McGraw Hill Education create™

Course Taking Sides:
Clashing Views in Science, Technology, and Society, 11e

Course Number **by Thomas A. Easton**

create™

http://create.mheducation.com

ISBN-10: 1308008791 ISBN-13: 9781308008790

Contents

Credits

Preface

Those who must deal with scientific and technological issues—scientists, politicians, sociologists, business managers, and anyone who is concerned about energy policy, genetically modified foods, government intrusiveness, expensive space programs, or the morality of medical research, among many other issues—must be able to consider, evaluate, and choose among alternatives. Making choices is an essential aspect of the scientific method. It is also an inescapable feature of every public debate over a scientific or technological issue, for there can be no debate if there are no alternatives.

The ability to evaluate and to select among alternatives—as well as to know when the data do not permit selection—is called critical thinking. It is essential not only in science and technology but in every other aspect of life as well. *Taking Sides: Clashing Views in Science, Technology, and Society* is designed to stimulate and cultivate this ability by holding up for consideration 19 issues that have provoked substantial debate. Each of these issues has at least two sides, usually more. However, each issue is expressed in terms of a single question in order to draw the lines of debate more clearly. The ideas and answers that emerge from the clash of opposing points of view should be more complex than those offered by the students before the reading assignment.

The issues in this book were chosen because they are currently of particular concern to both science and society. They touch on the nature of science and research, the relationship between science and society, the uses of technology, and the potential threats that technological advances can pose to human survival. And they come from a variety of fields, including computer and space science, biology, environmentalism, law enforcement, and public health. I wish to thank Jeff Hecht for sharing his memories of the dawn of the modern computer age.

Organization of the book For each issue, I have provided an *issue introduction,* which provides some historical background and discusses why the issue is important. I then present two selections, one pro and one con, in which the authors make their cases. Each issue concludes with a *exploring the issue* that brings the issue up to date and adds other voices and viewpoints. I have also provided relevant Internet site addresses (URLs) both in the text and on the *Internet References* page that accompanies each part opener. At the back of the book is a listing of all the *contributors to this volume,* which gives information on the scientists, technicians, professors, and social critics whose views are debated here.

Which answer to the issue question—yes or no—is the correct answer? Perhaps neither. Perhaps both. Students should read, think about, and discuss the readings and then come to their own conclusions without letting my or their instructor's opinions (which sometimes show!) dictate theirs. The additional readings mentioned in both the introductions and the exploring the issue should prove helpful. It is worth stressing that the issues covered in this book are all *live* issues; that is, the debates they represent are active and ongoing. In fact, they are so active and ongoing that when I teach this course, it often feels like a current events course!

Changes to this edition This eleventh edition represents a considerable revision of its predecessor. There are many completely new issues: "Should Scientific Papers Containing Potentially Hazardous Information Be Published in Their Entirety?"; "Should We Be Thinking about Changing People to Beat Global Warming?"; "Is Hydropower a Sound Choice for Renewable Energy?"; "Does a Hydrogen Economy Make Sense?"; "Should Society Impose a Moratorium on the Use and Release of 'Synthetic Biology' Organisms?"; "Will Robots Take Your Job?"; and "Is Cyber-War or Cyber-Terrorism a Genuine Threat?". Two issues have been renamed and given two new essays: "Do We Have a Population Problem?" and "Can We Stop an Asteroid or Comet Impact?".

In addition, for three of the issues retained from the previous edition, one or both readings have been replaced to bring the debate up to date: "Should the Public Have to Pay to See the Results of Federally Funded Research?"; "Are Genetically Modified Foods Safe to Eat?"; and "Do Humans Belong in Space?". In all, there are 21 new selections. The book's introduction and the issue introductions in the retained issues have been revised and updated where necessary.

A word to the instructor An *Instructor's Resource Guide with Test Questions* (multiple-choice and essay) is available through the publisher for the instructor using Taking Sides in the classroom. It includes suggestions for stimulating in-class discussion for each issue. A general guidebook, *Using Taking Sides in the Classroom,* which discusses methods and techniques for integrating the pro–con approach into any classroom setting, is also available. An online version of *Using Taking Sides in the Classroom* and a correspondence service for Taking Sides adopters can be found at www.mhhe.com/cls.

Taking Sides: Clashing Views in Science, Technology, and Society is only one title in the Taking Sides series. If you are interested in seeing the table of contents for any of the other titles, please visit the Taking Sides website at www.mhhe.com/cls.

Thomas A. Easton
Thomas College

Editor of This Volume

THOMAS A. EASTON is a professor of science at Thomas College in Waterville, Maine, where he has been teaching environmental science, science, technology, and society, and computer science since 1983. He received a BA in biology from Colby College in 1966 and a PhD in theoretical biology from the University of Chicago in 1971. He writes and speaks frequently on scientific and futuristic issues. His books include *Focus on Human Biology*, 2nd ed., coauthored with Carl E. Rischer (HarperCollins, 1995), *Careers in Science*, 4th ed. (VGM Career Horizons, 2004), *Classic Edition Sources: Environmental Studies*, 4th ed. (McGraw-Hill, 2011), *Taking Sides: Clashing Views on Controversial Issues in Science, Technology and Society*, 10th ed. (McGraw-Hill, 2011), and *Taking Sides: Clashing Views on Controversial Environmental Issues*, 14th ed. (McGraw-Hill, 2011). Dr. Easton is also a well-known writer and critic of science fiction.

Academic Advisory Board Members

Members of the Academic Advisory Board are instrumental in the final selection of articles for each edition of TAKING SIDES. Their review of articles for content, level, and appropriateness provides critical direction to the editors and staff. We think that you will find their careful consideration well reflected in this volume.

Grace Auyang
University of Cincinnati

Himanshu Baral
California State University—East Bay

James Barnard
Embry-Riddle Aeronautical University—Worlwide

Don Booker
Pace University

Claudius A. Carnegie
Florida International University

Robert Cole
Saint Louis University

Paul DiBara
Curry College

Wilton Duncan
ASA College

Michael Efthimiades
Vaughn College of Aeronautics

Sarah Greenwald
Appalachian State University

Keith Harman
Oklahoma Baptist University

Eric Height
Marist College

James Hollenbeck
Indiana University Southeast

Malynnda A. Johnson
Carroll University

JoAnne Juett
Indiana University Southeast

John A. Kromkowski
The Catholic University of America

Michael Martel
Ohio University

Timothy McGettigan
Colorado State University, Pueblo

Robert Moody
Fort Hays State University

Joseph B. Mosca
Monmouth University

Troy Nordman
Butler Community College

Nicholas J. Rowland
Pennsylvania State University

Viveca Sulich
Raritan Valley Community College

Mike Theiss
University of Wisconsin Marathon

Linda Wright-Smith
Cameron University

Topic Guide

This topic guide suggests how the selections in this book relate to the subjects covered in your course. You may want to use the topics listed on these pages to search the Web more easily.

All the articles that relate to each topic are listed below the bold-faced term.

Artificial Intelligence

Will Robots Take Your Job?
Should We Reject the "Transhumanist" Goal of the Genetically, Electronically, and Mechanically Enhanced Human Being?

Business

Should the Internet Be Neutral?
Will Robots Take Your Job?
Does Endorsing Open Source Software Fail to Respect Intellectual Property?

Crime

Is Cyber-War or Cyber-Terrorism a Genuine Threat?
Is "Animal Rights" Just Another Excuse for Terrorism?

Education

Should the Public Have to Pay to See the Results of Federally Funded Research?

Emerging Applications

Does a Hydrogen Economy Make Sense?
Will Robots Take Your Job?
Is Cyber-War or Cyber-Terrorism a Genuine Threat?
Should We Reject the "Transhumanist" Goal of the Genetically, Electronically, and Mechanically Enhanced Human Being?

Energy Options

Do We Need Research Guidelines for Geoengineering?
Is Hydropower a Sound Choice for Renewable Energy?
Does a Hydrogen Economy Make Sense?

Hardware and Software Design

Is There Sufficient Scientific Evidence to Conclude That Cell Phones Cause Cancer?
Will Robots Take Your Job?
Does Endorsing Open Source Software Fail to Respect Intellectual Property?

Health

Do We Have a Population Problem?
Is There Sufficient Scientific Evidence to Conclude That Cell Phones Cause Cancer?
Should Society Impose a Moratorium on the Use and Release of "Synthetic Biology" Organisms?
Can Infectious Animal Diseases Be Studied Safely in Kansas?
Are Genetically Modified Foods Safe to Eat?

Legal and Regulatory Issues

Should Scientific Papers Containing Potentially Hazardous Information Be Published in Their Entirety?
Should the Internet Be Neutral?
Is There Sufficient Scientific Evidence to Conclude That Cell Phones Cause Cancer?
Should Society Impose a Moratorium on the Use and Release of "Synthetic Biology" Organisms?
Can Infectious Animal Diseases Be Studied Safely in Kansas?
Are Genetically Modified Foods Safe to Eat?
Does Endorsing Open Source Software Fail to Respect Intellectual Property?
Is "Animal Rights" Just Another Excuse for Terrorism?

Philosophical/Historical/Cultural Issues

Should Scientific Papers Containing Potentially Hazardous Information Be Published in Their Entirety?
Should the Internet Be Neutral?
Does Endorsing Open Source Software Fail to Respect Intellectual Property?
Should We Reject the "Transhumanist" Goal of the Genetically, Electronically, and Mechanically Enhanced Human Being?

Politics

Should the Public Have to Pay to See the Results of Federally Funded Research?
Should Scientific Papers Containing Potentially Hazardous Information Be Published in Their Entirety
Should the Internet Be Neutral?
Do We Need Research Guidelines for Geoengineering?
Can Infectious Animal Diseases Be Studied Safely in Kansas?
Do Humans Belong in Space?
Is Cyber-War or Cyber-Terrorism a Genuine Threat?
Does Endorsing Open Source Software Fail to Respect Intellectual Property?
Should We Reject the "Transhumanist" Goal of the Genetically, Electronically, and Mechanically Enhanced Human Being?

Population

Do We Have a Population Problem?
Is There Sufficient Scientific Evidence to Conclude That Cell Phones Cause Cancer?
Should Society Impose a Moratorium on the Use and Release of "Synthetic Biology" Organisms?
Are Genetically Modified Foods Safe to Eat?
Should We Reject the "Transhumanist" Goal of the Genetically, Electronically, and Mechanically Enhanced Human Being?

Privacy

Should the Public Have to Pay to See the Results of Federally Funded Research?
Is Cyber-War or Cyber-Terrorism a Genuine Threat?

Space Technology

Can We Stop an Asteroid or Comet Impact?
Will the Search for Extraterrestrial Life Ever Succeed?
Do Humans Belong in Space?

Youth

Do We Have a Population Problem?
Will Robots Take Your Job?

Introduction

In his 2008 inaugural address, President Barack Obama said, "We will build the roads and bridges, the electric grids, and digital lines that feed our commerce and bind us together. We will restore science to its rightful place and wield technology's wonders to raise health care's quality and lower its costs." At the 2010 meeting of the American Association for the Advancement of Science, Eric Lander, cochair of the President's Council of Advisors on Science and Technology, asked, "What is the rightful place of science?" and answered that it belongs "in the president's cabinet and policy-making, in the nation's classrooms; as an engine to propel the American economy; as a critical investment in the federal budget, even in times of austerity; as a tool for diplomacy and international understanding and as an organizing principle for space exploration." (See Eric S. Lander, "Obama Advisor Weighs 'The Rightful Place of Science'," *Science News* (June 5, 2010); the question is also discussed in Daniel Sarewitz, "The Rightful Place of Science," *Issues in Science and Technology* (Summer 2009).) However, John Marburger, science advisor to President George W. Bush, notes in "Science's Uncertain Authority in Policy," *Issues in Science and Technology* (Summer 2010), that policymakers often ignore science in favor of preference, prejudice, and expedience.

The discussion of "the rightful place of science" is important for several reasons. One is simply that previous administrations have often made decisions based less on evidence than on politics and ideology. Today, the conservative or right-wing side of American society is waging what has been called a "war on science," refusing to accept scientific truths that threaten religious beliefs (e.g., evolution), desperate wishes (e.g., vaccine safety and alternative medicine), profit (e.g., global warming), and more; see Shawn Lawrence Otto, *Fool Me Twice: Fighting the Assault on Science in America* (Rodale, 2011); John Grant, *Denying Science: Conspiracy Theories, Media Distortions, and the War Against Reality* (Prometheus, 2011); and Shawn Lawrence Otto, "America's Science Problem," *Scientific American* (November 2012).

The other—closely related—reason for discussing "the rightful place of science" is that a great many of the issues that the United States and the world face today cannot be properly understood without a solid grounding in climatology, ecology, physics, and engineering (among other areas). This is not going to change. In the twenty-first century, we cannot escape science and technology. Their fruits—the clothes we wear, the foods we eat, the tools we use—surround us. They also fill us with both hope and dread for the future, for although new discoveries promise us cures for diseases and other problems, new insights into the wonders of nature, new gadgets, new industries, and new jobs (among other things), the past has taught us that technological developments can have unforeseen and terrible consequences.

Those consequences do *not* belong to science, for science is nothing more (or less) than a systematic approach to gaining knowledge about the world. Technology is the application of knowledge (including scientific knowledge) to accomplish things we otherwise could not. It is not just devices such as hammers and computers and jet aircraft, but also management systems and institutions and even political philosophies. And it is of course such *uses* of knowledge that affect our lives for good and ill.

We cannot say, "for good *or* ill." Technology is neither an unalloyed blessing nor an unmitigated curse. Every new technology offers both new benefits and new problems, and the two sorts of consequences cannot be separated from each other. Automobiles provide rapid, convenient personal transportation, but precisely because of that benefit, they also create suburbs, urban sprawl, crowded highways, and air pollution, and even contribute to global climate change.

Optimists Vs. Pessimists

The inescapable pairing of good and bad consequences helps to account for why so many issues of science and technology stir debate in our society. Optimists focus on the benefits of technology and are confident that we will be able to cope with any problems that arise. Pessimists fear the problems and are sure their costs will outweigh any possible benefits.

Sometimes the costs of new technologies are immediate and tangible. When new devices—steamship boilers or space shuttles—fail or new drugs prove to have unforeseen side effects, people die. Sometimes the costs are less obvious.

The proponents of technology answer that if a machine fails, it needs to be fixed, not banned. If a drug has side effects, it may need to be refined or its permitted recipients may have to be better defined (the banned tranquilizer thalidomide is famous for causing birth defects when taken early in pregnancy; it is apparently quite safe for men and nonpregnant women).

Certainty Vs. Uncertainty

Another root for the debates over science and technology is uncertainty. Science is by its very nature uncertain. Its truths are provisional, open to revision.

Unfortunately, most people are told by politicians, religious leaders, and newspaper columnists that truth is certain. They therefore believe that if someone admits uncertainty, their position is weak and they need not be heeded.

This is, of course, an open invitation for demagogues to prey upon fears of disaster or side effects or upon the wish to be told that the omens of greenhouse warming and ozone holes (etc.) are mere figments of the scientific imagination. Businesses may try to emphasize uncertainty to forestall government regulations; see David Michaels, *Doubt Is Their Product: How Industry's Assault on Science Threatens Your Health* (Oxford University Press, 2008).

Is Science Just Another Religion?

Science and technology have come to play a huge role in human culture, largely because they have led to vast improvements in nutrition, health care, comfort, communication, transportation, and humanity's ability to affect the world. However, science has also enhanced understanding of human behavior and of how the universe works, and in this it frequently contradicts what people have long thought they knew. Furthermore, it actively rejects any role of God in scientific explanation.

Many people therefore reject what science tells us. They see science as just another way of explaining how the world and humanity came to be; in this view, science is no truer than religious accounts. Indeed, some say science is just another religion, with less claim on followers' allegiance than other religions that have been divinely sanctioned and hallowed by longer traditions. Certainly, they see little significant difference between the scientist's faith in reason, evidence, and skepticism as the best way to achieve truth about the world and the religious believer's faith in revelation and scripture. This becomes very explicit in connection with the debates between creationists and evolutionists. Even religious people who do not favor creationism may reject science because they see it as denying both the existence of God and the importance of "human values" (meaning behaviors that are affirmed by traditional religion). This leads to a basic antipathy between science and religion, especially conservative religion, and especially in areas—such as human origins—where science and scripture seem to be talking about the same things but are contradicting each other. This point can be illustrated by mentioning the Italian physicist Galileo Galilei (1564–1642), who in 1616 was attacked by the Roman Catholic Church for teaching Copernican astronomy and thus contradicting the teachings of the Church. Another example arose when evolutionary theorist Charles Darwin first published *on The Origin of Species by Means of Natural Selection* in 1859. Mano Singham notes in "The Science and Religion Wars," *Phi Delta Kappan* (February 2000), that "In the triangle formed by science, mainstream religion, and fringe beliefs, it is the conflict between science and fringe beliefs that is usually the source of the most heated, acrimonious, and public debate." Michael Ruse takes a more measured tone when he asks "Is Evolution a Secular Religion?" *Science* (March 7, 2003); his answer is that "Today's professional evolutionism is no more a secular religion than is industrial chemistry" but there is also a "popular evolutionism" that treads on religious ground and must be carefully distinguished. In recent years, efforts to counter "evolutionism" by mandating the teaching of creationism or "intelligent design" (ID) in public schools have made frequent appearances in the news, but so have the defeats of those efforts. One of the most recent defeats was in Dover, Pennsylvania, where the judge declared that "ID is not science." See Jeffrey Mervis, "Judge Jones Defines Science—And Why Intelligent Design Isn't," *Science* (January 6, 2006), and Sid Perkins, "Evolution in Action," *Science News* (February 25, 2006).

Even if religion does not enter the debate, some people reject new developments in science and technology (and in other areas) because they seem "unnatural." For most people, "natural" seems to mean any device or procedure to which they have become accustomed. Very few realize how "unnatural" are such ordinary things as circumcision and horseshoes and baseball.

Yet new ideas are inevitable. The search for and the application of knowledge is perhaps the human species' single most defining characteristic. Other creatures also use tools, communicate, love, play, and reason. Only humans have embraced change. We are forever creating variations on our religions, languages, politics, and tools. Innovation is as natural to us as building dams is to a beaver.

Efforts to encourage innovation are a perennial topic in discussions of how nations can deal with problems and stimulate their economies (see David H. Guston, "Innovation Policy: Not Just a Jumbo Shrimp," *Nature* (August 21, 2008)). India has a National Innovation Foundation, and a similar government agency has been suggested for the United States (see Robert Atkinson and Howard Wial, "Creating a National Innovation Foundation," *Issues in Science and Technology* (Fall 2008); see also Robert Atkinson and Howard Wial, *Boosting Productivity, Innovation, and Growth through a National Innovation Foundation* (Washington, DC: Brookings Institution and Information Technology and Innovation Foundation, 2008), available online at www.brookings.edu/~/media/ Files/rc/reports/2008/04_federal_role_atkinson_wial/NIF%20Report.pdf or www.itif.org/files/NIF.pdf). The closest we have come so far is the Defense Advanced Research Projects Agency (DARPA; www.darpa.mil/), famous for its initiation of Internet technology, and ARPA-Energy (http://arpa-e.energy.gov/), launched in 2007 with hopes for equally impressive results in the field of energy.

Voodoo Science

Public confusion over science and technology is increased by several factors. One is the failure of public education. In 2002, the Committee on Technological Literacy of the National Academy of Engineering and the National Research Council published a report (*Technically Speaking: Why All Americans Need to Know More About Technology*) that said that although the United States is defined by and dependent on science and technology, "its citizens are not equipped to make well-considered decisions or to think critically about technology. As a society, we are not even fully aware of or conversant with the technologies we use every day."

A second factor is the willingness of some to mislead. Alarmists stress awful possible consequences of new technology without paying attention to actual evidence, they demand certainty when it is impossible, and they reject the new because it is untraditional or even "unthinkable." And then there are the marketers, hypesters, fraudsters, activists, and even legitimate scientists and critics who oversell their claims. Robert L. Park, author of *Voodoo Science: The Road from Foolishness to Fraud* (Oxford University Press, 2002), lists seven warning signs "that a scientific claim lies well outside the bounds of rational scientific discourse" and should be viewed warily:

- The discoverer pitches his claim directly to the media, without permitting peer review.
- The discoverer says that a powerful establishment is trying to suppress his or her work.
- The scientific effect involved is always at the very limit of detection.
- Evidence for a discovery is only anecdotal.
- The discoverer says a belief is credible because it has endured for centuries.
- The discoverer has worked in isolation.
- The discoverer must propose new laws of nature to explain an observation.

The Soul of Science

The standard picture of science—a world of observations and hypotheses, experiments and theories, a world of sterile white coats and laboratories and cold, unfeeling logic—is a myth of our times. It has more to do with the way science is presented by both scientists and the media than with the way scientists actually do their work. In practice, scientists are often less orderly, less logical, and more prone to very human conflicts of personality than most people suspect.

The myth remains because it helps to organize science. It provides labels and a framework for what a scientist does; it may thus be especially valuable to student scientists who are still learning the ropes. In addition, it embodies certain important ideals of scientific thought. It is these ideals that make the scientific approach the most powerful and reliable guide to truth about the world that human beings have yet devised.

The Ideals of Science: Skepticism, Communication, and Reproducibility

The soul of science is a very simple idea: *Check it out.* Scholars used to think that all they had to do to do their duty by the truth was to say "According to . . ." some ancient authority such as Aristotle or the Bible. If someone with a suitably illustrious reputation had once said something was so, it was so. Arguing with authority or holy writ could get you charged with heresy and imprisoned or burned at the stake.

This attitude is the opposite of everything that modern science stands for. As Carl Sagan says in *The Demon-Haunted World: Science as a Candle in the Dark* (Random House, 1995, p. 28), "One of the great commandments of science is, 'Mistrust arguments from authority'." Scientific knowledge is based not on authority but on reality itself. Scientists take nothing on faith. They are *skeptical.* When they want to know something, they do not look it up in the library or take others' word for it. They go into the laboratory, the forest, the desert—wherever they can find the phenomena they wish to know about—and they ask those phenomena directly. They look for answers in the book of nature. And if they think they know the answer already, it is not of books that they ask, "Are we right?" but of nature. This is the point of "scientific experiments"—they are how scientists ask nature whether their ideas check out.

This "check it out" ideal is, however, an ideal. No one can possibly check everything out for himself or herself. Even scientists, in practice, look things up in books. They too rely on authorities. But the authorities they rely on are other scientists who have studied nature and reported what they learned. In principle, everything those authorities report can be checked. Observations in the lab or in the field can be repeated. New theoretical or computer models can be designed. What is in the books can be confirmed.

In fact, a good part of the official "scientific method" is designed to make it possible for any scientist's findings or conclusions to be confirmed. Scientists do not say, "Vitamin D is essential for strong bones. Believe me. I know." They say, "I know that vitamin D is essential for proper bone formation because I raised rats without vitamin D in their diet, and their bones turned out soft and crooked. When I gave them vitamin D, their bones hardened and straightened. Here is the kind of rat I used, the kind of food I fed them, the amount of vitamin D I gave them. Go thou and do likewise, and you will see what I saw."

Communication is therefore an essential part of modern science. That is, in order to function as a scientist, you must not keep secrets. You must tell others not just what you have learned by studying nature, but how you learned it. You must spell out your methods in enough detail to let others repeat your work.

Scientific knowledge is thus *reproducible* knowledge. Strictly speaking, if a person says "I can see it, but you can't," that person is not a scientist. Scientific knowledge exists for everyone. Anyone who takes the time to learn the proper techniques can confirm it. They don't have to believe in it first.

As an exercise, devise a way to convince a red-green colorblind person, who sees no difference between red and green, that such a difference really exists. That is, show that a knowledge of colors is reproducible, and therefore scientific, knowledge, rather than something more like belief in ghosts or telepathy.

Here's a hint: Photographic light meters respond to light hitting a sensor. Photographic filters permit light of only a single color to pass through.

The Standard Model of the Scientific Method

As it is usually presented, the scientific method has five major components. They include *observation, generalization* (identifying a pattern), stating a *hypothesis* (a tentative extension of the pattern or explanation for why the pattern exists), and *experimentation* (testing that explanation). The results of the tests are then *communicated* to other members of the scientific community, usually by publishing the findings. How each of these components contributes to the scientific method is discussed briefly below.

Observation

The basic units of science—and the only real facts the scientist knows—are the individual *observations.* Using them, we look for patterns, suggest explanations, and devise tests for our ideas. Our observations can be casual, as when we notice a black van parked in front of the fire hydrant on our block. They may also be more deliberate, as what a police detective notices when he or she sets out to find clues to who has been burglarizing apartments in our neighborhood.

Generalization

After we have made many observations, we try to discern a pattern among them. A statement of such a pattern is a *generalization.* We might form a generalization if we realized that every time there was a burglary on the block, that black van was parked by the hydrant.

Cautious experimenters do not jump to conclusions. When they think they see a pattern, they often make a few more observations just to be sure the pattern holds up. This practice of strengthening or confirming findings by *replicating* them is a very important part of the scientific process. In our example, the police would wait for the van to show up again and for another burglary to happen. Only then might they descend on the alleged villains. Is there loot in the van? Burglary tools?

The Hypothesis

A tentative explanation suggesting why a particular pattern exists is called a *hypothesis.* In our example, the hypothesis that comes to mind is obvious: The burglars drive to work in that black van.

The mark of a good hypothesis is that it is *testable.* The best hypotheses are *predictive.* Can you devise a predictive test for the "burglars use the black van" hypothesis?

Unfortunately, tests can fail even when the hypothesis is perfectly correct. How might that happen with our example?

Many philosophers of science insist on *falsification* as a crucial aspect of the scientific method. That is, when a test of a hypothesis shows the hypothesis to be false, the hypothesis must be rejected and replaced with another.

The Experiment

The *experiment* is the most formal part of the scientific process. The concept, however, is very simple: An experiment is nothing more than a test of a hypothesis. It is what a scientist—or a detective—does to check an idea out.

If the experiment does not falsify the hypothesis, that does not mean the hypothesis is true. It simply means that the scientist has not yet come up with the test that falsifies it. The more times and the more different ways that falsification fails, the more probable it is that the hypothesis is true. Unfortunately, because it is impossible to do all the possible tests of a hypothesis, the scientist can never *prove* it is true.

Consider the hypothesis that all cats are black. If you see a black cat, you don't really know anything at all about all cats. If you see a white cat, though, you certainly know that not all cats are black. You would have to look at every cat on Earth to prove the hypothesis. It takes just one to disprove it.

This is why philosophers of science say that *science is the art of disproving,* not proving. If a hypothesis withstands many attempts to disprove it, then it may be a good explanation of what is going on. If it fails just one test, it is clearly wrong and must be replaced with a new hypothesis.

However, researchers who study what scientists actually do point out that the truth is a little different. Almost all scientists, when they come up with what strikes them as a good explanation of a phenomenon or pattern, do *not* try to disprove their hypothesis. Instead, they design experiments to *confirm* it. If an experiment fails to confirm the hypothesis, the researcher tries another experiment, not another hypothesis.

Police detectives may do the same thing. Think of the one who found no evidence of wrongdoing in the black van but arrested the suspects anyway. Armed with a search warrant, he later searched their apartments. He was saying, in effect, "I *know* they're guilty. I just have to find the evidence to prove it."

The logical weakness in this approach is obvious, but that does not keep researchers (or detectives) from falling in love with their ideas and holding onto them as long as possible. Sometimes they hold on so long, even without confirmation of their hypothesis, that they wind up looking ridiculous. Sometimes the confirmations add up over the years and whatever attempts are made to disprove the hypothesis fail to do so. The hypothesis may then be elevated to the rank of a *theory, principle,* or *law.* Theories are explanations of how things work (the theory of evolution *by means of* natural selection). Principles and laws tend to be statements of things that happen, such as the law of gravity (masses attract each other, or what goes up comes down) or the gas law (if you increase the pressure on an enclosed gas, the volume will decrease and the temperature will increase).

Communication

Each scientist is obligated to share her or his hypotheses, methods, and findings with the rest of the scientific community. This sharing serves two purposes. First, it supports the basic ideal of skepticism by making it possible for others to say, "Oh, yeah? Let me check that." It tells those others where to see what the scientist saw, what techniques to use, and what tools to use.

Second, it gets the word out so that others can use what has been discovered. This is essential because science is a cooperative endeavor. People who work thousands of miles apart build with and upon each other's discoveries, and some of the most exciting discoveries have involved bringing together information from very different fields, as when geochemistry, paleontology, and astronomy came together to reveal that what killed off the dinosaurs 65 million years ago was apparently the impact of a massive comet or asteroid with the Earth.

Scientific cooperation stretches across time as well. Every generation of scientists both uses and adds to what previous generations have discovered. As Isaac Newton said, "If I have seen further than [other men], it is by standing upon the shoulders of Giants" (Letter to Robert Hooke, February 5, 1675/6).

The communication of science begins with a process called "peer review," which typically has three stages. The first occurs when a scientist seeks funding—from government agencies, foundations, or other sources—to carry out a research program. He or she must prepare a report describing the intended work, laying out background, hypotheses, planned experiments, expected results, and even the broader impacts on other fields. Committees of other scientists then go over the report to see whether the scientist knows his or her area, has the necessary abilities, and is realistic in his or her plans.

Once the scientist has the needed funding, has done the work, and has written a report of the results, that report will go to a scientific journal. Before publishing the report, the journal's editors will show it to other workers in the same or related fields and ask whether the work was done adequately, the conclusions are justified, and the report should be published.

The third stage of peer review happens after publication, when the broader scientific community gets to see and judge the work.

This three-stage quality-control filter can, of course, be short-circuited. Any scientist with independent wealth can avoid the first stage quite easily, but such scientists are much, much rarer today than they were a century or so ago. Those who remain are the object of envy. Surely it is fair to say that they are not frowned upon as are those who avoid the later two stages of the "peer review" mechanism by using vanity presses and press conferences.

On the other hand, it is certainly possible for the standard peer review mechanisms to fail. By their nature, these mechanisms are more likely to approve ideas that do not contradict what the reviewers think they already know. Yet unconventional ideas are not necessarily wrong, as Alfred Wegener proved when he tried to gain acceptance for the idea of continental drift in the early twentieth century. At the time, geologists believed the crust of the Earth—which was solid rock, after all—did not behave like liquid. Yet Wegener was proposing that the continents floated about like icebergs in the sea, bumping into each other, tearing apart (to produce matching profiles like those of South America and Africa), and bumping again. It was not until the 1960s that most geologists accepted his ideas as genuine insights instead of hare-brained delusions.

The Need for Controls

Many years ago, I read a description of a wish machine. It consisted of an ordinary stereo amplifier with two unusual attachments. The wires that would normally be connected to a microphone were connected instead to a pair of copper plates. The wires that would normally be connected to a speaker were connected instead to a whip antenna of the sort we usually see on cars.

To use this device, one put a picture of some desired item between the copper plates. It could be a photo of a person with whom one wanted a date, a lottery ticket, a college, anything. One test case used a photo of a pest-infested cornfield. One then wished fervently for the date, a winning ticket, a college acceptance, or whatever else one craved. In the test case, that meant wishing that all the cornfield pests should drop dead.

Supposedly the wish would be picked up by the copper plates, amplified by the stereo amplifier, and then sent via the whip antenna wherever wish-orders have to go. Whoever or whatever fills those orders would get the message, and then. . . . Well, in the test case, the result was that when the testers checked the cornfield, there was no longer any sign of pests.

What's more, the process worked equally well whether the amplifier was plugged in or not.

I'm willing to bet that you are now feeling very much like a scientist—skeptical. The true, dedicated scientist, however, does not stop with saying, "Oh, yeah? Tell me another one!" Instead, he or she says something like, "Mmm. I wonder. Let's check this out." (Must we, really? After all, we can be quite sure that the wish machine does not work because if it did, it would be on the market.

Casinos would then be unable to make a profit for their backers. Deadly diseases would not be deadly. And so on.)

Where must the scientist begin? The standard model of the scientific method says the first step is observation. Here, our observations (as well as our necessary generalization) are simply the description of the wish machine and the claims for its effectiveness. Perhaps we even have an example of the physical device itself.

What is our hypothesis? We have two choices, one consistent with the claims for the device, one denying those claims: The wish machine always works, or the wish machine never works. Both are equally testable, but perhaps one is more easily falsifiable. (Which one?)

How do we test the hypothesis? Set up the wish machine, and perform the experiment of making a wish. If the wish comes true, the device works. If it does not, it doesn't.

Can it really be that simple? In essence, yes. But in fact, no.

Even if you don't believe that wishing can make something happen, sometimes wishes do come true by sheer coincidence. Therefore, if the wish machine is as nonsensical as most people think it is, sometimes it will *seem* to work. We therefore need a way to shield against the misleading effects of coincidence. We need a way to *control* the possibilities of error.

Coincidence is not, of course, the only source of error we need to watch out for. For instance, there is a very human tendency to interpret events in such a way as to agree with our preexisting beliefs, our prejudices. If we believe in wishes, we therefore need a way to guard against our willingness to interpret near misses as not quite misses at all. There is also a human tendency not to look for mistakes when the results agree with our prejudices. That cornfield, for instance, might not have been as badly infested as the testers said it was, or a farmer might have sprayed it with pesticide whether the testers had wished or not, or the field they checked might have been the wrong one.

We would also like to check whether the wish machine does indeed work equally well plugged in or not, and then we must guard against the tendency to wish harder when we know it's plugged in. We would like to know whether the photo between the copper plates makes any difference, and then we must guard against the tendency to wish harder when we know the wish matches the photo.

Coincidence is easy to protect against. All that is necessary is to repeat the experiment enough times to be sure we are not seeing flukes. This is one major purpose of replication.

Our willingness to shade the results in our favor can be defeated by having someone else judge the results of our wishing experiments. Our eagerness to overlook "favorable" errors can be defeated by taking great care to avoid any errors at all; peer reviewers also help by pointing out such problems.

The other sources of error are harder to avoid, but scientists have developed a number of helpful *control* techniques. One is "blinding." In essence, it means setting things up so the scientist does not know what he or she is doing.

In the pharmaceutical industry, this technique is used whenever a new drug must be tested. A group of patients are selected. Half of them—chosen randomly to avoid any unconscious bias that might put sicker, taller, shorter, male, female, homosexual, black, or white patients in one group instead of the other—are given the drug. The others are given a dummy pill, or a sugar pill, also known as a placebo. In all other respects, the two groups are treated exactly the same. Drug (and other) researchers take great pains to be sure groups of experimental subjects are alike in every way but the one way being tested. Here that means the only difference between the groups should be which one gets the drug and which one gets the placebo.

Unfortunately, placebos can have real medical effects, apparently because we *believe* our doctors when they tell us that a pill will cure what ails us. We have faith in them, and our minds do their best to bring our bodies into line. This mind-over-body "placebo effect" seems to be akin to faith healing.

Single Blind. The researchers therefore do not tell the patients what pill they are getting. The patients are "blinded" to what is going on. Both placebo and drug then gain equal advantage from the placebo effect. If the drug seems to work better or worse than the placebo, then the researchers can be sure of a real difference between the two.

Double Blind. Or can they? Unfortunately, if the researchers know what pill they are handing out, they can give subtle, unconscious cues. Or they may interpret any changes in symptoms in favor of the drug. It is therefore best to keep the researchers in the dark too; since both researchers and patients are now blind to the truth, the experiment is said to be "double blind." Drug trials often use pills that differ only in color or in the number on the bottle, and the code is not broken until all the results are in. This way nobody knows who gets what until the knowledge can no longer make a difference.

Obviously, the double-blind approach can work only when there are human beings on both sides of the experiment, as experimenter and as experimental subject. When the object of the experiment is an inanimate object such as a wish machine, only the single-blind approach is possible.

With suitable precautions against coincidence, self-delusion, wishful thinking, bias, and other sources of error, the wish machine could be convincingly tested. Yet it cannot be perfectly tested, for perhaps it works only sometimes, when the aurora glows green over Copenhagen, in months without an "r," or when certain people use it. It is impossible to rule out all the possibilities, although we can rule out enough to be pretty confident as we call the gadget nonsense.

Very similar precautions are essential in every scientific field, for the same sources of error lie in wait wherever experiments are done, and they serve very much the same function. However, we must stress that no controls and no peer review system, no matter how elaborate, can completely protect a scientist—or science—from error.

Here, as well as in the logical impossibility of proof (experiments only fail to disprove) and science's dependence on the progressive growth of knowledge (its requirement that each scientist make his or her discoveries while standing on the shoulders of the giants who went before, if you will) lies the uncertainty that is the hallmark of science. Yet it is also a hallmark of science that its methods guarantee that uncertainty will be reduced (not eliminated). Frauds and errors will be detected and corrected. Limited understandings of truth will be extended.

Those who bear this in mind will be better equipped to deal with issues of certainty and risk.

Something else to bear in mind is that argument is an inevitable part of science. The combination of communication and skepticism very frequently leads scientists into debates with each other. The scientist's willingness to be skeptical about and hence to challenge received wisdom leads to debates with everyone else. A book like this one is an unrealistic portrayal of science only because it covers such a small fraction of all the arguments available.

Is Science Worth It?

What scientists do as they apply their methods is called *research*. Scientists who perform *basic or fundamental research* seek no specific result. Basic research is motivated essentially by curiosity. It is the study of some intriguing aspect of nature for its own sake. Basic researchers have revealed vast amounts of detail about the chemistry and function of genes, explored the behavior of electrons in semiconductors, revealed the structure of the atom, discovered radioactivity, and opened our minds to the immensity in both time and space of the universe in which we live.

Applied or strategic research is more mission-oriented. Applied scientists turn basic discoveries into devices and processes, such as transistors, computers, antibiotics, vaccines, nuclear weapons and power plants, and communications and weather satellites. There are thousands of such examples, all of which are answers to specific problems or needs, and many of which were quite surprising to the basic researchers who first gained the raw knowledge that led to these developments.

It is easy to see what drives the effort to put science to work. Society has a host of problems that cry out for immediate solutions. Yet there is also a need for research that is not tied to explicit need because such research undeniably supplies a great many of the ideas, facts, and techniques that problem-solving researchers then use in solving society's problems. Basic researchers, of course, use the same ideas, facts, and techniques as they continue their probings into the way nature works.

In 1945—after the scientific and technological successes of World War II—Vannevar Bush argued in *Science, the Endless Frontier* (National Science Foundation, 1990) that science would continue to benefit society best if it were supported with generous funding but not controlled by society. On the record, he was quite right, for the next half-century saw an unprecedented degree of progress in medicine, transportation, computers, communications, weapons, and a great deal more.

There have been and will continue to be problems that emerge from science and its applications in technology. Some people respond like Bill Joy, who argues in "Why the Future Doesn't Need Us," *Wired* (April 2000), that some technologies—notably robotics, genetic engineering, and nanotechnology—are so hazardous that we should refrain from developing them. On the whole, however, argue those like George Conrades ("Basic Research: Long-Term Problems Facing a Long-Term Investment," *Vital Speeches of the Day* (May 15, 1999)), the value of the opportunities greatly outweighs the hazards of the problems. Others are less sanguine. David H. Guston and Kenneth Keniston ("Updating the Social Contract for Science," *Technology Review* (November/December 1994)) argue that despite the obvious successes of science and technology, public attitudes toward scientific research also depend on the vast expense of the scientific enterprise and the perceived risks. As a result, the public should not be "excluded from decision making about science." That is, decisions should not be left to the experts alone.

Conflict also arises over the function of science in our society. Traditionally, scientists have seen themselves as engaged in the disinterested pursuit of knowledge, solving the puzzles set before them by nature with little concern for whether the solutions to these puzzles might prove helpful to human enterprises such as war, health care, and commerce, among many more. Yet again and again the solutions found by scientists have proved useful. They have founded industries. And scientists love to quote Michael Faraday, who, when asked by politicians what good the new electricity might be, replied: "Someday, sir, you will tax it."

Not surprisingly, society has come to expect science to be useful. When asked to fund research, it feels it has the right to target research on issues of social concern, to demand results of immediate value, to forbid research it deems dangerous or disruptive, and to control access to research results that might be misused by terrorists or others (the issue of "unclassified but sensitive" research was included in the 8th edition of this book; see also Donald Kennedy, "Science and Security, Again," *Science* (August 22, 2008)).

Private interests such as corporations often feel that they have similar rights in regard to research they have funded. For instance, tobacco companies have displayed a strong tendency to fund research that shows tobacco to be safe and to cancel funding for studies that come up with other results, which might interfere with profits.

One argument for public funding is that it avoids such conflict-of-interest issues. Yet politicians have their own interests, and their control of the purse strings—just like a corporation's—can give their demands a certain undeniable persuasiveness.

Public Policy

The question of targeting research is only one way in which science and technology intersect the broader realm of public policy. Here the question becomes how society should allocate its resources in general: toward education or prisons; health care or welfare; research or trade; and encouraging new technologies or cleaning up after old ones?

The problem is that money is finite. Faced with competing worthy goals, we must make choices. We must also run the risk that our choices will turn out, in hindsight, to have been wrong.

The Purpose of This Book

Is there any prospect that the debates over the proper function of science, the acceptability of new technologies, or the truth of forecasts of disaster will soon fall quiet? Surely not, for some of the old issues will forever refuse to die (think of evolution versus creationism), and there will always be new issues to debate afresh. Some of the new issues will strut upon the stage of history only briefly, but they will in their existence reflect something significant about the way human beings view science and technology. Some will remain controversial as long as has evolution or the population explosion (which has been debated ever since Thomas Malthus' 1798 "Essay on the Principle of Population"). Some will flourish and fade and return to prominence; early editions of this book included the debate over whether the last stocks of smallpox virus should be destroyed; they were not, and the war on terrorism has brought awareness of the virus and the need for smallpox vaccine back onto the public stage. The loss of the space shuttle *Columbia* reawakened the debate over whether space should be explored by people or machines. Some issues will remain live but change their form, as has the debate over government interception of electronic communications. And there will always be more issues than can be squeezed into a book like this one—think, for instance, of the debate over whether elections should use electronic voting machines (discussed by Steve Ditlea, "Hack the Vote," *Popular Mechanics* (November 2004)).

Since almost all of these science and technology issues can or will affect the conditions of our daily lives, we should know something about them. We can begin by examining the nature of science and a few of the current controversies over issues in science and technology. After all, if one does not know what science, the scientific mode of thought, and their strengths and limitations are, one cannot think critically and constructively about any issue with a scientific or technological component. Nor can one hope to make informed choices among competing scientific, technological, or political and social priorities.

Unit 1

UNIT

The Place of Science and Technology in Society

The partnership between human society and science and technology is an uneasy one. Science and technology offer undoubted benefits, in both the short and long term, but they also challenge received wisdom and political ideology. The issues in this section deal with whether public access to publicly funded research should take precedence over the right of private interests to make money, whether the full results of scientific research should be available to all, and whether commerce or freedom is a better foundation for regulation.

Selected, Edited, and with Issue Framing Material by:
Thomas A. Easton, *Thomas College*

ISSUE

Should the Public Have to Pay to See the Results of Federally Funded Research?

YES: **Ralph Oman**, from "The Fair Copyright in Research Works Act," testimony regarding H.R 6845, before the Subcommittee on Courts, the Internet, and Intellectual Property of the Committee on the Judiciary (September 11, 2008)

NO: **Stuart M. Shieber**, from "Testimony Before the U.S. House of Representatives Committee on Science, Space and Technology, Subcommittee on Investigations and Oversight, Hearing on Examining Public Access and Scholarly Publication Interests" (March 29, 2012)

Learning Outcomes

After studying this issue, students will be able to:

- Explain how peer review helps to assure the quality of scientific publications.
- Explain why peer review and open access can coexist.
- Explain why university and college libraries favor open access publishing.
- Explain the role of profit in academic publishing.

ISSUE SUMMARY

YES: Attorney and past register of copyrights Ralph Oman contends that "If the NIH [National Institutes of Health] succeeds in putting all of the NIH-related peer-reviewed articles on its online database for free within one year of publication, the private publishers will be hard-pressed to survive." Allowing private publishers to continue to profit by publishing the results of publically funded research is the best way to ensure public benefit.

NO: Stuart M. Shieber argues that the concerns of traditional journal publishers that open access publishing will endanger their survival are not justified. The data show that publisher profitability has increased despite the recent economic downturn. Providing open access to the publicly funded research literature amplifies the diffusion of knowledge and benefits researchers, taxpayers, and everyone who gains from new medicines, new technologies, new jobs, and new solutions to long-standing problems of every kind.

According to Peter Suber's "Open Access Overview" (www.earlham.edu/~peters/fos/overview.htm), "open access" refers to the broad-based movement to put peer-reviewed research articles online, free of charge, and without most copyright and licensing restrictions. According to his "Timeline of the Open Access Movement" (www.earlham.edu/~peters/fos/timeline.htm), the movement has roots in the 1960s, well before the Internet came to exist as we know it today. Project Gutenberg (www.gutenberg.org/wiki/Main_Page), which makes public-domain novels and other books freely available, was launched in 1971. For many years, the open access movement was no threat to the standard modes of scientific publishing, but by 2004 it was clear that scientific (and other) journals were becoming so expensive that university and college libraries were being forced to cut back on the number of journals they could subscribe to; on April 17, 2012, Harvard's Faculty Advisory Council sent a memo to faculty saying "Major Periodical Subscriptions Cannot Be Sustained" (http://isites.harvard.edu/icb/icb.do?keyword=k77982&tabgroupid=icb.tabgroup143448).

In response to a report from the House Appropriations Committee urging the National Institutes of Health to require NIH-funded research reports to be deposited in NIH's Internet archive, PubMed Central, NIH director Elias Zerhouni convened meetings with representatives of academic publishers, and others. Publishers expressed concern that making reports freely available would threaten their continued existence. See Jocelyn Kaiser, "House Weighs Proposal to Block Mandatory 'Open Access'," *Science* (September 19, 2008).

Pressure was rising to do something about the problem, and open access looked like a possible solution, as exemplified by the Public Library of Science (PLoS) (see Theodora Bloom, et al., "PLoS Biology at 5: The Future Is Open Access," *PLoS Biology* (October 2008). Leah Hoffman, "Open for Business," *Communications of the ACM* (April 2012), notes that "Open access is growing fast in both recognition and popularity, making it a force to be reckoned with in the future of academic publishing."

According to Walt Crawford, "Open Access: It's Never Simple," *Online* (July/August 2008), one major objection to the traditional mode of scholarly publication—meaning that university and college libraries pay to subscribe to a journal—is that subscriptions have become remarkably expensive. Springer-Verlag's journal prices for 2010 can be seen at www.springer.com/librarians/price+lists?SGWID=0-40585-0-0-0; sixteen of those journals are priced at over $10,000 a year. The prices of Elsevier's titles are listed at www.elsevier.com/wps/find/journalpricing.cws_home/subscrippricelistlibr/description; *Life Sciences* cost a library $7,399 for 2012 compared to $4,031 a year in 2000 and $2,325 in 1995. Subscription prices for print journals have grown about 10 percent per year, with electronic access and mixed access being priced even higher. Aggregated (multi-journal) electronic-access packages appeared in 2001 to help stabilize prices; see Frances L. Chen, Paul Wrynn, and Judith L. Rieke, "Electronic Journal Access: How Does It Affect the Print Subscription Price?" *Bulletin of the Medical Library Association* (October 2001). Michael P. Taylor, "Opinion: Academic Publishing Is Broken: The Current System by Which Academics Publish Their Scientific Discoveries Is a Massive Waste of Money," *The Scientist* (March 19, 2012), reinforces these points.

Today aggregated packages (such as Ebsco) are commonplace, with many academic libraries using them to replace paper subscriptions. But even these can be expensive. It is no surprise that libraries are among the strongest backers of the open access movement in the United States and elsewhere (for a Canadian view, see Heather Morrison and Andrew Waller, "Open Access and Evolving Scholarly Communication," *C&RL News*, September 2008). Some researchers are addressing the concern that open access journals are somehow inferior to subscription journals in terms of quality control by studying their "impact factor" (how often papers are cited); K. A. Clauson, et al., "Open-Access Publishing for Pharmacy-Focused Journals," *American Journal of Health-System Pharmacists* (August 15, 2008), find that impact factors are actually greater for journals with some form of open access. Yet as open access journals proliferate, it is clear that some are of much less quality than others; see Martin Enserink, "As Open Access Explodes, How to Tell the Good from the Bad and the Ugly?" *Science* (November 23, 2012).

The pressure for open access does not come only from government agencies such as NIH. Some see open access as a movement to democratize what has until recently been an elite resource; see Ron Miller, "Open Access Battles to Democratize Academic Publishing," *EContent* (April 2009). Leslie Chan, Subbiah Arunachalam, and Barbara Kirsop, "Open Access: A Giant Leap Towards Bridging Health Inequities," *Bulletin of the World Health Organization* (August 2009), argue that only through open access publishing can the latest research results reach those who need them. Harvard University's arts and sciences faculty "has directly challenged the authority of academic journals to control access to research results" by voting to put faculty work in a free online repository, following similar moves by the Howard Hughes Medical Institute and the Wellcome Trust in London. A comment by Patricia Schroeder of the Association of American Publishers that "Publishers may not be as quite as excited to take articles from Harvard" seems more than a little wishful, considering Harvard's reputation. See Andrew Lawler, "Harvard Faculty Votes to Make Open Access Its Default Mode," *Science* (February 22, 2008). In December 2009, Robin Peek, "OAW [Open Access Week] 2009 Exceeds Expectations," *Information Today*, noted that 100 universities had already announced plans to require researchers to deposit research information in open access repositories. The Obama administration has opened discussions over whether to broaden open access beyond the NIH program; see Jocelyn Kaiser, "White House Mulls Plan to Broaden Access to Published Papers," *Science* (January 15, 2010). In July 2010, the Information Policy, Census, and National Archives Subcommittee of the House Committee on Oversight and Government Reform held a hearing to discuss the open access debate, touching on two bills, one that would extend the NIH policy to eleven other research agencies and shorten the 12-month delay before depositing papers in an open archive to just 6 months, and one that would revise copyright law to forbid the practice entirely. Testimony recapitulated many of the points mentioned here; see Jocelyn Kaiser, "House Hearing Explores Debate over Free Access to Journal Articles," *ScienceInsider* (July 30, 2010).

Are print journals actually threatened by the open access movement? Many commentators remark that journals offer much more than just research reports. However, they may not prove able to sustain high subscription prices. They will be obliged to adapt, as many are already doing, according to Jennifer Howard, "Scholarly Presses Discuss How They're Adapting to a Brave New E-World," *Chronicle of Higher Education* (July 11, 2008). One such adaptation is publishing books that can be freely downloaded in hope that actual book sales will follow; see John Murphy, "New Entry Tries New Publishing Model," *Research Information* (December 2008). Charles Oppenheim, "Electronic Scholarly Publishing and Open Access," *Journal of Information Science* (vol. 34, no. 4, 2008), expects pressure for open access publishing to continue, and not just in the United States. In 2012 the United Kingdom announced a requirement to require open access publishing of publicly funded research. Still, no one really expects open access publishing to completely displace the traditional mode; see Jocelyn Kaiser, "Free Journals Grow Amid Ongoing Debate," *Science* (August 20, 2010).

In 2007, legislation mandated that federally funded research reports be given to PubMed Central. The resulting Public Access Policy is described in Robin Peek, "Coming to Grips with the NIH Policy," *Information Today* (September 2008); see also Robin Peek, "The Battle over PubMed Central Continues," *Information Today* (November 2008). The debate continued into 2012, but when journal publisher Elsevier pulled its support from the latest bill, it appeared dead, at least for now; see Jennifer Howard, "Legislation to Bar Public-Access Requirement on Federal Research Is Dead," *The Chronicle of Higher Education* (February 27, 2012). On February 22, 2013, the White House's Office of Science and Technology Policy issued a "policy memorandum" directing all Federal agencies with more than $100 million in R&D spending to develop plans to make publically accessible within one year of publication the results of all their research; see Jocelyn Kaiser, "U.S. Agencies Directed to Make Research Papers Available," *Science* (March 1, 2013).

A hearing on an earlier bill was held on September 11, 2008. Publisher representatives such as Martin Frank, executive director of the American Physiological Society, supported the bill, arguing that "By protecting copyright for research works, [it] will continue to provide incentives for private-sector investment in the peer review process which helps to ensure the quality and integrity of scientific research." In the YES selection, attorney and past register of copyrights Ralph Oman contends in his testimony that "If the NIH [National Institutes of Health] succeeds in putting all of the NIH-related peer-reviewed articles on its online database for free within one year of publication, the private publishers will be hard-pressed to survive." Allowing private publishers to continue to profit by publishing the results of publically funded research is the best way to ensure public benefit. In the NO selection, from a 2012 hearing of the House Committee on Science, Space and Technology, Subcommittee on Investigations and Oversight, on Examining Public Access and Scholarly Publication, Stuart M. Shieber argues that the concerns of traditional journal publishers that open access publishing will endanger their survival are not justified. The data show that publisher profitability has increased despite the recent economic downturn. Providing open access to the publicly funded research literature amplifies the diffusion of knowledge and benefits researchers, taxpayers, and everyone who gains from new medicines, new technologies, new jobs, and new solutions to long-standing problems of every kind.

YES

Ralph Oman

The Fair Copyright in Research Works Act

Mr. Chairman and members of the Subcommittee. It is a great honor to appear again before this distinguished panel. It has been a few years since my last appearance.

Thank you for the opportunity to testify on this matter of importance to copyright generally, and to the public, to the research community, to the authors of scientific, technical, and medical articles, and to the publishers of STM journals. I would like to focus on the larger policy issues that undergird the American copyright system and discuss the proposal of the National Institutes of Health that requires recipients of NIH research grants to effectively renounce copyright in their peer-reviewed article manuscripts just 12 months after publication. I will also briefly mention the bill introduced by Chairman Conyers that seeks to moderate the impact of the NIH proposal in a way that will encourage the broadest possible dissemination of high quality, peer-reviewed articles without running roughshod over the rights of authors and copyright owners.

This hearing is important on another level. The language in the appropriations bill that has given rise to this controversy was never vetted by the Judiciary Committee—the committee with intellectual property expertise. With your scrutiny today, the Subcommittee puts this narrow dispute in the larger context of the constitutional mandate—to promote the progress of science for the public interest. Other than celebrating the Judiciary Committee's involvement, I will not comment on the wisdom of legislating on appropriations bills. Into that Serbonian Bog I will not wade.

Instead, I simply applaud your decision, Mr. Chairman, to give a full airing of these issues before your expert Subcommittee. They bear directly on the copyright policies of our government and the incentives to authorship and publication under U.S. copyright law. For reasons I will discuss, the NIH proposal seems short-sighted, counterproductive, damaging to U.S. creativity, which this subcommittee fosters and safeguards, and contrary to the NIH's own interests in encouraging broad public dissemination of peer-reviewed learned articles. The Appropriations Committee, to its credit, sensed that the NIH proposal ventured into sensitive territory and added a very important proviso. That proviso directed the NIH to "implement the public access policy in a manner consistent with copyright law." In my opinion, the NIH has fallen short of that dictate in several respects, and, with this committee's expert guidance, they should refine their proposal in ways that are true to both the letter and spirit of the copyright law, and the essential policies behind it.

In this debate, three key questions must be answered. First, what policy will result in the broadest dissemination of high quality, peer-reviewed scholarly articles? Second, is it fair for the U.S. government to appropriate the value-added contributions of the private STM publishers? And, third, is the NIH correct in its assumption that the STM publishers will continue to publish their journals even if they lose 50 percent of their paid subscriptions?

Many of my colleagues in academia recognize that the STM publishers perform many vital functions in bringing these articles into the public forum. For one thing, they make substantial investments in the peer-review process. While they do not as a general rule pay the reviewers, the publishers hire in-house teams to support outside specialists. These teams arrange and coordinate effective distribution, stay close to the academic experts in the discipline personally and professionally, follow the literature, and engage in on-going communications with the authors about the reviewers' comments and the incorporation of those comments into the manuscript.

In addition to the peer-review process, the publishers make judgments about which of the manuscripts to publish, depending on their quality and the level of interest in the research itself. They also edit the manuscripts and make them presentable for publication.

My basic concern about the NIH proposal is that it will, sooner rather than later, destroy the commercial market for these scientific, technical, and medical journals. If this dark prophesy comes to pass, who, I wonder, will handle all of these expensive and sensitive administrative details? Some of my academic colleagues are confident that this change in the mechanics of scientific publishing will have little or no impact on the private sector, and that it will remain as robust as ever, even if the NIH freely publishes all of the NIH peer-reviewed article manuscripts shortly after private publication. Some claim that they have "evidence" that STM publishing will continue to flourish. I have not seen that evidence. To me, it suggests an element of wishful thinking. In my experience, Congress is normally reluctant to hang major legislative change in copyright policy on the thin reed of wishful thinking. With the prospect of free copies available in the near term, who in the face of experience and reality can reasonably expect that subscribers to STM journals, faced

Oman, Ralph. The U.S. House of Representatives, September 11, 2008.

with their own budgetary constraints and needs, will not look with real favor on alternative free sources? I can't. It is belied by common sense. Certainly, many university and industry librarians will cancel their subscriptions to these learned journals, with some estimates of a cancellation rate approaching 50 percent. With plummeting sales, how could the STM publishers stay in business? This is a critical point, and one that this committee has a special sensitivity to. It really goes to the heart of the matter, in terms of public policy.

It is a basic premise of copyright that the law is designed to benefit the public, not reward authors or publishers. But, as James Madison wrote in the Federalist Papers, "the public good fully coincides" with the rights of authors and copyright owners. With that admonition, we consider the NIH proposal. It seems clear that Congress would not want the NIH free access policy to cause many or all of the private STM publishers to fade away. Of course, if fair market competition, or a change in the culture of academic publishing, or costly overhead were eventually to drive the private publishers out of business, so be it. It is one thing that they should suffer demise because of changes in the marketplace, and it is another to be brought down by an ill-considered governmental fiat. The NIH does not intend to perform any of the vetting, selection, and editing functions now performed by the learned societies, by the professional organizations, and by the STM publishers, and I doubt if Congress wants to increase their budget so they can take on these additional responsibilities. So the question occurs: who is going to do it? I do not see replacements for the publishers raising their hands to volunteer. For this reason alone, I question the wisdom of the NIH provision. And there are larger issues as well. Experience teaches that as a general rule Congress prefers to keep the hairy snout of the federal government out of the peer-review and manuscript selection process. We live in an open society, and, with a weather eye on the First Amendment, we try to keep the government at arms length from these delicate publication decisions, so as not to skew the process.

That being said, the NIH provision brings back vivid memories of the debate we had in 1980 with the Small Business and University Patent Procedure Act. In that debate, Senator Russell Long, Chairman of the Senate Finance Committee, following the script written by Admiral Rickover, the father of the nuclear submarine, argued in favor of existing government policy—that patents developed with government research money belong to the taxpayers who subsidize the research. Senator Bayh and Senator Dole reasoned that the taxpayers would get a far greater return on their investment if we instead facilitated private sector ownership and commercialization of the inventions, putting these inventions to work for the people. We are about to celebrate the 30th anniversary of Bayh/Dole, and no one is arguing for its repeal.

The same policy arguments apply in the NIH case. If the NIH succeeds in putting all of the NIH-related peer-reviewed articles on its online database for free within one year of publication, the private publishers will be hard-pressed to survive. To me, it seems far more likely that the U.S. taxpayer will achieve the desired objective—the broadest possible dissemination of the peer-reviewed article manuscripts—under the current system. With the private STM publishers running the peer-review process, selecting the articles, and aggressively marketing their journals to libraries and other research institutions, both foreign and domestic, the current system lets the publishers bring their professional judgment and expertise into the process and ensures high quality scholarship. Paid subscriptions keep the current system perking along, without intrusive government involvement, and without an infusion of funds from the government fisc. If the NIH provision is fully implemented, it will almost certainly end this self-policing and self-financing system and get the federal government deeply into the STM publishing business.

Finally, Mr. Chairman, I would like to mention a few related issues. First, I wonder if any of the manuscript articles that the NIH will publish contain preexisting materials that the NIH researcher did not create and therefore does not own. Here, I am thinking of charts, diagrams, photographs, and illustrations. Will the NIH commandeer the rights of those creators as well, or will it require the NIH researcher to clear all of those ancillary rights as part of the "contract." Today, of course, the publishers often help the author clear these rights, including electronic distribution rights. Will the NIH undertake this task if the publishers drop out of the picture?

Second, I wonder if the NIH proposal really serves our international interests. Our trade negotiators are constantly fighting for strong intellectual property protection, which is under siege in many countries around the world. I assume that some of the authors (or at least co-authors) are foreign nationals, and would fall under the protection of the Berne Convention. And I assume some of the impacted publisher/copyright owners are foreign as well. As I will note in a moment, the NIH policy will seriously threaten the protection of American authored and published works in foreign countries. This government edict from the NIH, not promulgated "in a manner consistent with copyright law," has a crippling effect on the value of the copyright in these works. Some of my academic colleagues argue that the Berne Convention has no relevance to the NIH policy. They see it as a simple contract matter, and they note that the researchers get very valuable consideration for their assignment of copyright to the NIH under the contract. Granted, the researchers do receive a generous stipend, averaging $400,000, but that fact also makes the whole arrangement suspect. To a serious researcher, an NIH grant is a matter of life and death professionally. To claim that the assignment of the reproduction right is "voluntary"—the product of a free market negotiation—strikes me as disingenuous.

In fact, the government involvement puts the NIH "contract" in a suspect category in the Berne and TRIPs context. It is not a private contract between commercial interests. Let me draw a hypothetical. The U.S. motion picture industry is now permitted to exhibit theatrically only 10 or so films per year in China. Suppose the government of China were to offer the American film producers a deal: "If you sign a contract waiving your reproduction right, we will allow you to exhibit 100 films a year." The producers would crunch the numbers and calculate the bottom line, even while complaining bitterly that the deal is outrageous and clearly a violation of the spirit of copyright and the Berne Convention. Nonetheless, they might conclude that on balance they would make more money with the proffered deal than they now make with limited access to the huge Chinese market. So, in the end, they might sign on the dotted line. Could the United States take that "contract" to the WTO and press a claim under TRIPs that China is not complying with its treaty obligations? I think so. The ensuing mass piracy of American films in China would be a direct result of this unwaivering government action that diminishes copyright, disguised as a "contract." In any case, the NIH free access policy is an unfortunate international precedent for a country like the United States, whose great strength is intellectual property.

The NIH should reconsider the long term consequences of its proposal. The dedicated researchers who benefit from the NIH grants take great professional pride in being published in prestigious learned journals, all of which constitute a valuable and reliable resource for future research. The NIH itself recognizes that "publication in peer-reviewed journals is a major factor in determining the professional standing of scientists; institutions use publication in peer-reviewed journals in making hiring, promotion, and tenure decisions."

Despite some grumbling about high subscription prices, very few researchers, academics, or librarians are suggesting that the journals have outlived their usefulness. The STM publishers should be given the right to compete fairly in a changing marketplace, in which they will innovate and have the opportunity to flourish on their own merits, as long as their copyrights are protected. Congress should require the NIH to demonstrate convincingly that their free access policy will not jeopardize the existence of the STM publishers and the indispensable role they play in vetting and selecting peer-reviewed articles. Absent that proof, the NIH should rethink their current policy of involuntary assignment. Current law gives the NIH some discretion in implementing their open access policy in a manner consistent with copyright. If the NIH do not amend their policy, Congress should direct them to do so. The Chairman's bill will allow the publishers to continue publishing. It will preserve the STM journals as valuable professional tools for scientific research, thereby promoting the progress of science. By restoring the status quo ante, the Chairman's bill will give the evolving free market a chance to come to grips with the new online technologies without undercutting the incentives that publishers have relied on for two hundred years. I would urge its enactment.

Ralph Oman is Pravel Professorial Lecturer in Intellectual Property Law and fellow of the Creative and Innovative Economy Center, The George Washington University Law School. He is a counsel for the intellectual property practice group of the firm Dechert, LLP, and has served as register of copyrights of the United States and as chief counsel of the Senate Subcommittee on Patents, Copyrights, and Trademarks.

Stuart M. Shieber

NO

Testimony Before the U.S. House of Representatives Committee on Science, Space and Technology, Subcommittee on Investigations and Oversight, Hearing on Examining Public Access and Scholarly Publication Interests

The Potential for Open Access

The mission of the university is to create, preserve, and disseminate knowledge to the benefit of all. In Harvard's Faculty of Arts and Sciences (FAS), where I hold my faculty post, we codify this in the FAS Grey Book, which states that research policy "should encourage the notion that ideas or creative works produced at the University should be used for the greatest possible public benefit. This would normally mean the widest possible dissemination and use of such ideas or materials."

At one time, the widest possible dissemination was achieved by distributing the scholarly articles describing the fruits of research in the form of printed issues of peer-reviewed journals, sent to the research libraries of the world for reading by their patrons, and paid for by subscription fees. These fees covered the various services provided to the authors of the articles—management of the peer review process, copy-editing, typesetting, and other production processes—as well as the printing, binding, and shipping of the physical objects.

Thanks to the forward thinking of federal science funding agencies, including NSF, DARPA, NASA, and DOE, we now have available computing and networking technologies that hold the promise of transforming the mechanisms for disseminating and using knowledge in ways not imaginable even a few decades ago. The internet allows nearly instantaneous distribution of content for essentially zero marginal cost to a large and rapidly increasing proportion of humanity. Ideally, this would ramify in a universality of access to research results, thereby truly achieving the widest possible dissemination.

The benefits of such so-called *open access* are manifold. The signatories of the 2002 Budapest Open Access Initiative state that

> The public good [open access] make[s] possible is the world-wide electronic distribution of the peer-reviewed journal literature and completely free and unrestricted access to it by all scientists, scholars, teachers, students, and other curious minds. Removing access barriers to this literature will accelerate research, enrich education, share the learning of the rich with the poor and the poor with the rich, make this literature as useful as it can be, and lay the foundation for uniting humanity in a common intellectual conversation and quest for knowledge.

From a more pragmatic point of view, a large body of research has shown that public research has a large positive impact on economic growth, and that access to the scholarly literature is central to that impact. Martin and Tang's recent review of the literature concludes that "there have been numerous attempts to measure the economic impact of publicly funded research and development (R&D), all of which show a large positive contribution to economic growth." It is therefore not surprising that Houghton's modeling of the effect of broader public access to federally funded research shows that the benefits to the US economy come to the billions of dollars and are eight times the costs.

Opening access to the literature makes it available not only to human readers, but to computer processing as well. There are some million and a half scholarly articles published each year. No human can read them all or even the tiny fraction in a particular subfield, but computers can, and computer analysis of the text, known as *text mining,* has the potential not only to extract high-quality structured data from article databases but even to generate new research hypotheses. My own field of research, computational linguistics, includes text mining. I have collaborated with colleagues in the East Asian Languages and Civilization department on text mining of tens of thousands of classical Chinese biographies and with colleagues in the History department on computational analysis of pre-modern Latin texts. Performing similar analyses on the current research literature, however, is encumbered by proscriptions of copyright and contract because the dominant publishing mechanisms are not open.

Shieber, Stuart M. From statement before U.S. House of Representatives, March 29, 2012.

In Harvard's response to the Office of Science and Technology Policy's request for information on public access, Provost Alan Garber highlighted the economic potential for the kinds of reuse enabled by open access.

> Public access not only facilitates innovation in research-driven industries such as medicine and manufacturing. It stimulates the growth of a new industry adding value to the newly accessible research itself. This new industry includes search, current awareness, impact measurement, data integration, citation linking, text and data mining, translation, indexing, organizing, recommending, and summarizing. These new services not only create new jobs and pay taxes, but they make the underlying research itself more useful. Research funding agencies needn't take on the job of provide all these services themselves. As long as they ensure that the funded research is digital, online, free of charge, and free for reuse, they can rely on an after-market of motivated developers and entrepreneurs to bring it to users in the forms in which it will be most useful. Indeed, scholarly publishers are themselves in a good position to provide many of these value-added services, which could provide an additional revenue source for the industry.

Finally, free and open access to the scholarly literature is an intrinsic good. It is in the interest of the researchers generating the research and those who might build upon it, the public who take interest in the research, the press who help interpret the results, and the government who funds these efforts. All things being equal, open access to the research literature ought to be the standard.

Systemic Problems in the Journal Publishing System

Unfortunately, over the last several years, it has become increasingly clear to many that this goal of the "widest possible dissemination" was in jeopardy because of systemic problems in the current mechanisms of scholarly communication, which are not able to take full advantage of the new technologies to maximize the access to research and therefore its potential for social good.

By way of background, I should review the standard process for disseminating research results. Scholars and researchers—often with government funding—perform research and write up their results in the form of articles, which are submitted to journals that are under the editorial control of the editor-in-chief and editorial boards made up of other scholars. These editors find appropriate reviewers, also scholars, to read and provide detailed reviews of the articles, which authors use to improve the quality of the articles. Reviewers also provide advice to the editors on whether the articles are appropriate for publication in the journal, the final decisions being made by the editors. Participants in these aspects of the publishing process are overwhelmingly volunteers, scholars who provide their time freely as a necessary part of their engagement in the research enterprise. The management of this process, handling the logistics, is typically performed by the journal's publisher, who receives the copyright in the article from the author for its services. The publisher also handles any further production process such as copy-editing and typesetting of accepted articles and their distribution to subscribers through print issue or more commonly these days through online access. This access is provided to researchers by their institutional libraries, which pay for annual subscriptions to the journals.

Libraries have observed with alarm a long-term dramatic rise in subscription costs of journals. The Association of Research Libraries, whose members represent the leading research libraries of the United States and Canada, have tracked serials expenditures for over three decades. From 1986 through 2010 (the most recent year with available data), expenditures in ARL libraries have increased by a factor of almost 5. Even discounting for inflation, the increase is almost 2.5 times. These increases correspond to an annualized rate of almost 7% per year, during a period in which inflation has averaged less than 3%.

Another diagnostic of the market dysfunction in the journal publishing system is the huge disparity in subscription costs between different journals. Bergstrom and Bergstrom showed that even within a single field of research, commercial journals are *on average* five times more expensive per page than non-profit journals. When compared by cost per citation, which controls better for journal quality, the disparity becomes even greater, a factor of 10 times. Odylzko notes that "The great disparity in costs among journals is a sign of an industry that has not had to worry about efficiency." Finally, the extraordinary profit margins, increasing even over the last few years while research libraries' budgets were under tremendous pressure, provide yet another signal of the absence of a functioning competitive market.

The Harvard library system is the largest academic library in the world, and the fifth largest library of any sort. In attempting to provide access to research results to our faculty and students, the university subscribes to tens of thousands of serials at a cost of about 9 million dollars per year. Nonetheless, we too have been buffeted by the tremendous growth in journal costs over the last decades, with Harvard's serials expenditures growing by a factor of 3 between 1986 and 2004. Such geometric increases in expenditures could not be sustained indefinitely. Over the years since 2004 our journal expenditure increases have been curtailed through an aggressive effort at deduplication, elimination of print subscriptions, and a painful series of journal cancellations. As a researcher, I know that Harvard does not subscribe to all of the journals that I would like access to for my own research, and if Harvard, with its scale, cannot provide optimal subscription access, other universities without our resources are in an even more restricted position.

Correspondingly, the articles that we ourselves generate as authors are not able to be accessed as broadly as we would like. We write articles not for direct financial gain—we are not paid for the articles and receive no royalties—but rather so that others can read them and make use of the discoveries they describe. To the extent that access is limited, those goals are thwarted.

The economic causes of these observed phenomena are quite understandable. Journal access is a monopolistic good. Libraries can buy access to a journal's articles only from the publisher of that journal, by virtue of the monopoly character of copyright. In addition, the high prices of journals are hidden from the "consumers" of the journals, the researchers reading the articles, because an intermediary, the library, pays the subscriptions on their behalf. The market therefore embeds a moral hazard. Under such conditions, market failure is not surprising; one would expect inelasticity of demand, hyperinflation, and inefficiency in the market, and that is what we observe. Prices inflate, leading to some libraries canceling journals, leading to further price increases to recoup revenue—a spiral that ends in higher and higher prices paid by fewer and fewer libraries. The market is structured to provide institutions a Hobson's choice between unsustainable expenditures or reduced access.

The unfortunate side effect of this market dysfunction has been that as fewer libraries can afford the journals, access to the research results they contain is diminished. In 2005, then Provost of Harvard Steven Hyman appointed an ad hoc committee, which I chaired, to examine these issues and make recommendations as to what measures Harvard might pursue to mitigate this problem of access to our writings. Since then, we have been pursuing a variety of approaches to maximize access to the writings of Harvard researchers.

Addressing Insufficient Access Through an Open Access Policy

One of these approaches involves the self-imposition by faculty of an open-access policy according to which faculty grant a license to the university to distribute our scholarly articles and commit to providing copies of our manuscript articles for such distribution. By virtue of this kind of policy, the problem of access limitation is mitigated by providing a supplemental venue for access to the articles. Four years ago, in February of 2008, the members of the Faculty of Arts and Sciences at Harvard became the first school to enact such a policy, by unanimous vote as it turned out.

In order to guarantee the freedom of faculty authors to choose the rights situation for their articles, the license is waivable at the sole discretion of the author, so faculty retain control over whether the university is granted this license. But the policy has the effect that by default, the university holds a license to our articles, which can therefore be distributed from a repository that we have set up for that purpose. Since the FAS vote, six other schools at Harvard—Harvard Law School, Harvard Kennedy School of Government, Harvard Graduate School of Education, Harvard Business School, Harvard Divinity School, and Harvard Graduate School of Design—have passed this same kind of policy, and similar policies have been voted by faculty bodies at many other universities as well, including Massachusetts Institute of Technology, Stanford, Princeton, Columbia, and Duke. Notably, the policies have seen broad faculty support, with faculty imposing these policies on themselves typically by unanimous or near unanimous votes.

Because of these policies in the seven Harvard schools, Harvard's article repository, called DASH (for Digital Access to Scholarship at Harvard), now provides access to over 7,000 articles representing 4,000 Harvard-affiliated authors. Articles in DASH have been downloaded almost three-quarters of a million times. The number of waivers of the license has been very small; we estimate the waiver rate at about 5%. Because of the policy, as faculty authors we are retaining rights to openly distribute the vast majority of the articles that we write.

The process of consultation in preparation for the faculty vote was a long one. I started speaking with faculty committees, departments, and individuals about two years before the actual vote. During that time and since, I have not met a single faculty member or researcher who objected to the principle underlying the open-access policies at Harvard, to obtain the widest possible dissemination for our scholarly results, and have been struck by the broad support for the kind of open dissemination of articles that the policy and the repository allow.

This approach to the access limitation problem, the provision of supplemental access venues, is also seen in the extraordinarily successful public access policy of the National Institutes of Health (NIH), which Congress mandated effective April, 2008. By virtue of that policy, researchers funded by NIH provide copies of their articles for distribution from NIH's PubMed Central (PMC) repository. Today, PMC provides free online access to 2.4 million articles downloaded a million times per day by half a million users. NIH's own analysis has shown that a quarter of the users are researchers. The hundreds of thousands of articles they are accessing per day demonstrates the large latent demand for articles not being satisfied by the journals' subscription base. Companies account for another 17%, showing that the policy benefits small businesses and corporations, who need access to scientific advances to spur innovation. Finally, the general public accounts for 40% of the users, some quarter of a million people per day, demonstrating that these articles are of tremendous interest to the taxpayers who fund the research in the first place and who deserve access to the results that they have underwritten.

The Standard Objection to Open Access Policies

The standard objection to these open-access policies is that supplemental access to scholarly articles, such as that provided by institutional repositories like Harvard's DASH or subject-based repositories like NIH's PubMed Central, could supplant subscription access to such an extent that subscriptions would come under substantial price pressure. Sufficient price pressure, in this scenario, could harm the publishing industry, the viability of journals, and the peer review and journal production processes.

There is no question that the services provided by journals are valuable to the research enterprise, so such concerns must be taken seriously. By now, however, these arguments have been aired and addressed in great detail. I recommend the report "The Future of Taxpayer-Funded Research: Who Will Control Access to the Results?" by my co-panelist Elliott Maxwell, which provides detailed support for the report's conclusion that "There is no persuasive evidence that increased access threatens the sustainability of traditional subscription-supported journals, or their ability to fund rigorous peer review." The reasons are manifold, including the fact that supplemental access covers only a fraction of the articles in any given journal, is often delayed relative to publication, and typically provides a manuscript version of the article rather than the version of record. Consistent with this reasoning, the empirical evidence shows no such discernible effect. After four years of the NIH policy, for instance, subscription prices have continued to increase, as have publisher margins. The NIH states that "while the U.S. economy has suffered a downturn during the time period 2007 to 2011, scientific publishing has grown: The number of journals dedicated to publishing biological sciences/agriculture articles and medicine/health articles increased 15% and 19%, respectively. The average subscription prices of biology journals and health sciences journals increased 26% and 23%, respectively. Publishers forecast increases to the rate of growth of the medical journal market, from 4.5% in 2011 to 6.3% in 2014."

Open Access Journal Publishing as an Alternative to Subscription Journal Publishing

Nonetheless, it does not violate the laws of economics that increased supplemental access (even if delayed) to a sufficiently high proportion of articles (even if to a deprecated version) could put price pressure on subscription journals, perhaps even so much so that journals would not be able to recoup their costs. In this hypothetical case, would that be the end of journals? No, because even if publishers (again, merely by hypothesis and counterfactually) add no value for the readers (beyond what the readers are already getting in the [again hypothetical] universal open access), the author and the author's institution gain much value: vetting, copyediting, typesetting, and most importantly, imprimatur of the journal. This is value that authors and their institutions should be, would be, and are willing to pay for. The upshot is that journals will merely switch to a different business model, in which the journal charges a one-time *publication fee* to cover the costs of publishing the article.

I state this as though this publication-fee revenue model is itself hypothetical, but it is not. Open-access journals already exist in the thousands. They operate in exactly the same way as traditional subscription journals—providing management of peer review, production services, and distribution—with the sole exception that they do not charge for online access, so that access is free and open to anyone. The publication-fee revenue model for open-access journals is a proven mechanism. The prestigious non-profit open-access publisher Public Library of Science is generating surplus revenue and is on track to publish some 3% of the world biomedical literature through its journal *PLoS ONE* alone. The BioMed Central division of the commercial publisher Springer is generating profits for its parent company using the same revenue model. Indeed, the growth of open-access journals over the past few years has been meteoric. There are now over 7,000 open-access journals, many using the publication-fee model, and many of the largest, most established commercial journal publishers—Elsevier, Springer, Wiley-Blackwell, SAGE—now operate open-access journals using the publication-fee revenue model. Were supplemental access to cause sufficient price pressure to put the subscription model in danger, the result would merely be further uptake of this already burgeoning alternative revenue model.

In this scenario, the cost of journal publishing would be borne not by the libraries on behalf of their readers, but by funding agencies and research institutions on behalf of their authors. Already, funding agencies such as Wellcome Trust and Howard Hughes Medical Institute underwrite open access author charges, and in fact mandate open access. Federal granting agencies such as NSF and NIH allow grant funds to be used for open-access publication fees as well (though grantees must prebudget for these unpredictable charges). Not all fields have the sort of grant funding opportunities that could underwrite these fees. For those fields, the researcher's employing institution, as de facto funder of the research, should underwrite charges for publication in open-access journals. Here again, Harvard has taken an early stand as one of the initial signatories—along with Cornell, Dartmouth, MIT, and University of California, Berkeley—of the Compact for Open-Access Publishing Equity, which commits these universities and the dozen or so additional signatories to establishing mechanisms for underwriting reasonable open-access publication fees. The Compact acknowledges the fact that the services that journal publishers provide are important, cost money, and deserve to be funded, and commits the universities to doing so, albeit with a revenue model that avoids the market dysfunction of the subscription journal system.

Advantages of the Open Access Publishing System

The primary advantage of the open-access journal publishing system is the open access that it provides. Since revenue does not depend on limiting access to those willing to pay, journals have no incentive to limit access, and in fact have incentive to provide as broad access as possible to increase the value of their brand. In fact, open-access journals can provide access not only in the traditional sense, allowing anyone to access the articles for the purpose of reading them, but can provide the articles unencumbered by any use restrictions, thereby allowing the articles to be used, re-used, analyzed, and data-mined in ways we are not even able to predict.

A perhaps less obvious advantage of the publication-fee revenue model for open-access journals is that the factors leading to the subscription market failure do not inhere in the publication-fee model. Bergstrom and Bergstrom explain why:

> Journal articles differ [from conventional goods such as cars] in that they are not substitutes for each other in the same way as cars are. Rather, they are complements. Scientists are not satisfied with seeing only the top articles in their field. They want access to articles of the second and third rank as well. Thus for a library, a second copy of a top academic journal is not a good substitute for a journal of the second rank. Because of this lack of substitutability, commercial publishers of established second-rank journals have substantial monopoly power and are able to sell their product at prices that are much higher than their average costs and several times higher than the price of higher quality, nonprofit journals.
>
> By contrast, the market for authors' inputs appears to be much more competitive. If journals supported themselves by author fees, it is not likely that one Open Access journal could charge author fees several times higher than those charged by another of similar quality. An author, deciding where to publish, is likely to consider different journals of similar quality as close substitutes. Unlike a reader, who would much prefer access to two journals rather than to two copies of one, an author with two papers has no strong reason to prefer publishing once in each journal rather than twice in the cheaper one.
>
> If the entire market were to switch from Reader Pays to Author Pays, competing journals would be closer substitutes in the view of authors than they are in the view of subscribers. As publishers shift from selling complements to selling substitutes, the greater competition would be likely to force commercial publishers to reduce their profit margins dramatically.

Again, the empirical evidence supports this view. Even the most expensive open-access publication fees, such as those of the prestigious Public Library of Science journals, are less than $3,000 per article, with a more typical value in the $1,000–1,500 range. By contrast, the average revenue per article for subscription journal articles is about $5,000. Thus, the open-access model better leverages free market principles: Despite providing unencumbered access to the literature, it costs no more overall per article, and may end up costing much less, than the current system. The savings to universities and funding agencies could be substantial.

Conclusion

I began my comments by quoting the mission of academics such as myself to provide the widest possible dissemination—open access—to the ideas and knowledge resulting from our research. Government, too, has an underlying goal of promoting the dissemination of knowledge, expressed in Thomas Jefferson's view that "by far the most important bill in our whole code is that for the diffusion of knowledge among the people." The federal agencies and science policies that this committee oversees have led to knowledge breakthroughs of the most fundamental sort—in our understanding of the physical universe, in our ability to comprehend fundamental biological processes, and, in my own field, in the revolutionary abilities to transform and transmit information.

Open access policies build on these information technology breakthroughs to maximize the return on the taxpayers' enormous investment in that research, and magnify the usefulness of that research. They bring economic benefits that far exceed the costs. The NIH has shown one successful model, which could be replicated at other funding agencies, as envisioned in the recently re-introduced bipartisan Federal Research Public Access Act (FRPAA).

Providing open access to the publicly-funded research literature—amplifying the "diffusion of knowledge"—will benefit researchers, taxpayers, and every person who gains from new medicines, new technologies, new jobs, and new solutions to longstanding problems of every kind.

Stuart M. Shieber is the James O. Welch, Jr., and Virginia B. Welch Professor of computer science at Harvard University. As a faculty member, he led the development and enactment of Harvard's open access policies. He also serves as the faculty director of Harvard's Office for Scholarly Communication.

EXPLORING THE ISSUE

Should the Public Have to Pay to See the Results of Federally Funded Research?

Critical Thinking and Reflection

1. How does peer review help to ensure the quality of scientific publications?
2. Are "open access" and "peer review" mutually contradictory concepts?
3. Why can university libraries not subscribe to all available high-quality academic journals?
4. Should academic publishing be profit oriented?

Is There Common Ground?

At the core of the debate lie two points: the right of academic publishers to make a profit and the right of the public to have access to the fruits of scientific research. High journal prices favor the former while impeding the latter. In one form, open access publishing says the academic publishers can make a profit for a limited time before articles get put into open access archives. On the other hand, no one really expects open access publishing to completely displace the traditional mode; see Jocelyn Kaiser, "Free Journals Grow Amid Ongoing Debate," *Science* (August 20, 2010).

1. Is this form of open access publishing a viable compromise?
2. Some areas of science have long circulated preprints of articles to give other scientists and even the public a first look at reports. Journals later publish edited, peer-reviewed versions of the reports. Is this a viable compromise?
3. What services do journal publishers provide to researchers? Do these services justify high journal prices?
4. If we reject the idea that academic publishing should be profit oriented, how can the publishers remain in business? Should academic publishing be run by the government?

Create Central

www.mhhe.com/createcentral

Additional Resources

Theodora Bloom, et al., "PLoS Biology at 5: The Future Is Open Access," *PLoS Biology* (October 2008).

Jennifer Howard, "Legislation to Bar Public-Access Requirement on Federal Research Is Dead," *The Chronicle of Higher Education* (February 27, 2012).

Jocelyn Kaiser, "Free Journals Grow Amid Ongoing Debate," *Science* (August 20, 2010).

Michael P. Taylor, "Opinion: Academic Publishing Is Broken: The Current System by Which Academics Publish Their Scientific Discoveries Is a Massive Waste of Money," *The Scientist* (March 19, 2012).

Internet References . . .

Directory of Open Access Journals

The Directory of Open Access Journals lists over 8,000 free, full-text, quality-controlled scientific and scholarly journals, many of which can be searched at the article level.

www.doaj.org/

BioMed Central Open Access Charter

BioMed Central calls itself the "open access publisher." It defines open access publishing as making materials "universally and freely accessible via the Internet, in an easily readable format . . . immediately upon publication" and commits itself to maintaining an open access policy.

www.biomedcentral.com

Selected, Edited, and with Issue Framing Material by:
Thomas A. Easton, *Thomas College*

ISSUE

Should Scientific Papers Containing Potentially Hazardous Information Be Published in Their Entirety?

YES: Daniel R. Perez, from "H5N1 Debates: Hung Up on the Wrong Questions," *Science* (February 11, 2012)

NO: Michael T. Osterholm and Donald A. Henderson, from "Life Sciences at a Crossroads: Respiratory Transmissible H5N1," *Science* (February 11, 2012)

Learning Outcomes

After studying this issue, students will be able to:

- Explain what "dual-use" research is.
- Explain why a government agency would ask researchers and journal editors to leave details out of a scientific paper.
- Explain why bird flu is not currently a major threat to the human population.

ISSUE SUMMARY

YES: Daniel R. Perez argues that if we hope to prevent a future bird-flu pandemic, we need all the information we can get. Two papers detailing how to engineer a bird flu virus that can move more easily between ferrets—and thus potentially between humans—should be published in their entirety.

NO: Michael T. Osterholm and Donald A. Henderson argue that the risks of releasing all the details of these papers far outweigh any potential benefits.

H5N1 bird flu is deadly to domestic poultry. Occasionally it infects people, and the death rate among those who are taken to hospitals is about 60 percent (no one knows how many cases are not taken to hospitals; the actual death rate may be much less). Fortunately, the virus does not spread easily from human to human. In an effort to understand why, research teams led by Ron Fouchier of Erasmus MC in Rotterdam, the Netherlands, and Yoshihiro Kawaoka of the University of Wisconsin, Madison, modified the virus so that it could move more easily through the air between ferrets (which respond to flu similarly to humans), and potentially from human to human. In the fall of 2011, the two teams submitted papers to *Nature* and *Science* explaining how they had modified the virus. The journals accepted the papers but delayed publication while the United States' National Science Advisory Board for Biosecurity (NSABB) deliberated over whether key details should be removed or "redacted" from the papers (and made available only to researchers with a clear need to know) in order to prevent terrorists from learning how to create a flu pandemic (widespread epidemic). Critics called the modified virus an "Armageddon virus," and the media—CNN, the *New York Times*, *Time*, and many other magazines and blogs—gave the story major attention. There was even a call on Facebook to suppress the research. The potentials for bioterrorism and accidental releases from labs were major concerns; see Laurie Garrett, "The Bioterrorist Next Door," *Foreign Policy* (December 15, 2011); Fred Guterl, "Waiting to Explode," *Scientific American* (June 2012); and Tina Hesman Saey, "Designer Flu," *Science News* (June 2, 2012).

Those who oppose redaction argue that the details may be crucial to identifying a dangerous pandemic in its early stages and mounting an appropriate response; see Carl Zimmer, "Could Information about a Lab-Made Virus Really Help Evildoers Create a Biological Weapon?" *Slate* (December 22, 2011; www.slate.com/articles/technology/future_tense/2011/12/h5n1_the_lab_made_virus_the_u_s_fears_could_be_made_into_a_biological_weapon_.html); and Jon Cohen, "Does Forewarned = Forearmed with Lab-Made Avian Influenza Strains?" *Science* (February 17, 2012). In December 2011 the NSABB recommended redaction, and soon thereafter the researchers announced a

60-day moratorium on further research (the moratorium has since then been extended); see Josh Fischman, "Science and Security Clash on Bird-Flu Papers," *Chronicle of Higher Education* (January 6, 2012); and Alice Park, "Scientists Agree to Halt Work on Dangerous Bird Flu Strain," *Time* (January 20, 2012).

Some scientists cautioned that the modified flu virus may not actually be a serious threat and urged the NSABB to reconsider its decision. In February 2012, the World Health Organization convened a group of flu researchers, public health officials, and journal editors from eleven countries to discuss the issue. The group recommended that the papers be published with all their details. See Jon Cohen, "WHO Group: H5N1 Papers Should Be Published in Full," *Science* (February 24, 2012), and "Surprising Twist in Debate over Lab-Made H5N1," *Science* (March 9, 2012). On March 29, 2012, the U.S. government issued a "Policy for Oversight of Life Sciences Dual Use Research of Concern" (http://oba.od.nih.gov/oba/biosecurity/pdf/united_states_government_policy_for_oversight_of_durc_final_version_032812.pdf). Very shortly afterwards, the NSABB rereviewed the H5N1 papers and recommended publication in full. See Jon Cohen and David Malakoff, "On Second Thought, Flu Papers Get Go-Ahead," *Science* (April 6, 2012). The *Nature* paper, Masaki Imai, et al., "Experimental Adaptation of an Influenza H5 HA Confers Respiratory Droplet Transmission to a Reassortant H5 HA/H1N1 Virus in Ferrets" (www.nature.com/nature/journal/vaop/ncurrent/full/nature10831.html), appeared online May 2, 2012, and on paper June 21, 2012. The *Science* paper, Sander Herfst, et al., "Airborne Transmission of Influenza A/H5N1 Virus Between Ferrets" (www.sciencemag.org/content/336/6088/1534.full), was published on June 22, 2012, along with several essays reviewing the situation and an attempt to assess the likelihood that the virus could actually jump to humans and cause problems; see Colin A. Russell, "The Potential for Respiratory Droplet-Transmissible A/H5N1 Influenza Virus to Evolve in a Mammalian Host," *Science* (June 22, 2012). Critics remain concerned that, as Thomas Ingleby of the Center for Biosecurity of the University of Pittsburgh Medical Center said, "We are playing with fire"; see Libby Lewis, "Science Journal Could Give Recipe for Deadly Avian Flu Virus," CNN (May 12, 2012) (www.cnn.com/2012/05/12/us/journal-avian-flu/index.html). By late 2012, a National Institutes of Health (NIH) plan that would call for stringent reviews of whether similar research should receive government funding, or even be classified, was being discussed by the NSABB; see David Malakoff, "Proposed H5N1 Research Reviews Raise Concerns," *Science* (December 7, 2012), and David Malakoff and Martin Enserink, "New U.S. Rules Increase Oversight of H5N1 Studies, Other Risky Science," *Science* (March 1, 2013).

The debate over whether publication of the details of the bird-flu papers should be redacted or not has been intense. Concern that they may lead to new and more onerous controls on research and publication seem to have been justified; see David Malakoff, "U.S. Agencies to Start Screening Biomedical Proposals for Dual Use," *Science* (April 6, 2012). Despite new controls, however, researchers are eager to resume research in this area; see David Malakoff, "H5N1 Researchers Ready as Moratorium Nears End," *Science* (January 4, 2013).

The basic question of control over scientific and technical knowledge is not new. In 2001, the destruction of New York's World Trade Towers and the unrelated mailing of anthrax spores to several public figures created a climate of fear and mistrust that led to heightened concern about security. Part of that fear and mistrust was aimed at science and technology, for the Al Qaeda terrorists had used computers and the Internet for communicating with each other and the person responsible for the anthrax scare (currently thought to be anthrax researcher Bruce Ivins; see David Willman, *The Mirage Man: Bruce Ivins, the Anthrax Attacks, and America's Rush to War* [Bantam, 2011]) obviously knew too much about anthrax.

"Even before . . . 2001, White House directives and agencies used the label SBU (sensitive but unclassified) to safeguard from public disclosure information that does not meet the standards for classification"; see Genevieve J. Knezo, "'Sensitive but Unclassified' and Other Federal Security Controls on Scientific and Technical Information: History and Current Controversy" (Congressional Research Service Report for Congress, April 2, 2003). See also John D. Kraemer and Lawrence O. Gostin, "The Limits of Government Regulation of Science," *Science* (March 2, 2012). In March 2002, the Bush administration declared that some information—notably the results of scientific research, especially in the life sciences—might not be classified in the ways long familiar to researchers in nuclear physics (for instance), but it could still be considered "sensitive" and thus worthy of restrictions on publication and dissemination. The Defense Department announced—and promptly dropped—plans to restrict the use and spread of unclassified DoD-funded research. However, a National Academy of Sciences report on agricultural bioterrorism that contained no classified information was censored on the insistence of the Department of Agriculture "to keep potentially dangerous information away from enemies of the United States." National security experts warned "that the current system of openness in science could lead to dire consequences." See Richard Monastersky, "Publish and Perish?" *Chronicle of Higher Education* (October 11, 2002). However, many have objected to inventing and attempting to restrict the new "sensitive but unclassified" category of information. Steven Teitelbaum, president of the Federation of American Societies for Experimental Biology, said, "information should be either classified or not classified." Charles M. Vest, in "Response and Responsibility: Balancing Security and Openness in Research and Education," *Report of the President for the Academic Year 2001–2002* (Cambridge, MA: Massachusetts Institute of Technology, 2002), argued that openness in science must preempt fears of the consequences of scientific knowledge falling into the wrong hands.

In July 2002, researchers announced that they had successfully assembled a polio virus from biochemicals and the virus's gene map. Members of Congress called for more care in releasing such information, and the American Society for Microbiology (ASM) began to debate voluntary restrictions on publication. By August 2002, the ASM had policy guidelines dictating that journal submissions that contain "information . . . that could be put to inappropriate use" be carefully reviewed and even rejected; see David Malakoff, "Researchers See Progress in Finding the Right Balance," *Science* (October 18, 2002). Soon thereafter, the federal government took its own steps in the same direction with the formation of the NSABB; see Jennifer Couzin, "U.S. Agencies Unveil Plan for Biosecurity Peer Review," *Science* (March 12, 2004).

In October 2005, scientists reassembled the deadly 1918 flu from synthesized subunits (see Phillip A. Sharp, "1918 Flu and Responsible Science" (Editorial), *Science,* October 7, 2005). In 2006, there were calls for authors, journal editors, and reviewers to do risk-benefit analysis before publishing "dual-use" work (see Yudhijit Bhattacharjee, "U.S. Panel Calls for Extra Review of Dual-Use Research," *Science* (July 21, 2006), and Robert F. Service, "Synthetic Biologists Debate Policing Themselves," *Science* (May 26, 2006)). The relevance of the debate outside biology became clear when researchers omitted important details from a study of how a dirty-bomb attack could affect Los Angeles harbor (see Yudhijit Bhattacharjee, "Should Academics Self-Censor Their Findings on Terrorism?" *Science* (May 19, 2006)).

A paper by Lawrence M. Wein and Yifan Liu, "Analyzing a Bioterror Attack on the Food Supply: The Case of Botulinum Toxin in Milk," on how terrorists might attack the United States' milk supply and on how to safeguard it, was scheduled for the May 30, 2005, issue of the *Proceedings of the National Academy of Sciences.* However, Stewart Simonson, Assistant Secretary of the Department of Health and Human Services, asked the NAS not to publish the paper on the grounds that it provides "a road map for terrorists and publication is not in the interests of the United States." The journal put the paper on hold while it studied the issue; it appeared online (www.pnas.org/cgi/content/abstract/0408526102v1) on June 28, 2005, and in print in the July 12, 2005, issue of *PNAS.* The Department of Health and Human Services continues to believe publication is a mistake, for the "consequences could be dire." It should come as no surprise that Frida Kuhlau, Anna T. Hoglund, Kathinka Evers, and Stefan Eriksson, "A Precautionary Principle for Dual Use Research in the Life Sciences," *Bioethics* (January 2011), note that the precautionary principle—more familiar in environmental and public health contexts—may reasonably be applied to dual-use biological research.

When in March/April 2006, *Technology Review* published Mark Williams' "The Knowledge," which stressed the ominous implications of current knowledge and the ready availability of materials and equipment (DNA synthesizers can be bought on eBay!), it also published a rebuttal. Allison M. Macfarlane, "Assessing the Threat," *Technology Review* (March/April 2006), noted that turning biological agents of destruction into useful weapons is much harder than it seems and the real hazards are impossible to estimate without more research. For now, she thinks, it makes more sense to focus on more imminent threats, such as those involving nuclear weapons.

Are there other possible answers besides restricting—voluntarily or otherwise—publication of potentially hazardous work? John D. Steinbruner and Elisa D. Harris, "Controlling Dangerous Pathogens," *Issues in Science and Technology* (Spring 2003), call for a global body that could oversee and regulate potentially dangerous disease research. Robert H. Sprinkle proposes "The Biosecurity Trust" (*Bioscience,* March 2003). Ruth R. Faden and Ruth A. Karron, "The Obligation to Prevent the Next Dual-Use Controversy," *Science* (February 11, 2012), argue that the need for some such oversight mechanism is urgent. No such organization yet exists, although the new screening rules (see above) are a step in that direction.

In the YES selection, Daniel Perez argues that if we hope to prevent a future bird-flu pandemic, we need all the information we can get. The papers at the heart of the current controversy should be published in their entirety. In the NO selection, Michael Osterholm and Donald Henderson argue that the risks of releasing all the details of these papers far outweigh any potential benefits. Despite the March 2012 decision of the NSABB to approve full publication, they continue to oppose it.

YES

Daniel R. Perez

H5N1 Debates: Hung Up on the Wrong Questions

Over the past few months, there has been an ever-increasing debate, echoed by the media, about the wisdom of publishing the details of two studies that have looked at the respiratory transmission potential of the so-called "bird flu" (H5N1 highly pathogenic avian influenza viruses or H5N1 HPAIV). Some voices have gone as far as asking for stopping or restricting this type of research. In the next paragraphs, I would like to argue against such calls and argue that it is important for this research to be continued under the current conditions. It is also important that the information gathered from these studies finds the necessary channels to benefit public health worldwide. The attention on this issue should be redirected to the larger problem of how to eradicate a bird flu that has the capacity to affect us on a global scale.

The H5N1 bird flu emerged in Southeast Asia in the late 1990s. In 1997, it crossed to humans in Hong Kong, where 18 people were diagnosed with the virus, and the infection resulted in six fatalities. Live bird markets were associated with the source of the virus. Culling of birds from these markets prevented new human cases. Until this incident, the prevailing dogma was that HPAIVs—bird flu H5N1 being just one of them—were viruses restricted to poultry, with no direct consequences to humans. Far from being eradicated, H5N1 viruses have had an unprecedented geographic spread, not typical of HPAIVs, spreading from Southeast Asia into the Middle East, Europe, and Africa. A combination of factors has contributed to this spread, including live poultry trade and transport, other agricultural activities, the failure of poultry vaccination campaigns, and introduction of these viruses into the wild bird population. From 2003 onward, the reported human cases of H5N1 in several countries have been associated with outbreaks of the disease in domestic poultry. So far, 576 human cases and 339 resulting deaths have been reported. Countries that eradicated the disease from domestic poultry have had no additional reports of human cases.

The H5N1 situation, however, is far from over. These viruses have continued to evolve genetically and antigenically at a pace that resembles the evolution of human influenza viruses. In Indonesia and Egypt, H5N1 is endemic in poultry and, not surprisingly, these two countries continue to report human cases. The cumulative case-fatality rate of H5N1 is 35% in Egypt and 82% in Indonesia. It is not clear whether the differences in fatality rate between these two countries are related to differences in molecular attributes of the prevalent H5N1 strains in each country, or environmental conditions and/or timing of the diagnosis and/or treatment options and regimes.

The uncontrolled spread of H5N1 viruses in poultry continues to pose a major pandemic threat. If we do not "take the bull by the horns" and make a worldwide concerted effort to help countries eradicate H5N1 viruses from domestic poultry, we will continue to face a potential H5N1 influenza pandemic.

An influenza virus is only capable of causing a pandemic if it acquires the ability to maintain sustained human-to-human transmission. The prevailing thought is that pandemic influenza strains must transmit efficiently by respiratory droplets, particularly by droplet nuclei or aerosols. A distinctive feature of avian influenza viruses in general, and H5N1 viruses in particular, is that they are incapable of being transmitted among humans by aerosol. Because pandemic influenza strains originated in avian influenza viruses, it can be argued that past pandemic influenza viruses were once avian influenza viruses that "learned" how to jump to and transmit by aerosol in humans. Understanding the molecular attributes that make influenza viruses transmissible by aerosol is the key to predicting and/or preventing the emergence of pandemic strains.

Receptor specificity plays a major role in the ability of influenza viruses to perpetuate in the human population. Pandemic influenza strains ultimately evolve in the human population with a preference for receptors with α2,6-linked sialic acid (α2,6SA)—sialic acids bound to the adjacent galactose residue in an α2,6 conformation. In contrast, most avian influenza viruses recognize α2,3SA receptors. However, this simplistic observation does not explain the fact that the highly prevalent H9N2 strains in Eurasia and the Middle East have α2,6SA humanlike receptor specificity but have yet to cause a pandemic, despite serological evidence showing considerable human exposure to these viruses. Likewise, this narrow approach does not explain why H5N1 viruses with typical α2,3SA avian-like receptor specificity can jump from birds to humans and replicate efficiently in the human host but fail to be transmitted among humans.

We are certainly only making our first steps into understanding influenza transmission; we are in the infancy stage when it comes to predicting the transmission potential of influenza strains. In this regard, the independent work by Fouchier's and Kawaoka's groups showing that H5N1 can be transmitted by respiratory droplets in the ferret model is of great importance. Ferrets are considered the best animal model for predicting the transmission of influenza in humans. If there ever was a sense of complacency about H5N1 viruses, these studies are a wake-up call. More important, the molecular changes associated with this phenotype are surprisingly few, and although the combination of these changes has yet to be found in a field isolate, the mutations themselves are not unique or exclusive to the viruses produced in these two laboratories. Make no mistake, it is likely that these viruses can emerge in the field.

Nature has an uncontrolled environment and thousands of susceptible subjects at its disposal versus the handful available to scientists in the laboratory, and therefore, it is just a matter of chance for these or viruses with a similar phenotype to emerge naturally. Just as researchers use new findings to learn how to predict earthquakes and tsunamis, the key elements that have made these viruses transmissible by respiratory droplets in the laboratory must be properly communicated to help public health officials make informed decisions if they are faced with similar field viruses.

The National Science Advisory Board for Biosecurity (NSABB)—an independent expert committee that advises the U.S. Department of Health and Human Services (HHS) and other federal departments and agencies on matters of biosecurity—has recommended that "the general conclusions highlighting the novel outcome be published, but that the manuscripts not include the methodological and other details that could enable replication of the experiments by those who would seek to do harm." Although I greatly respect the views of the NSABB, the fact that these two and other research groups have already published similar studies in the past makes it almost impossible to prevent access to details on the methodology. Preventing access to crucial pieces of information will hamper our ability to develop better vaccines and antivirals against these viruses.

The relations between receptor binding, transmissibility, and antigenic make up of the virus are intricate. Therefore, it is possible that changes that affect transmissibility can affect antigenicity and, thus, vaccine efficacy. Access to the virus sequence information could be used to increase eradication efforts if a similar field isolate is identified. The question now is not whether H5N1 viruses can be transmitted by aerosol but when it will happen in nature. In this regard, the World Health Organization highlights the importance of this research and "notes that studies conducted under appropriate conditions must continue to take place so that critical scientific knowledge needed to reduce the risks posed by the H5N1 virus continues to increase."

The worst mistake that we could make is to stop this type of research out of fear for the potential misuse of it. We should avoid the temptation to increase the containment levels for handling these viruses under laboratory conditions. Currently, these viruses are handled under Biosafety Level-3 (BSL3-Ag) conditions, which include biological safety cabinets, controlled access to the laboratory, protective equipment for investigators, filtration of supply and exhaust air, sewage decontamination, exit personnel showers, and facility integrity testing. This is historically the type of containment that many countries around the world use for these viruses. No containment condition is fail-proof, but it must be emphasized that there have been no human H5N1 cases reported from laboratory contamination and no accidental release into the environment from any laboratory. At present, far more people are at risk of infection with H5N1 in countries where the virus remains endemic. In these countries, backyard poultry owners and their families, from where most human cases have been reported, use no protection whatsoever. Smallpox was not defeated out of fear. Smallpox was defeated because Edward Jenner, among others, was fearless in his pursuit of controlling an infectious disease and, in the process, conferred a scientific status to the process of vaccination. We are much better prepared to confront infectious diseases now than in Jenner's time. We know a great deal more about influenza than was known during the 1918 Spanish influenza.

We were ill prepared to cope with the logistics of mass vaccine production during the 1957 and 1968 pandemics. In 2009, we dealt with an H1N1 pandemic virus that was not growing properly in eggs, the primary substrate for preparation of influenza vaccines, which caused a major delay in vaccine availability. However, through technology and the tireless efforts of dedicated virologists, an optimal vaccine against the H1N1 virus was produced. This initial road-block triggered many countries to build their own capacity for making vaccines. The H5N1 grows well in eggs, and the United States has been committed since 1997 to making vaccine seed stocks for viruses with pandemic potential. If the laboratory variants are cross-reactive with the seed stock, then we have a vaccine candidate. If they are not, then the question becomes whether we wait or begin now stockpiling vaccines against these variants.

Yet there are still fundamental questions about influenza viruses that we must discover in order to prevent the next influenza pandemic. We failed at containing the 2009 pandemic influenza simply because, among other factors, we do not have a comprehensive understanding of what makes an influenza strain transmissible in humans. We still do not know whether an H5N1 virus that gained the capacity to transmit by respiratory droplets in ferrets can effectively transmit by the same route in humans. We do know that the potential is there, but it is not through fear that we will stop H5N1 from becoming pandemic. The pursuit of knowledge is what has made humans resilient—a species capable of overcoming our worst fears.

Daniel R. Perez is an associate professor in the Department of Veterinary Medicine of the University of Maryland.

Michael T. Osterholm and Donald A. Henderson

NO

Life Sciences at a Crossroads: Respiratory Transmissible H5N1

Two recently submitted manuscripts to *Science* and *Nature* report success in creating mutant isolates of influenza A/H5N1 that are able to be transmitted by respiratory droplet or aerosol between mammals (ferrets). The studies imply that human-to-human transmission could be possible as well. Shortly after the submission of the papers to the journals, the National Science Advisory Board for Biosecurity (NSABB) was asked by the U.S. government to address this question. The NSABB recommended that the papers not be fully published; rather, the basic results of the studies should be communicated without methods or detailed results but in sufficient detail to maximize the benefits to society of the studies' findings. In turn, these recommendations were accepted by the U.S. government and shared with the authors and the editors of *Science* and *Nature*.

Some have asserted that these recommendations represent unwarranted censorship of scientific research and that the sharing of the results, particularly the specific viral mutations, is necessary to protect global public health. They argue that sharing the virus mutation information with global influenza surveillance organizations would result in the rapid identification of a potential H5N1 pandemic virus in birds or humans. This early information might permit health authorities to quash an emerging human influenza pandemic. In addition, they believe that knowledge of the mutations could enhance H5N1 vaccine research and manufacturing.

While considering the possible merits of a wider dissemination of more complete information regarding mutational changes of the newly created H5N1 strains, one fact must be kept in mind. The current circulating strains of influenza A/H5N1, with their human case-fatality rate of 30 to 80%, place this pathogen in the category of causing one of the most virulent known human infectious diseases.

Moreover, detecting an emerging pandemic virus in animals before the occurrence of a human pandemic is unrealistic; rather, the pandemic virus documentation will be "an after-the-fact record of what just happened." For example, in the six countries of the world where highly pathogenic avian influenza H5N1 is endemic (Bangladesh, Cambodia, China, Egypt, Indonesia, and Viet Nam), the quality of public and private veterinary and animal production services is variable and low in some places. These countries are not often able to detect and respond to influenza A/H5N1 infections in birds. When H5N1 isolates are obtained, little to no gene sequencing is conducted, meaning that a mutation map of possible prepandemic viruses will not be generally available. Even if such laboratory support were readily available and samples from ill birds were processed in a timely manner, these countries lack the commitment to deal vigorously with H5N1. This conclusion was recently highlighted by the United Nations Food and Agriculture Organization.

The World Health Organization (WHO) is also well aware of the magnitude of the challenge of identifying an emerging human influenza pandemic and stopping it before it spreads globally. Experiences with pandemic H1N1 [influenza A(H1N1)pmd09] show the problems of a strategy based on the assumption that an emerging influenza pandemic could be identified quickly in a localized geographic area with no, or very limited, travel in or out of the pandemic zone. As a result of extensive global travel, influenza A(H1N1)pmd09 infection was already occurring in a number of countries before the first isolate was identified. That experience dashed WHO's expectations of using antiviral drugs to stop initial outbreaks of an emerging pandemic influenza virus.

With regard to H5N1 vaccine research, licensed influenza vaccines for human use, whether inactivated or live attenuated, are based on the use of the hemagglutinin and neuraminidase antigens, not on the other novel antigens that are potentially altered by mutational changes. Although H5N1 candidate vaccines using the isolates from these studies should be developed and tested, this does not require sharing all of the mutational data outside of a small select group of established researchers already working within the WHO network. Rather, the real challenge that we face in preparing for the next influenza pandemic is developing, licensing, and manufacturing 21st-century game-changing influenza vaccines that are effective against multiple strains and readily available on a global basis in time for the earliest days of the pandemic. One of us (M.T.O.) recently summarized the serious challenges we face with the relative effectiveness and availability of our current hemagglutinin antigen vaccines. First, the effectiveness of vaccines both with and without adjuvant against influenza A(H1N1)pmd09–related illness was limited despite the very close match between the circulating virus and the vaccine strain. In the United States, the effectiveness of the vaccine without adjuvant in children and adults 10 to 49 years was 59%, and for mostly vaccines with adjuvant in Europe and Canada in those primarily under 65 years of age, the median effectiveness was 72%. In addition, influenza vaccines produced for each of the last three pandemics (1957, 1969, and 2009) prevented very little disease, because supplies of vaccine were not available until after most of the cases had occurred because of lengthy manufacturing requirements.

In summary, disseminating the entirety of the methods and results of the two H5N1 studies in the general scientific literature will not materially increase our ability to protect the public's health from a future H5N1 pandemic. Even targeting dissemination of the information to scientists who request it will likely not enhance the public's health. Rather, making every effort to ensure that this information does not easily fall into the hands of those who might use it for nefarious purposes or that a biosafety accident resulting in an unintended release does not occur should be our first and highest priority. We can't unring a bell; should a highly transmissible and virulent H5N1 influenza virus that is of human making cause a catastrophic pandemic, whether as the result of intentional or unintentional release, the world will hold those who work in the life sciences accountable for what they did or did not do to minimize that risk.

Michael T. Osterholm is director of the Center for Infectious Disease Research and Policy (CIDRAP) and a professor in the Division of Environmental Health Sciences, School of Public Health, and an adjunct professor in the Medical School, University of Minnesota. He is also a member of the Institute of Medicine (IOM) of the National Academy of Sciences, the Council of Foreign Relations, and the National Science Advisory Board on Biosecurity (NSABB).

Donald A. Henderson is a distinguished scholar at the University of Pittsburgh Medical Center's Center for Biosecurity and a professor of public health and medicine at the University of Pittsburgh. During the 1960s, he headed the international effort to eliminate smallpox.

EXPLORING THE ISSUE

Should Scientific Papers Containing Potentially Hazardous Information Be Published in Their Entirety?

Critical Thinking and Reflection

1. Discuss whether scientific papers should fully explain how results were obtained and what the results were.
2. Does publishing the full methods and results of the Fouchier and Kawaoka H5N1 studies seem likely to increase our ability to protect public health from a future H5N1 pandemic?

Is There Common Ground?

An essential component of the scientific method (see this book's Introduction) is communication. This includes publishing hypotheses, theories, and experimental results in the scientific literature. Since many of those involved in the debate over whether to publish all the details of the Fouchier and Kawaoka H5N1 studies are scientists, they take the value of communication as a given. The question on which they differ is just how much to communicate.

1. What are the purposes of communication (as part of the scientific method)?
2. Are some details more important than others to communicate?
3. Can one separate those details according to purpose?

Create Central

www.mhhe.com/createcentral

Additional Resources

Jon Cohen, "Does Forewarned = Forearmed with Lab-Made Avian Influenza Strains?" *Science* (February 17, 2012).

Fred Guterl, "Waiting to Explode," *Scientific American* (June 2012).

Sander Herfst, et al., "Airborne Transmission of Influenza A/H5N1 Virus Between Ferrets," *Science* (June 22, 2012) (www.sciencemag.org/content/336/6088/1534.full).

Masaki Imai, et al., "Experimental Adaptation of an Influenza H5 HA Confers Respiratory Droplet Transmission to a Reassortant H5 HA/H1N1 Virus in Ferrets," *Nature* (June 21, 2012) (www.nature.com/nature/journal/vaop/ncurrent/full/nature10831.html).

Carl Zimmer, "Could Information about a Lab-Made Virus Really Help Evildoers Create a Biological Weapon?" *Slate* (December 22, 2011) (www.slate.com/articles/technology/future_tense/2011/12/h5n1_the_lab_made_virus_the_u_s_fears_could_be_made_into_a_biological_weapon_.html).

Internet References . . .

National Science Advisory Board for Biosecurity (NSABB)

The NSABB is a federal advisory committee chartered to provide advice, guidance, and leadership regarding biosecurity oversight of dual use research, defined as biological research with legitimate scientific purpose that may be misused to pose a biologic threat to public health and/or national security.

http://oba.od.nih.gov/biosecurity/about_nsabb.html

Selected, Edited, and with Issue Framing Material by:
Thomas A. Easton, *Thomas College*

ISSUE

Should the Internet Be Neutral?

YES: Julius Genachowski, from "Preserving a Free and Open Internet: A Platform for Innovation, Opportunity, and Prosperity," speech at The Brookings Institution (September 21, 2009)

NO: Kyle McSlarrow, from "The Future of the Internet," Testimony before the Senate Committee on Commerce, Science, and Transportation Hearing (April 22, 2008)

Learning Outcomes

After studying this issue, students will be able to explain:

- The value of network neutrality.
- Why large content providers are opposed to network neutrality.
- The difficulty of maintaining network neutrality.
- The need for government regulation to protect network neutrality.

ISSUE SUMMARY

YES: FCC Chairman Julius Genachowski argues that we must preserve the openness and freedom of the Internet to ensure that the Internet continues to support innovation, opportunity, economic growth, and democracy in the twenty-first century.

NO: Kyle McSlarrow, president and chief executive officer of the National Cable & Telecommunications Association, argues that "net neutrality" mandates would interfere with the ability of broadband providers to improve Internet access and thus would ultimately undermine consumer choice and welfare.

When the Internet was young—just two decades ago—any content provider could send any kind of data they wanted to any and all users. It was all bits—ones and zeroes—and from the standpoint of the computers or servers that accepted, transferred, and delivered the data, there was no difference between one stream of bits and another. The Communications Act of 1934, which regulated the phone companies which owned the wires over which almost all network traffic then ran, outlawed treating one kind of traffic or one source's traffic differently from any other. The result was that if one could figure out a way to turn a new kind of data into bits, or a new way to package the bits, or a new way to coordinate different bit streams, one could create a new business. It didn't matter whether one was a teenager in a bedroom in Indiana or a big business in New York. It also didn't matter whether the bits—or "content"—meant stock tips or porn. Everyone had a chance to innovate and make money.

The result was a virtual explosion of innovation. Today it is hard to imagine a world without e-mail, instant messaging, file sharing, web pages, eBay, PayPal, Google, blogging, social networking, Monster, wireless connectivity, web cameras, and smart phones, among many other things. We have also gone from an Internet that ran on slow dial-up connections to one dominated by much faster broadband—DSL and cable—connections, which makes it possible to deliver television and film over the Internet. Media and phone companies now deliver content, and at least some of them would like to facilitate the flow of their own content to their own customers and to interfere with the flow of content from other sources, unless those other sources pay a fee. Such a change has been likened to turning the open highway of the present Internet into a toll road. See Wendy M. Grossman, "Who Pays?" *Scientific American* (July 2006). At the same time, traffic on the Internet has increased tremendously, to the point where the flow of content is sometimes greatly slowed. Tom Giovanetti, "Network Neutrality? Welcome to the Stupid Internet," *Mercury News* (June 9, 2006), argues that a non-neutral Internet that gave priority to such things as VoIP (Internet phone) traffic from police and fire departments, 911 calls, and so on would be vastly preferable to a neutral Internet that did not. The debate has been and continues to be vigorous. Opposition from broadband providers remains strong, however. And that opposition can take bizarre forms. In May 2012, a Florida VoIP carrier complained that a local broadband provider had charged it with theft of service for not paying extra for providing voice services (broadband providers such as cable companies now offer phone service as an extra), police were investigating the charge; see Grant Gross, "VoIP Provider Files Net Neutrality Complaint with FCC," *PC World* blog (May 22, 2012) (www.pcworld.com/businesscenter/article/255990/voip_provider_files_net_neutrality_complaint_with_fcc.html).

In June 2006, the U.S. House of Representatives passed the Communications Opportunity, Promotion and Enhancement Act after deleting a provision that would have mandated network neutrality. As passed, the Act "would let the [Federal Communications Commission] investigate complaints about broadband providers blocking Internet content only after the fact." See Grant Gross, "House Rejects Net Neutrality, Passes Telecom Reform Bill," *Network World* (June 12, 2006). In the Senate, attempts to amend a similar bill to mandate network neutrality failed. See Tom Abate, "Net Neutrality Amendment Dies: Telecommunications Bill Goes to Senate Without Provision Sought by Web Firms," *San Francisco Chronicle* (June 29, 2006). Some have credited the telecommunications industry's heavy investment in lobbyists and campaign contributions with the result to that point. Lauren Weinstein, "Ma Bell's Revenge: The Battle for Network Neutrality," *Communications of the ACM* (January 2007), says that "Much of the anti-neutrality argument is simple greed in action" and warns that "most Internet users simply don't realize how drastically and negatively they could be affected if anti-neutrality arguments hold sway. Getting true network neutrality back after it's been lost is likely to be effectively impossible. Except for the anti-neutrality camp itself, we'd all be worse off with a non-neutral Internet, and that's a risk we simply must not accept."

The overall significance of the issue is discussed by Daniel Krauss, "Net Neutrality and How It Just Might Change Everything," *American Libraries* (September 2006), and Michael Baumann, "Net Neutrality: The Internet's World War," *Information Today* (September 2006). Since then, the debate has gained new impetus with the proposal of new legislation and charges that Comcast and other broadband providers are surreptitiously causing large file downloads to fail (see "Comcast, Cox slowing P2P traffic 24X7," *Network World* [May 19, 2008]), and "Elude Your ISP's BitTorrent Blockade," *PC World* (July 2008)). In August 2008, the Federal Communications Commission declared network blocking illegal and told Comcast to stop interfering with its customers' use of the Internet (John Eggerton, "FCC: Comcast Violated Internet Open-Access Guidelines," *Broadcasting & Cable* (August 1, 2008), www.broadcastingcable.com/article/CA6583586.html). Comcast immediately took the issue to the U.S. Court of Appeals, which ruled in April 2010 that the FCC did not have the authority to enforce network neutrality; see Cecilia Kang, "Court Rules for Comcast over FCC in 'Net Neutrality' Case," *Washington Post* (April 7, 2010). In response, the FCC has proposed reversing a past rule, which defined Internet service providers (ISPs) as "information-provider" companies instead of "telecommunications" companies and returning to the old rules, which required network neutrality; see George H. Pike, "What the Future Holds for Net Neutrality," *Information Today* (June 2010). See also Jeffrey A. Hart, "The Net Neutrality Debate in the United States," *Journal of Information Technology & Politics* (2011), and Alexander Reicher, "Redefining Net Neutrality after Comcast v. FCC," *Berkeley Technology Law Journal, 2011 Annual Review* (2011).

In testimony before the Senate Committee on Commerce, Science and Transportation Hearing on "The Future of the Internet" (April 22, 2008), Professor of Law Lawrence Lessig argues that in order to protect the growth and economic vitality of the Internet, Congress should enact "network neutrality" legislation to prevent broadband providers from interfering with free competition among application and content providers. But net neutrality is not just a matter of promoting innovation, growth, and economic vitality. Devon Greyson, "Net Neutrality: A Library Issue," *Feliciter* (vol. 56, no. 2, 2010), notes that Canadian libraries are defending net neutrality as a matter of intellectual freedom. Joe Dysart, "The Quest for Net Neutrality," *American School Board Journal* (May 2008), says that broadband providers such as AT&T and Comcast are pushing for a two-tiered Internet, with one tier free but slow and a second tier that provides more speed at a premium price. Dysart notes that this would adversely impact institutions such as public schools, whose limited budgets would confine them to the inferior tier. Religious groups have similar concerns. Testifying at the same "The Future of the Internet" hearing that provided the McSlarrow selection for this issue, Michele Combs, vice president of Communications for the Christian Coalition of America, argued that net neutrality has been abused by many ISPs: "Verizon Wireless censored text messages sent by the pro-choice advocacy group, NARAL, to its own members who had voluntarily signed up to receive them. . . . AT&T [has] cut off political speech during live concerts . . . [and] Comcast was blocking consumers' ability to download the King James Bible." Combs says that, "Increasingly, faith-based groups are turning to the Internet to promote their political rights, to engage in what Ronald Reagan called 'the hard work of freedom.' We should not let the phone and cable companies interfere with that work." Unfortunately, the 2010 election put many anti-net neutrality senators and representatives in office. The conclusion of this debate is by no means clear, but Internet founder Tim Berners-Lee, "Long Live the Web," *Scientific American* (December 2010), considers the Web of interconnected information sources essential to both prosperity and liberty; therefore, he says, it needs defending. In the wake of the "Arab Spring" of 2011, Hilary Rodham Clinton, "Internet Freedom and Human Rights," *Issues in Science and Technology* (Spring 2012), argues that an open, free Internet is essential to the principles inherent in the Universal Declaration of Human Rights (www.un.org/en/documents/udhr/).

In December 2010, the FCC announced rules intended to protect neutrality; see the FCC press release, "FCC Acts to Preserve Internet Freedom and Openness: Action Helps Ensure Robust Internet for Consumers, Innovation, Investment, Economic Prosperity" at www.fcc.gov/Daily_Releases/Daily_Business/2010/db1221/DOC-303745A1.pdf. Perhaps unfortunately, they were designed as a compromise and many say they are not satisfied. Are better rules needed to keep the Internet neutral? In the YES selection, FCC Chairman Julius Genachowski argues that we must preserve the openness and freedom of the Internet in order to ensure that the Internet continues to support innovation, opportunity, economic growth, and democracy in the 21st century. In the NO selection, Kyle McSlarrow, president and chief executive officer of the National Cable & Telecommunications Association, argues that "net neutrality" mandates would interfere with the ability of broadband providers to improve Internet access and thus would ultimately undermine consumer choice and welfare.

YES

Julius Genachowski

Preserving a Free and Open Internet: A Platform for Innovation, Opportunity, and Prosperity

. . . Just over forty years ago, a handful of engineers in a UCLA lab connected two computers with a 15-foot gray cable and transferred little pieces of data back and forth. It was the first successful test of the ARPANET, the U.S.-government-funded project that became the Internet—the most transformational communications breakthrough since the printing press.

Today, we can't imagine what our lives would be like without the Internet—any more than we can imagine life without running water or the light bulb. Millions of us depend upon it every day: at home, at work, in school—and everywhere in between. The Internet has unleashed the creative genius of countless entrepreneurs and has enabled the creation of jobs—and the launch of small businesses and the expansion of large ones—all across America.

That's why Congress and the President have charged the FCC with developing a National Broadband Plan to ensure that every American has access to open and robust broadband.

The fact is that we face great challenges as a nation right now, including health care, education, energy, and public safety. While the Internet alone will not provide a complete solution to any of them, it can and must play a critical role in solving each one.

Openness Is the Key

Why has the Internet proved to be such a powerful engine for creativity, innovation, and economic growth? A big part of the answer traces back to one key decision by the Internet's original architects: to make the Internet an open system.

Historian John Naughton describes the Internet as an attempt to answer the following question: How do you design a network that is "future proof"—that can support the applications that today's inventors have not yet dreamed of? The solution was to devise a network of networks that would not be biased in favor of any particular application. The Internet's creators didn't want the network architecture—or any single entity—to pick winners and losers. Because it might pick the wrong ones. Instead, the Internet's open architecture pushes decision-making and intelligence to the edge of the network—to end users, to the cloud, to businesses of every size and in every sector of the economy, to creators and speakers across the country and around the globe. In the words of Tim Berners-Lee, the Internet is a "blank canvas"—allowing anyone to contribute and to innovate without permission.

It is easy to look at today's Internet giants—and the tremendous benefits they have supplied to our economy and our culture—and forget that many were small businesses just a few years ago, founded on little more than a good idea and a no-frills connection to the Internet. Marc Andreessen was a graduate student when he created Mosaic, which led to Netscape, the first commercially successful Web browser. Mark Zuckerberg was a college student in 2004 when he started Facebook, which just announced that it added its 300 millionth member. Pierre Omidyar originally launched eBay on his own personal website. Today more than 600,000 Americans earn part of their living by operating small businesses on eBay's auction platform, bringing jobs and opportunity to Danvers, Massachusetts, Durham, North Carolina and Lincoln, Nebraska, and many other communities in both rural and urban America. This is the power of the Internet: distributed innovation and ubiquitous entrepreneurship, the potential for jobs and opportunity everywhere there is broadband.

And let us not forget that the open Internet enables much more than commerce. It is also an unprecedented platform for speech, democratic engagement, and a culture that prizes creative new ways of approaching old problems.

In 2000, Jimmy Wales started a project to create a free online encyclopedia. He originally commissioned experts to write the entries, but the project only succeeded after moving to volunteers to write them collaboratively. The result is Wikipedia, one of the top 10 most visited websites in the world and one of the most comprehensive aggregations of human knowledge in our history. The potential of collaboration and social media continues to grow. It is changing and accelerating innovation. And we've seen new media tools like Twitter and YouTube used by democratic movements around the globe.

Even now, the Internet is beginning to transform health care, education, and energy usage for the better. Health-related applications, distributed over a widely con-

Genachowski, Julius. From a speech given at The Brookings Institution, September 21, 2009. Published 2009 by Federal Communications Commission.

nected Internet, can help bring down health care costs and improve medical service. Four out of five Americans who are online have accessed medical information over the Internet, and most say this information affected their decision-making. Nearly four million college students took at least one online course in 2007, and the Internet can potentially connect kids anywhere to the best information and teachers everywhere. And the Internet is helping enable smart grid technologies, which promise to reduce carbon dioxide emissions by hundreds of millions of metric tons.

At the same time, we have also seen great strides in the center of the network. Most Americans' early exposure to the Internet was through analog modems, which allowed a trickle of data through the phone lines to support early electronic bulletin boards and basic email. Over the last two decades, thanks to substantial investment and technological ingenuity, companies devised ways to retrofit networks initially designed for phones and one-way video to support two-way broadband data streams connecting homes and businesses across the country. And a revolution in wireless technologies—using licensed and unlicensed spectrum—and the creation of path-breaking devices like the Blackberry and iPhone have enabled millions of us to carry the Internet in our pockets and purses.

The lesson of each of these stories, and innumerable others like them, is that we cannot know what tomorrow holds on the Internet, except that it will be unexpected; that the genius of American innovators is unlimited; and that the fewer obstacles these innovators face in bringing their work to the world, the greater our opportunity as citizens and as a nation.

At a Crossroads

Notwithstanding its unparalleled record of success, today the free and open Internet faces emerging and substantial challenges. We've already seen some clear examples of deviations from the Internet's historic openness. We have witnessed certain broadband providers unilaterally block access to VoIP applications (phone calls delivered over data networks) and implement technical measures that degrade the performance of peer-to-peer software distributing lawful content. We have even seen at least one service provider deny users access to political content. And as many members of the Internet community and key Congressional leaders have noted, there are compelling reasons to be concerned about the future of openness.

One reason has to do with limited competition among service providers. As American consumers make the shift from dial-up to broadband, their choice of providers has narrowed substantially. I don't intend that remark as a policy conclusion or criticism—it is simply a fact about today's marketplace that we must acknowledge and incorporate into our policymaking.

A second reason involves the economic incentives of broadband providers. The great majority of companies that operate our nation's broadband pipes rely upon revenue from selling phone service, cable TV subscriptions, or both. These services increasingly compete with voice and video products provided over the Internet. The net result is that broadband providers' rational bottom-line interests may diverge from the broad interests of consumers in competition and choice.

The third reason involves the explosion of traffic on the Internet. With the growing popularity of high-bandwidth applications, Internet traffic is roughly doubling every two years. Technologies for managing broadband networks have become more sophisticated and widely deployed. But these technologies are just tools. They cannot by themselves determine the right answers to difficult policy questions—and they raise their own set of new questions.

In acknowledging the existence of challenging competitive, economic, and technological realities for today's Internet, I want to underscore that this debate, as I see it, isn't about white hats or black hats among companies in and around the network. Rather, there are inevitable tensions built into our system; important and difficult questions that we have an obligation to ask and to answer correctly for our country.

When I worked in the private sector I was fortunate to work with some of the greatest innovators of our time. That taught me some lessons about the importance of innovation and investment. It also taught me the importance of developing clear goals and then being focused and practical in achieving them, making sure to have the best input and ideas from the broadest group possible.

I am convinced that there are few goals more essential in the communications landscape than preserving and maintaining an open and robust Internet. I also know that achieving this goal will take an approach that is smart about technology, smart about markets, smart about law and policy, and smart about the lessons of history.

We Must Choose to Preserve the Open Internet

The rise of serious challenges to the free and open Internet puts us at a crossroads. We could see the Internet's doors shut to entrepreneurs, the spirit of innovation stifled, a full and free flow of information compromised. Or we could take steps to preserve Internet openness, helping ensure a future of opportunity, innovation, and a vibrant marketplace of ideas.

I understand the Internet is a dynamic network and that technology continues to grow and evolve. I recognize that if we were to create unduly detailed rules that attempted to address every possible assault on openness, such rules would become outdated quickly. But the fact that the Internet is evolving rapidly does not mean we can, or should, abandon the underlying values fostered by an open network, or the important goal of setting rules of the road to protect the free and open Internet.

Saying nothing—and doing nothing—would impose its own form of unacceptable cost. It would deprive innovators and investors of confidence that the free and open Internet we depend upon today will still be here tomorrow. It would deny the benefits of predictable rules of the road to all players in the Internet ecosystem. And it would be a dangerous retreat from the core principle of openness—the freedom to innovate without permission—that has been a hallmark of the Internet since its inception, and has made it so stunningly successful as a platform for innovation, opportunity, and prosperity.

In view of these challenges and opportunities, and because it is vital that the Internet continue to be an engine of innovation, economic growth, competition and democratic engagement, I believe the FCC must be a smart cop on the beat preserving a free and open Internet.

What We Can Do

This is how I propose we move forward: To date, the Federal Communications Commission has addressed these issues by announcing four Internet principles that guide our case-by-case enforcement of the communications laws. These principles can be summarized as: Network operators cannot prevent users from accessing the lawful Internet content, applications, and services of their choice, nor can they prohibit users from attaching non-harmful devices to the network.

The principles were initially articulated by Chairman Michael Powell in 2004 as the "Four Freedoms," and later endorsed in a unanimous 2005 policy statement issued by the Commission under Chairman Kevin Martin and with the forceful support of Commissioner Michael Copps, who of course remains on the Commission today. In the years since 2005, the Internet has continued to evolve and the FCC has issued a number of important bipartisan decisions involving openness. Today, I propose that the FCC adopt the existing principles as Commission rules, along with two additional principles that reflect the evolution of the Internet and that are essential to ensuring its continued openness.

Fifth Principle of Non-Discrimination

The fifth principle is one of non-discrimination—stating that broadband providers cannot discriminate against particular Internet content or applications.

This means they cannot block or degrade lawful traffic over their networks, or pick winners by favoring some content or applications over others in the connection to subscribers' homes. Nor can they disfavor an Internet service just because it competes with a similar service offered by that broadband provider. The Internet must continue to allow users to decide what content and applications succeed.

This principle will not prevent broadband providers from reasonably managing their networks. During periods of network congestion, for example, it may be appropriate for providers to ensure that very heavy users do not crowd out everyone else. And this principle will not constrain efforts to ensure a safe, secure, and spam-free Internet experience, or to enforce the law. It is vital that illegal conduct be curtailed on the Internet. As I said in my Senate confirmation hearing, open Internet principles apply only to lawful content, services and applications—not to activities like unlawful distribution of copyrighted works, which has serious economic consequences. The enforcement of copyright and other laws and the obligations of network openness can and must co-exist.

I also recognize that there may be benefits to innovation and investment of broadband providers offering managed services in limited circumstances. These services are different than traditional broadband Internet access, and some have argued they should be analyzed under a different framework. I believe such services can supplement—but must not supplant—free and open Internet access, and that we must ensure that ample bandwidth exists for all Internet users and innovators. In the rulemaking process I will discuss in a moment, we will carefully consider how to approach the question of managed services in a way that maximizes the innovation and investment necessary for a robust and thriving Internet.

I will propose that the FCC evaluate alleged violations of the non-discrimination principle as they arise, on a case-by-case basis, recognizing that the Internet is an extraordinarily complex and dynamic system. This approach, within the framework I am proposing today, will allow the Commission to make reasoned, fact-based determinations based on the Internet before it—not based on the Internet of years past or guesses about how the Internet will evolve.

Sixth Principle of Transparency

The sixth principle is a transparency principle—stating that providers of broadband Internet access must be transparent about their network management practices.

Why does the FCC need to adopt this principle? The Internet evolved through open standards. It was conceived as a tool whose user manual would be free and available to all. But new network management practices and technologies challenge this original understanding. Today, broadband providers have the technical ability to change how the Internet works for millions of users—with profound consequences for those users and content, application, and service providers around the world.

To take one example, last year the FCC ruled on the blocking of peer-to-peer transmissions by a cable broadband provider. The blocking was initially implemented with no notice to subscribers or the public. It was discovered only after an engineer and hobbyist living in Oregon realized that his attempts to share public domain recordings of old barbershop quartet songs over a home Internet connection were being frustrated. It was not until he brought the problem to the attention of the media and

Internet community, which then brought it to the attention of the FCC, that the improper network management practice became known and was stopped.

We cannot afford to rely on happenstance for consumers, businesses, and policymakers to learn about changes to the basic functioning of the Internet. Greater transparency will give consumers the confidence of knowing that they're getting the service they've paid for, enable innovators to make their offerings work effectively over the Internet, and allow policymakers to ensure that broadband providers are preserving the Internet as a level playing field. It will also help facilitate discussion among all the participants in the Internet ecosystem, which can reduce the need for government involvement in network management disagreements.

To be clear, the transparency principle will not require broadband providers to disclose personal information about subscribers or information that might compromise the security of the network, and there will be a mechanism to protect competitively sensitive data.

Application to the Internet, However Accessed

In considering the openness of the Internet, it is also important to recognize that our choice of technologies and devices for accessing the Internet continues to expand at a dizzying pace. New mobile and satellite broadband networks are getting faster every day, and extraordinary devices like smartphones and wireless data cards are making it easier to stay connected while on the go. And I note the beginnings of a trend towards openness among several participants in the mobile marketplace.

Even though each form of Internet access has unique technical characteristics, they are all are different roads to the same place. It is essential that the Internet itself remain open, however users reach it. The principles I've been speaking about apply to the Internet however accessed, and I will ask my fellow Commissioners to join me in confirming this.

Of course, how the principles apply may differ depending on the access platform or technology. The rulemaking process will enable the Commission to analyze fully the implications of the principles for mobile network architectures and practices—and how, as a practical matter, they can be fairly and appropriately implemented. As we tackle these complex questions involving different technologies used for Internet access, let me be clear that we will be focused on formulating policies that will maximize innovation and investment, consumer choice, and greater competition.

Rulemaking Process

I've talked about what we need to do; now I'd like to talk about how we should do it. I will soon circulate to my fellow Commissioners proposed rules prepared by Commission staff embodying the principles I've discussed, and I will ask for their support in issuing a notice of proposed rulemaking. This notice will provide the public with a detailed explanation of what we propose to do and why.

Equally importantly, the notice will ask for input and feedback on the proposed rules and their application, such as how to determine whether network management practices are reasonable, and what information broadband providers should disclose about their network management practices and in what form. And—as I indicated earlier—it will pose a series of detailed questions on how the Internet openness principles should apply to mobile broadband.

While my goals are clear—to ensure the Internet remains a free and open platform that promotes innovation, investment, competition, and users' interests—our path to implementing them is not pre-determined. I will ensure that the rulemaking process will be fair, transparent, fact-based, and data-driven. Anyone will be able to participate in this process, and I hope everyone will. We will hold a number of public workshops and, of course, use the Internet and other new media tools to facilitate participation. Today we've launched a new website, www.openinternet.gov, to kick off discussion of the issues I've been talking about. We encourage everyone to visit the site and contribute to the process.

Moving Forward

Some have argued that the FCC should not take affirmative steps to protect the Internet's openness. Let me be clear about what this is about, and what it isn't.

The fundamental goal of what I've outlined today is preserving the openness and freedom of the Internet.

We have an obligation to ensure that the Internet is an enduring engine for U.S. economic growth, and a foundation for democracy in the 21st century. We have an obligation to ensure that the Internet remains a vast landscape of innovation and opportunity.

This is not about government regulation of the Internet. It's about fair rules of the road for companies that control access to the Internet. We will do as much as we need to do, and no more, to ensure that the Internet remains an unfettered platform for competition, creativity, and entrepreneurial activity.

This is not about protecting the Internet against imaginary dangers. We're seeing the breaks and cracks emerge, and they threaten to change the Internet's fundamental architecture of openness. This would shrink opportunities for innovators, content creators, and small businesses around the country, and limit the full and free expression the Internet promises. This is about preserving and maintaining something profoundly successful and ensuring that it's not distorted or undermined. If we wait too long to preserve a free and open Internet, it will be too late.

Some will seek to invoke innovation and investment as reasons not to adopt open Internet rules. But history's lesson is clear: Ensuring a robust and open Internet is the best thing we can do to promote investment and innovation. And while there are some who see every policy decision as either pro-business or pro-consumer, I reject that approach; it's not the right way to see technology's role in America.

An open Internet will benefit both consumers and businesses. The principles that will protect the open Internet are an essential step to maximize investment and innovation in the network and on the edge of it—by establishing rules of the road that incentivize competition, empower entrepreneurs, and grow the economic pie to the benefit of all.

I believe we share a common purpose—we want the Internet to continue flourishing as a platform for innovation and communication, with continued investment and increasing deployment of broadband to all Americans. I believe my fellow Commissioners share this purpose, and I look forward to working collaboratively with them in this endeavor.

In closing, we are here because 40 years ago, a bunch of researchers in a lab changed the way computers interact and, as a result, changed the world. We are here because those Internet pioneers had unique insights about the power of open networks to transform lives for the better, and they did something about it. Our work now is to preserve the brilliance of what they contributed to our country and the world. It's to make sure that, in the 21st century, the garage, the basement, and the dorm room remain places where innovators can not only dream but bring their dreams to life. And no one should be neutral about that.

Julius Genachowski is the chair of the Federal Communications Commission.

Kyle McSlarrow

NO

The Future of the Internet

. . . The cable industry is the nation's largest provider of high-speed Internet access, making cable broadband service available to 92 percent of Americans, and has invested $130 billion to build a two-way interactive network with fiber-optic technology. Cable companies also provide state-of-the-art digital telephone service to more than 15 million American consumers. Cable operators are committed to delivering an open and satisfying Internet experience to their customers, and the dramatic growth in cable broadband subscribers is evidence of their success in doing so.

The cable industry has consistently demonstrated its commitment to policies that ensure all Americans have access to affordable broadband. We supported, for example, proposals advanced by Senator Dorgan and Senator Stevens to create a fund tailored to expanding broadband into unserved areas. We support Senator Inouye's Broadband Data Improvement Act, because we believe that improving federal data collection and dissemination regarding where broadband services have been deployed in the United States is necessary in order to achieve the goal of ubiquitous broadband availability for all Americans. And we continue to support:

- Tax credits or other tax incentives to providers that build out in rural areas that are unserved by an existing broadband provider.
- Reform of the RUS broadband loan program so that funding is targeted specifically to unserved areas.
- Expansion of the FCC's Lifeline and Link-Up Programs to help ensure that broadband access is extended to low-income households.
- Public–private partnerships to provide broadband in unserved areas.

We support these initiatives because we recognize that the government can play an important role in making certain that the economic and social benefits of broadband connectivity are extended to all areas of this country, and we look forward to working with you further to achieve these goals. But while broadband deployment to every community in America merits the full attention of policymakers, legislation calling for "network neutrality" or government intervention into the operation of networks would undermine the goals of broadband deployment and adoption. The development of the Internet, expansion of broadband networks, and creation of innovative Internet applications we have seen would not have occurred at such a rapid pace if providers were restricted in how they could engineer their networks to accommodate these dynamic developments. The government's consistent light regulatory touch since the introduction of broadband has worked. And only that continued regulatory freedom is likely to spur the investment and innovation that consumers have come to expect.

Today, I would like to focus on three points that illustrate why the Internet and broadband services should not be subject to greater and more intrusive government regulation. First, cable broadband providers have demonstrated and remain committed to providing Americans the very best broadband service available. Second, every cable modem subscriber today can access the content he or she seeks over the Internet. Broadband providers do not block access to content. Reasonable network optimization techniques not only enable the growth and development of the Internet, they protect consumers and their legitimate expectations.

Finally, the national policy of leaving the Internet unregulated has been a resounding success. Government intervention in broadband network management would only slow the pace of innovation and prevent the natural development of traffic solutions that is already occurring today.

I. Cable Brought Broadband to America

The industry's commitment to the deployment of broadband is reflected in the plain statistics. By any benchmark, the cable industry is leading efforts to spur broadband use and deployment.

Investment. The cable industry has done more to stimulate broadband growth and innovation than any other industry. Cable operators have invested $130 billion in private capital since the passage of the Telecommunications Act of 1996 to build broadband networks across the United States. Today 92% of American households, or about 117 million homes, have access to cable broadband service, including 96% of American homes to which cable television service is available. This investment and expansion took place without any government subsidies.

Competition. The cable industry's efforts to deploy broadband have stimulated tremendous investment in the

McSlarrow, Kyle. U.S. Senate, April 22, 2008.

provision of Internet access by competing providers, first by telephone companies and now wireless and satellite companies. This competition has spurred cable broadband providers and their competitors to develop better and better networks and applications to meet consumer demand and compete for their business. As former FTC Chairman Timothy Muris has explained, "competition [among providers] spurs producers to meet consumer expectations because the market generally imposes strict discipline on sellers who disappoint consumers and thus lose sales to producers who better meet consumer needs. These same competitive pressures also encourage producers to provide truthful information about their offerings."

Most notably, as the availability of broadband service has grown, the price-per-megabit has fallen significantly, and the speeds cable broadband offers have shot up dramatically. When cable first offered high-speed broadband service as an alternative to dial-up access in the mid-90s, the speeds were approximately 1–1.5 Mbps. Today, most cable operators offer broadband speeds topping 5 Mbps and some operators, such as Cablevision and Comcast, offer speeds up to 50 Mbps. Comcast and Cox Communications also offer a service that provides for "boosts" of higher speeds that double the throughput on an on-demand, capacity-available basis.

Now the cable industry is on the verge of making the next leap—from "broadband" to "wideband"—with a technology which can enable dramatically higher download and upload speeds well above 100 Megabits per second. Several weeks ago, for example, Comcast launched a "wideband" service in Minneapolis–St. Paul that offers speeds of 50 Megabits per second. Comcast expects to have wideband available to 20% of its systems by year-end 2008 and to all homes passed by mid-2010.

Increased Use and Demand. The high quality and easy availability of cable broadband has led to the widespread adoption of broadband use. Today, the cable industry has more than 35 million broadband customers. Overall, approximately 64 million broadband households nationwide have broadband service, and that number continues to grow.

New Content, Web Services, and Applications. The efforts of broadband network providers to build larger and faster networks have helped ensure the success of countless numbers of new Internet businesses and applications—online video services, social networking websites, data-sharing services, and online interactive game services, to name a few. Despite concerns about alleged limited access to broadband, use of Internet video on demand has grown at the most dramatic rate. In July 2006, 107 million Americans watched video online and about 60% of Internet users downloaded more than 7 billion videos off the Internet. In February 2008, nearly 135 million U.S. Internet users spent an average of 204 minutes viewing 10.1 billion online videos. YouTube represented 34% of those online videos, or nearly 3.5 billion in total. To put it into context, in 2006, YouTube consumed as much bandwidth as the entire Internet consumed in the year 2000.

Television networks are now offering cable modem and other broadband customers video online, such as NBC Universal and News Corp.'s new Hulu service. Book retailers are now offering online digital novels; and music sales websites, such as iTunes, continue to grow. Social networking websites, where users share home videos, pictures, and music content, are also on the rise—in 2007, an estimated 126.5 million people in North America participated in an online social networking website. Internet commerce also continues to grow. Last year, over $135 billion was spent purchasing goods and services over the Internet.

For years, net neutrality proponents have argued that without government intervention, broadband providers would stifle competing services and content providers; Internet development and usage would stagnate; and consumers would be unable to use their broadband connections to download video or access other emerging applications. In fact, cable's investment in broadband has driven innovation and investment in new content and applications at the edge—the exact opposite of what was predicted by advocates of net regulation.

There is no better proof that there presently exists no "problem" needing a "solution" than YouTube. YouTube would have been a pipe dream in 2002. Six years later, however, YouTube—the proverbial "two guys in a garage" who allegedly could not survive, let alone thrive, unless the Internet were regulated—has become a multibillion dollar enterprise. And YouTube is now owned by Google, which itself has grown to become one of the largest companies in the world with a market capitalization of $169 billion.

Here's an incontrovertible truth: the staggering growth of these companies would not have occurred without cable's investment in and deployment of the reliable high-speed broadband service that provides the ecosystem in which Google, YouTube, Yahoo! and other Internet services can flourish.

II. Network Optimization Enhances and Enables the Internet Experience

In 2006, I testified before this Committee and stated that cable operators do not and would not block subscribers' access to any lawful content, applications or services. That statement remains true today. Cable modem subscribers have the ability to do anything they want to on the Internet. They can download or stream videos, upload and send pictures to friends, or call family across the world. They can also attach gaming devices, or any other computing device they want to use to the network. They can use file-sharing software from peer-to-peer networks. If they couldn't do what they wanted, they would soon not be cable modem subscribers. They would go to our competitors.

Cable subscribers can enjoy the most advanced and cutting-edge Internet sites and applications because of the extensive efforts cable operators constantly undertake to make all content and applications flow smoothly and work seamlessly together over the network. In 1999, there were only 2 million households with broadband service in the United States; today there are approximately 64 million. This is a great success story—but with this success comes the need to manage the network so that every household has good user experience.

Cable providers built a smart infrastructure that has the capability to evolve and meet the challenges of multimedia, file sharing, and other bandwidth-intensive applications. But cable broadband subscribers currently enjoy the full benefits of broadband only because cable operators manage their networks on a content-agnostic basis to provide seamless connectivity, deter spam and viruses, and make sure that a tiny minority of users don't slow down the Internet for everyone else. Various estimates are that as few as 5% of customers use from 50 to 90% of the total capacity of the network. In Japan, it is estimated that 1% of Internet users consume 47% of the total Internet traffic. Faced with these voracious bandwidth consumers, cable operators may engage in reasonable, content-agnostic network management practices—triggered by objective criteria based upon network traffic levels—to ensure that the relatively few customers who utilize bandwidth-heavy applications do not degrade or otherwise adversely affect broadband Internet access for the vast majority of customers.

There have been some recent concerns that network management practices affecting certain high-bandwidth-consuming peer-to-peer (P2P) applications are "discriminatory." P2P traffic can consume a disproportionately large amount of network resources—far, far more than any other Internet use. If even a small fraction of customers are using these bandwidth-intensive applications at the same time, it can interfere with the ability of the vast majority of all other customers in that area to surf the web, watch streaming video, make voice-over-IP calls, or engage in other routine uses of the Internet.

Providers can't build their way out of this problem—in spite of increasing capacity, many P2P protocols are written specifically to commandeer as much bandwidth as is available. Instead, providers optimize their networks in order to balance the needs of all of their customers.

Far from inhibiting access, smart network techniques protect the ability of our customers to make the greatest and most flexible use of the Internet. They are a reasonable response to an identified congestion problem that has the benefit of allowing all other applications—particularly latency-sensitive applications like VoIP and streaming video—to work better. As the Institute for Policy Innovation recently stated, "[i]n almost all cases, network management today is unnoticed by consumers. The opposite, a total lack of management, would not be true. If network operators were precluded from managing their networks, consumers would be negatively affected." Sound network management is essential to ensuring a stable broadband platform. Google, Yahoo!, Amazon, and service providers like Vonage could not carry on their businesses if bandwidth-consuming applications were allowed to block customers from accessing their Web sites or completing their transactions. Because of network management, such businesses can develop business models that hinge on the expectation that their service will not be crowded out by congestion caused by heavy bandwidth-using software. Far from being "neutral," a network that is not managed simply allows those who want to demand all the bandwidth for themselves to do so unchecked.

Reasonable network management practices are also vital to combating the well-documented, illegal distribution of copyrighted material on the Internet. We cannot ignore the problem of piracy. It is a problem that affects not just broadband service providers, legitimate broadband application providers and content providers, but also law-abiding consumers. Ultimately they are the ones that bear the burden of congestion caused by those who abuse their network access to engage in the widespread distribution of infringing works. Technology is agnostic, but, according to one source, 90 percent of P2P downloads are pirated material. Broadband providers, content owners and others all have a stake in exploring technology solutions that address piracy in ways that respect our customers' expectations and respect the copyright owner's rights, not simply to curtail congestion but for reasons of fairness to those who invest in content and make an important contribution to our economy. Government action that would inhibit development of innovative approaches to thwarting piracy and enhancing the online experience for the vast majority of Internet users would harm content creation and ultimately consumers.

So, is there evidence that these challenges are insurmountable and require more government regulation? Quite the contrary. The same technological innovation that gives rise to some of these challenges has produced creative ways to fight spam and viruses. The same private sector collaboration that allowed the countless number of networks that make up the Internet to exchange traffic and engage in peering has and continues to focus on new challenges.

Some P2P developers are creating new ways to make that technology more bandwidth-efficient and network-friendly, so that it may continue to emerge as a useful way to distribute legal content. Cable companies and other broadband providers are working hard to find ways to address concerns about network congestion and create consumer-friendly options that allow the majority of users to access content at the speeds needed. The "P4P Working Group"—a collaborative industry effort to develop network management solutions that benefit cable and other broadband operators, P2P software firms, and consumers—is one such effort.

Broadband providers have also begun testing and dialogue with P2P applications providers to make networks and P2P applications friendlier to one another. For example, Verizon has been working with Pando Networks, a P2P software developer, and the P4P Working Group to develop a more bandwidth efficient file-sharing protocol. Just last week, Comcast and Pando announced their intention to lead an industry-wide effort to create a "P2P Bill of Rights and Responsibilities." And Comcast and BitTorrent recently reached an agreement in which Comcast pledged to adopt a capacity management technique based on individual users' consumption during peak periods rather than based on a particular protocol.

Broadband providers and Internet content and service providers have mutual incentives to develop workable solutions that enhance customers' Internet experiences. Cable operators' tremendous investments have laid the foundation for robust broadband networks that have spurred the remarkable explosion of new services and innovations on the Internet. In turn, the vast array of applications and services now available on the Internet drive more and more people to become broadband users.

III. The Government Should Continue to Refrain from Regulation

Congress should resist calls to interfere with broadband providers' freedom to manage their respective networks in order to satisfy the evolving needs of American consumers. Cable modem service has never been subject to regulation. Six years after the FCC classified cable's broadband offering as an unregulated information service and nearly three years after the FCC determined that no regulation was needed to encourage broadband deployment and preserve and promote Internet usage and demand, there has been no evidence of any practices that would change those conclusions or warrant government intervention generally or specifically with respect to permissible network management activities. The disaster scenarios voiced by network neutrality proponents for many years have never happened. In fact, the opposite has happened—the Internet is booming without regulation. There is quite simply no problem requiring a government solution.

Under the guise of preventing discrimination, "net neutrality" proponents would have the government determine which network management techniques are permissible. But putting every network management strategy up for debate before regulators would severely hamper the ability of network providers to ensure high-quality and reliable Internet access for their subscribers. Depriving network operators of certain bandwidth management tools only makes the network less efficient for everyone. Ultimately, interfering with an operator's ability to manage its network would harm consumers and prevent them from accessing the content they desire. Adept network optimization techniques are fundamental to creating and preserving the stable "ecosystem" for online service providers that ensures an optimal customer experience.

Government intervention in a fast-changing technological world could result in very real problems developing very quickly. Network management practices are constantly changing and evolving—as networks grow, consumer usage patterns change, and new technologies emerge. It would be impossible for any regulation to keep up with these changes. Nor does the government have the expertise or resources to second-guess the thousands of network management decisions broadband network engineers must make every day. It is far more likely that government interference in the development of the market could foreclose or prevent the emergence of cross-industry efforts that are more likely to get the solutions right.

Conclusion

Misplaced concerns over legitimate and reasonable network management practices do not justify the enactment of open-ended regulation of the Internet, particularly where the costs of such regulation are foreseeable and substantial. Given the growth of broadband competition and the breathtaking pace of technological change, government intervention is unwarranted. As the Federal Trade Commission has warned, regulation of Internet access at this stage of market development could have "potentially adverse and unintended effects," including reduced product and service innovation. And net neutrality requirements would frustrate the Federal policy of "preserv[ing] the vibrant and competitive free market that presently exists for the Internet . . . , unfettered by Federal or State regulation." Today's hands-off policy has given us the flexibility to innovate and respond to consumer demand. By contrast, proposals for "net neutrality" amount to regulation of the Internet that would undermine—not promote—consumer choice and welfare.

Kyle McSlarrow is the president and chief executive officer of the National Cable & Telecommunications Association.

EXPLORING THE ISSUE

Should the Internet Be Neutral?

Critical Thinking and Reflection

1. In what ways does increased traffic on the Internet make it difficult to maintain perfect network neutrality?
2. Society depends on many "networks" (interconnected channels through which something moves) such as the highway system, the electrical grid, and even municipal water distribution systems. In what ways does the concept of "network neutrality" apply to these networks (if it does)?
3. How do users pay for use of these other networks?
4. What are the risks involved in letting broadband providers control what kinds of information can be sent over the Internet?

Is There Common Ground?

Everyone involved in this debate agrees that the Internet is valuable to society. They differ in the nature of that value and to whom that value should accrue. Everyone also agrees that government regulation is a bad idea, but they differ on the reasons why.

1. To those who favor net neutrality, in what ways is the Internet valuable to society?
2. To those who oppose net neutrality, in what ways is the Internet valuable to society?
3. To those who favor net neutrality, what does "government regulation" mean?
4. To those who oppose net neutrality, what does "government regulation" mean?

Create Central

www.mhhe.com/createcentral

Additional Resources

Hilary Rodham Clinton, "Internet Freedom and Human Rights," *Issues in Science and Technology* (Spring 2012).

Jeffrey A. Hart, "The Net Neutrality Debate in the United States," *Journal of Information Technology & Politics* (2011).

Lauren Weinstein, "Ma Bell's Revenge: The Battle for Net Neutrality," *Communications of the ACM* (January 2007).

Internet References . . .

SavetheInternet.Com

The SavetheInternet.com Coalition believes that the Internet is a crucial engine for economic growth and free speech and lobbies to preserve network neutrality.

www.savetheinternet.com

Unit 2

UNIT

Energy and the Environment

As the damage that human beings do to their environment in the course of obtaining food, water, wood, ore, energy, and other resources has become clear, many people have grown concerned. Some of that concern is for the environment—the landscapes and living things with which humanity shares its world. Some of that concern is more for human welfare; it focuses on the ways in which environmental damage threatens human health, prosperity, or even survival.

Among the major environmental issues are those related to energy. By releasing vast amounts of carbon dioxide, fossil fuels threaten to change the world's climate. Potential solutions include warding off excess solar heating, greatly expanding the use of hydroelectric power, and replacing fossil fuels with hydrogen.

Selected, Edited, and with Issue Framing Material by:
Thomas A. Easton, *Thomas College*

ISSUE

Do We Need Research Guidelines for Geoengineering?

YES: M. Granger Morgan, Robert R. Nordhaus, and Paul Gottlieb, from "Needed: Research Guidelines for Solar Radiation Management," *Issues in Science and Technology* (Spring 2013)

NO: Jane C. S. Long and Dane Scott, from "Vested Interests and Geoengineering Research," *Issues in Science and Technology* (Spring 2013)

Learning Outcomes

After studying this issue, students will be able to:

- Describe some of the ways climate change may harm people around the world.
- Describe some of the methods that have been proposed for stopping or limiting climate change.
- Describe what is meant by "solar radiation management" or "geoengineering" and why it may be a useful approach to combating climate change.
- Describe how various vested interests prevent society from effectively addressing the risks of climate change.

ISSUE SUMMARY

YES: M. Morgan, Robert Nordhaus, and Paul Gottlieb argue that before we can embark on geoengineering a great deal of research will be needed. First, however, we need a plan to guide research by developing standards and ensuring open access to research results.

NO: Jane Long and Dane Scott argue that though we need to do much research into geoengineering, not all issues are technical. Vested interests (whose fortunes may be threatened by change, who may fear consequences, who may be driven by the craving for fame, or whose thinking may be dominated by ideology rather than facts), mismanagement, and human weakness must be addressed before engaging in geoengineering.

Exactly what will global warming do to the world and its people? Projections for the future have grown steadily worse; see Eli Kintisch, "Projections of Climate Change Go from Bad to Worse, Scientists Report," *Science* (March 20, 2009). Effects include rising sea level, more extreme weather events (Richard A. Kerr, "Humans Are Driving Extreme Weather; Time to Prepare," *Science* (November 25, 2011)), reduced global harvests (Constance Holden, "Higher Temperatures Seen Reducing Global Harvests," *Science* (January 9, 2009)), and threats to the economies and security of nations (Michael T. Klare, "Global Warming Battlefields: How Climate Change Threatens Security," *Current History* (November 2007); and Scott G. Bergerson, "Arctic Meltdown: The Economic and Security Implications of Global Warming," *Foreign Affairs* (March/April 2008)). As rainfall patterns change and the seas rise, millions of people will flee their homelands; see Alex de Sherbinin, Koko Warner, and Charles Erhart, "Casualties of Climate Change," *Scientific American* (January 2011). Perhaps worst of all, even if we somehow stopped emitting greenhouse gases today, the effects would continue for 1,000 years or more, during which sea level rise may exceed "several meters"; see Susan Solomon, et al., "Irreversible Climate Change Due to Carbon Dioxide Emissions," *Proceedings of the National Academy of Sciences* (February 10, 2009). And more and more climate scientists are now saying that all projections to date have been far too conservative; see John Carey, "Global Warming: Faster than Expected?" *Scientific American* (November 2012).

It seems clear that something must be done, but what? How urgently? And with what aim? Should we be trying to reduce or prevent human suffering? Or to avoid political conflicts? Or to protect the global economy—meaning standards of living, jobs, and businesses? The humanitarian and economic approaches are obviously connected, for protecting jobs certainly has much to do with easing or preventing suffering. However, these approaches can also conflict. In October 2009, the Government Accountability Office (GAO) released "Climate Change Adaptation: Strategic Federal Planning Could Help Government Officials Make More Informed Decisions" (GAO-10-113; www.gao.gov/products/GAO-10-113), which noted the need for multiagency coordination and strategic (long-term) planning, both of which are often resisted by bureaucrats and politicians. Robert Engelman, *Population, Climate Change, and Women's Lives* (Worldwatch Institute, 2010), notes that addressing population size and growth would help but "Despite its key contribution to climate change, population plays little role in current discussions on how to address this serious challenge."

The U.S. Climate Change Science Program's "Scientific Assessment of the Effects of Global Change on the United States, A Report of the Committee on Environment and Natural Resources, National Science and Technology Council" (May 29, 2008; available at www.whitehouse.gov/files/documents/ostp/NSTC%20Reports/Scientific%20Assessment%20FULL%20Report.pdf) describes the current and potential impacts of climate change. In sum, it says that the evidence is clear and getting clearer that global warming is "very likely" due to greenhouse gases largely released by human activity and there will be consequent changes in precipitation, storms, droughts, sea level, food production, fisheries, and more. Dealing with these effects may require changes in many areas, particularly relating to energy use.

President Barack Obama has indicated that his administration will take global warming more seriously. In June 2009, the U.S. House of Representatives passed an Energy and Climate bill that promised to cap carbon emissions and stimulate use of renewable energy. The Senate version of the bill failed to pass; see Daniel Stone, "Who Killed the Climate and Energy Bill?" *Newsweek* (September 15, 2010). There are few signs that the world is ready to take the extensive actions deemed necessary by many; see, for example, Janet L. Sawin and William R. Moomaw, "Renewing the Future and Protecting the Climate," *World Watch* (July/August 2010). The December 2011 United Nations Framework Convention on Climate Change, held in Durban, South Africa, came to no conclusion more substantive than an agreement to come up by 2015 with a firm international agreement to deal with the problem. "Denialists," largely funded by the fossil fuel industry, insist that the specter of global warming is a political bogeyman; for an example, see Steve Goreham's *The Mad, Mad, Mad World of Climatism* (New Lenox Books, 2013), a book that has been promoted intensively by the Heartland Institute.

What can be done, if we ever decide to do anything? It seems possible to make enormous headway; according to Jane C. S. Long and Jeffery Greenblatt, "The 80% Solution: Radical Carbon Emission Cuts for California," *Issues in Science and Technology* (Spring 2012), the 2005 call by California's governor to reduce carbon dioxide emissions to 80% below the 1990 level by 2050 is achievable; much of the necessary technology already exists, making the problem one of practical implementation. But there remain immense political obstacles.

The same may be said of technological solutions such as geoengineering. The basic idea behind geoengineering springs from the realization that natural events such as volcanic eruptions can cool climate, sometimes dramatically, by injecting large quantities of dust and sulfates into the stratosphere, where they serve as a "sunshade" that reflects a portion of solar heat back into space before it can warm the Earth (see, e.g., Clive Oppenheimer, "Climatic, Environmental and Human Consequences of the Largest Known Historic Eruption: Tambora Volcano (Indonesia) 1815," *Progress in Physical Geography* (June 2003).

Such effects have prompted many researchers to think that global warming is not just a matter of increased atmospheric content of greenhouse gases such as carbon dioxide (which slow the loss of heat to space and thus warm the planet) but also of the amount of sunlight that reaches Earth from the sun. So far most attempts to find a solution to global warming have focused on reducing human emissions of greenhouse gases. But it does not seem unreasonable to consider the other side of the problem, the energy that reaches Earth from the sun. After all, if you are too warm in bed at night, you can remove the blanket *or* turn down the furnace. Suggestions that something similar might be done on a global scale go back more than forty years; see Robert Kunzig, "A Sunshade for Planet Earth," *Scientific American* (November 2008).

Paul Crutzen suggested in "Albedo Enhancement by Stratospheric Sulfur Injections: A Contribution to Resolve a Policy Dilemma?" *Climate Change* (August 2006) that adding sulfur compounds to the stratosphere (as volcanoes have done) could reflect some solar energy and help relieve the problem. Such measures would not be cheap, and at present there is no way to tell whether they would have undesirable side effects, although G. Bala, P. B. Duffy, and K. E. Taylor, "Impact of Goengineering Schemes on the Global Hydrological Cycle," *Proceedings of the National Academy of Sciences of the United States of America* (June 3, 2008), suggest it is likely that precipitation would be significantly reduced.

Roger Angel, "Feasibility of Cooling the Earth with a Cloud of Small Spacecraft near the Inner Lagrange Point (L1)," *Proceedings of the National Academy of Sciences of the United States of America* (November 14, 2006), argues that if dangerous changes in global climate become inevitable, despite greenhouse gas controls, it may be possible to solve the problem by reducing the amount of solar energy that hits the Earth by using reflective spacecraft. He does not suggest that climate engineering solutions such as this or injecting sulfur compounds into the stratosphere should be tried *instead of* reducing greenhouse gas emissions. Rather, he suggests that such solutions should be evaluated for use *in extremis*, if greenhouse gas reductions are not sufficient or if global warming runs out of control. This position may make a good deal of sense. In January 2009, a survey of climate scientists found broad support for exploring the geoengineering approach and even developing techniques; see "What Can We Do to Save Our Planet?" *The Independent* (January 2, 2009) (www.independent.co.uk/environment/climate-change/what-can-we-do-to-save-our-planet-1221097.html). However, any such program will require much more international cooperation than is usually available; see Jason J. Blackstock and Jane C. S. Long, "The Politics of Geoengineering," *Science* (January 29, 2010). Jamais Cascio, "The Potential and Risks of Geoengineering," *Futurist* (May/June 2010), argues that there will be a place in international diplomacy for efforts "to control climate engineering technologies and deal with their consequences." Among those consequences may be major changes in the amount and distribution of rain and snow; see Gabriele C. Hegerl and Susan Solomon, "Risks of Climate Engineering," *Science* (August 21, 2009).

James R. Fleming, "The Climate Engineers," *Wilson Quarterly* (Spring 2007), argues that climate engineers fail to consider both the risks of unintended consequences to human life and political relationships and the ethics of the human relationship to nature. They also, he says, display signs of overconfidence in technology as a solution of first resort. A similar criticism has been levied against S. Matthew Liao, Anders Sandberg, and Rebecca Roache, "Human Engineering and Climate Change," *Ethics, Policy and the Environment* (Summer 2012), who argue that because behavioral, market-based, and technological solutions to human-caused climate change do not appear able or likely to solve the problem, it is appropriate to consider alternatives such as human engineering (meaning using embryo selection to reduce the average size of humans and using drugs to create an aversion to meat or increased altruism). Thomas Sterner, et al., "Quick Fixes for the Environment: Part of the Solution or Part of the Problem?" *Environment* (December 2006), say that "Quick fixes are sometimes appropriate because they work sufficiently well and/or buy time to design longer term solutions . . . [but] When quick fixes are deployed, it is useful to tie them to long-run abatement measures." Fundamental solutions (such as reducing emissions of greenhouse gases to solve the global warming problem) are to be preferred, but they may be opposed because of "lack of understanding of ecological mechanisms, failure to recognize the gravity of the problem, vested interests, and absence of institutions to address public goods and intergenerational choices effectively."

It is worth noting that much of the discussion of climate engineering presumes that we will try as a global society to reduce carbon emissions but that our efforts will be insufficient. However, the United Nations Global Climate Change Conference, held in Copenhagen in December 2009, failed to produce a binding agreement to start reducing emissions. Instead, it achieved only an agreement to meet again in 2010 and "start tackling climate change and step up work toward a legally binding treaty." Many people feel that if we do not move faster, geoengineering may be our only option. Robert B. Jackson and James Salzman, "Pursuing Geoengineering for Atmospheric Restoration," *Issues in Science and Technology* (Summer 2010), argue that we need to move toward increased energy efficiency and greater use of renewable energy and explore ways to remove carbon from the atmosphere. If we are successful, we will be less likely to need "sunshades" approaches to geoengineering; however, research into such approaches is essential. Ken Caldeira and David W. Keith, "The Need for Climate Engineering Research," *Issues in Science and Technology* (Fall 2010), say that climate engineering may prove to be "the only affordable and fast-acting option to avoid a global catastrophe." Research into the subject is essential because "the stakes are too high for us to think that ignorance is a good policy."

In the YES selection, M. Morgan, Robert Nordhaus, and Paul Gottlieb argue that before we can embark on geoengineering a great deal of research will be needed. First, however, we need a plan to guide research by developing standards and ensuring open access to research results. In the NO selection, Jane Long and Dane Scott argue that though we need to do much research into geoengineering, not all issues are technical. Vested interests (whose fortunes may be threatened by change, who may fear consequences, who may be driven by the craving for fame, or whose thinking may be dominated by ideology rather than facts), mismanagement, and human weakness must be addressed before engaging in geoengineering.

YES

M. Granger Morgan, Robert R. Nordhaus, and Paul Gottlieb

Needed: Research Guidelines for Solar Radiation Management

As this approach to geoengineering gains attention, a coordinated plan for research will make it possible to understand how it might work and what dangers it could present.

Emissions of carbon dioxide (CO_2) and other greenhouse gases (GHGs) continue to rise. The effects of climate change are becoming ever more apparent. Yet prospects for reducing global emissions of CO_2 by an order of magnitude, as would be needed to reduce threats of climate change, seem more remote than ever.

When emissions of air pollutants, such as sulfur dioxide and oxides of nitrogen, are reduced, improvements occur in a matter of days or weeks, because the gases quickly disappear from the atmosphere. This is not true for GHGs. Once emitted, they remain in the atmosphere for many decades or centuries. As a result, to stabilize atmospheric concentrations, emissions must be dramatically reduced. Further, there is inertia in the earth-ocean system, so the full effects of the emissions that have already occurred have yet to be felt. If the planet is to avoid serious climate change and its largely adverse consequences, global emissions of GHSs will have to fall by 80 to 90% over the next few decades.

Because the world has already lost so much time, and because it does not appear that serious efforts will be made to reduce emissions in the major economies any time soon, interest has been growing in the possibility that warming might be offset by engineering the planet: a concept called geoengineering. The term solar radiation management (SRM) is used to refer to a number of strategies that might be used to increase the fraction of sunlight reflected back into space by just a couple of percentage points in order to offset the temperature increase caused by rising atmospheric concentrations of CO_2 and other GHGs. Of these strategies, the one that appears to be most affordable and most capable of being quickly implemented involves injecting small reflective particles into the stratosphere.

There is nothing theoretical about whether SRM could cool the planet. Every time a large volcano explodes and injects tons of material into the stratosphere, Earth's average temperature drops. When Mount Pinatubo exploded in 1991, the result was a global-scale cooling that averaged about half a degree centigrade for more than a year.

So SRM could work. As undesirable impacts from climate changes mount up, the temptation to engage in SRM will grow. But what if someone tries to do it before we knew if it will work, or what dangers might come with it? The time has come for serious research that can get the world answers before it is too late. To that end, we offer a plan.

Variable Effects—and Benefits

SRM could be designed to bring average temperatures around the world back to something close to their present levels. But because particles injected into the stratosphere distribute themselves around the planet, it is doubtful whether strategies can be found to cool just some vulnerable region, such as the Arctic. Even with a uniform distribution of particles, the spatial distribution of the temperature reductions will not be uniform. For example, work by Katharine Ricke, then at Carnegie Mellon University and now at the Carnegie Institution for Science, has shown that over many decades the level of SRM that might be optimal for China will move further away from the level that might be optimal for India, although in both cases the regional climates would be closer to today's climate than they would have been without SRM.

Change in precipitation patterns induced by climate change might present a particularly strong inducement to undertake SRM. But here again, there are some variables and some unknowns. Although the best current estimates suggest that SRM, on average, could probably restore precipitation patterns to approximately those of today, the ability of climate models to predict the details of precipitation is still not very good. Also, some parts of the world are likely to find at least a little bit of warming or other climate change to be beneficial, and so later in this century countries in those regions might not want to return to the climate of the past few centuries, even if they could. In the short term, modest warming and elevated CO_2 will probably enhance some agricultural production, although with further warming most agriculture will suffer.

Although SRM could offset future warming, it does nothing to slow the steadily rising atmospheric concentrations of CO_2. The higher concentration of CO_2 in the atmosphere is already having notable effects on terrestrial and oceanic ecosystems. Some plant species are able to metabolize CO_2 much more efficiently than others, giving them a comparative advantage in a high-CO_2 world. This is beginning to disrupt and shift the makeup of terrestrial ecosystems.

Over a third of the CO_2 that human activities are adding to the atmosphere is being absorbed by the world's oceans. Today the oceans are roughly 30% more acidic than they were in preindustrial times. Sarah Cooley and colleagues at the Woods Hole Oceanographic Institution have estimated that by late in this century, there will be a dramatic drop in harvest yields of molluscs, resulting in a serious decline in the protein available to low-income coastal populations. Also, acidification is already affecting the ability of many coral species to make reef structures. Many marine experts believe that if emissions and ocean acidification continue to increase, most coral reefs will be gone by the end of this century. In addition to being aesthetically and economically important, reefs (along with coastal mangroves) provide the breeding grounds for many oceanic species and form the base of many oceanic food chains.

Political Landscape

Today in the United States, there are many people who doubt that climate change is occurring, or if it is, that those changes result from human action. Congress is no longer pursuing legislation to mandate reduced emissions of GHGs, and many political leaders have been avoiding the issue.

Federal regulatory actions to advance energy efficiency and reduce emissions from coal-fired power plants are making modest contributions to reducing emissions of GHGs, as is the tightening of the Corporate Average Fuel Economy, or CAFE, standards covering vehicles. Indeed, as Dallas Burtraw and Matthew Woerman of Resources for the Future recently observed, these regulations, together with the dramatic growth in the use of natural gas, have placed the United States on a path to achieve President Obama's goal for reducing U.S. emissions of GHGs. The goal calls for cutting emissions by 2020 to a level that is 17% below levels emitted in 2005. Of course, a 17% reduction does not come close to the U.S. share of reductions needed to stabilize the climate. A few states, most notably California and some in the northeast, are taking direct steps to reduce emissions. Overall, however, the United States shows no signs of being ready to adopt policies to implement the large economy-wide emission reductions necessary to deal with climate change.

Explicit climate policy has progressed further in Europe, where there is a widely shared understanding of the reality of climate change and the risks that it holds. But even as Europe has taken steps to begin reducing emissions of GHGs, these efforts also remain modest when compared with what will be needed to stabilize climate. In the 27 nations that comprise the European Union, per capita CO_2 emissions are roughly half those of the United States. However, Europe's present economic difficulties, together with Germany's growing dependence on coal as it moves to abandon nuclear power, have resulted in a rate of emissions reduction that now lags that of the United States.

Across the major developing nations—China, India, and Brazil—the primary focus is, of course, on economic growth. China is actively developing wind and solar power, as well as technologies for carbon capture and sequestration. China is doing this because it faces local and regional air pollution that is prematurely killing millions of people, because the government realizes that the country will need to wean itself from coal, and because the government assumes that sooner or later the rest of the world will get serious about reducing emissions and, when that happens, China wants to be a strong player in the international markets.

A Tempting Quick Fix

Although subtle impacts from climate change have been apparent for decades, it is only recently that changes have become more obvious and widespread. Over the next few decades, such changes will become ever more apparent. Because reducing atmospheric concentrations of GHGs is inherently slow and expensive, as more and more people and nations grow concerned, SRM could become a tempting quick fix.

SRM is a technology that has enormous leverage. Recent analysis by a university/industry team of researchers, led by Justin McClellan of the Aurora Flight Science Corporation, suggests that a small fleet of specially designed aircraft could deliver enough mass to the stratosphere in the form of small reflecting particles to offset all of the warming anticipated by the end of this century for a cost of less than $10 billion per year, or roughly one ten-thousandth of today's global gross domestic product of $70 trillion (in U.S. dollars). In contrast, estimates by the Intergovernmental Panel on Climate Change in its fourth assessment report suggest that the annual cost of controlling emissions of GHGs to a level sufficient to limit warming will be between half a percent and a few percent of global gross domestic product.

Clearly, given this enormous cost difference, as the impacts of warming and other climate change become more apparent, SRM is going to look increasingly tempting to countries and policymakers who face serious adverse impacts from climate change. Adding to this temptation is the fact that implementing SRM could be done unilaterally by any major nation, which is far from the case with reducing global emissions of GHGs, which would require cooperation among a number of sovereign nations around the world.

Planning a Research Agenda

Although it is well established scientifically that adding fine particles to the stratosphere would, on average, cool Earth, science cannot be at all sure about what else might happen. For example, science cannot be confident about the fate and transport of particles (or precursor materials) once they are injected. It is unknown whether and how the distribution of particles could best be maintained. The surfaces of some types of particles could provide catalytic reaction sites for ozone depletion, but again details are uncertain. Researchers have documented the transient effects of large volcanic injections, but it is not known whether a planned continuous injection of particles might produce large and unanticipated dynamic effects. In short, if the United States or some other actor were to undertake SRM today, it would be "jumping off a cliff" without knowing much about where it, and the planet, would land. Humans have a long tradition of overconfidence and hubris in considering such matters. In our view, anyone who undertook SRM based on what is known today would be imposing an unacceptably large risk on the entire planet.

The climate science community has been aware of the possibility of performing SRM for decades. However, most researchers have shied away from working in this area, in part because of a concern that the more that is known, the greater the chance that someone will try to do it. Although such concerns may have been valid in the past, we believe that the world has now passed a tipping point. In our view, the risks today of not knowing whether and how SRM might work are greater than any risks associated with performing such research.

We reach this conclusion for two reasons. First, the chances are growing that some major state might choose to embark on such a program. If science has not studied SRM and its consequences before that happens, the rest of the world will not be in a position to engage in informed discourse, or mount vigorous scientifically informed opposition if the risks are seen as too great. Second, given the slow pace at which efforts to abate global emissions of GHGs have been proceeding, the chances are growing that when the world does finally get serious about abatement, the United States and other nations may in fact need to collectively engage in a bit of SRM, if it can be done safely, in order to limit damages, while simultaneously scrambling to reduce emissions rapidly and perhaps also scrub CO_2 from the atmosphere.

There have been several calls for a significantly expanded research program on SRM. For example, the House Science Committee and an analogous committee in the UK's Parliament have explored the issue. The United Kingdom has also undertaken a modest program of research support. A task force of the Bipartisan Policy Center, an independent think tank based in Washington, DC, recently developed recommendations for a program of research by the U.S. government. However, most of the limited research now under way in the United States is occurring as part of existing programs that focus on climate and atmospheric science more generally.

Because SRM could rapidly modify the climate of the entire planet at a very modest cost, and because it holds the potential to have profound impacts on all living things, we believe that there is an urgent need for research to clarify its potential impacts and consequences and to provide sufficient reliable information to enable the establishment of appropriate regulatory controls. Building on the work of the Bipartisan Policy Center, the scientific community needs to develop a robust SRM research agenda and obtain the public and private funding necessary to carry it out. In parallel, the community needs to develop guidelines that ensure that such research is responsibly carried out. Finally, as we discuss in detail below, SRM research should be conducted in an open and transparent manner by providing public notification of proposed field experiments and providing decisionmakers and the public with full access to the results of the research.

Except for limited U.S. authority under the National Weather Modification Reporting Act to require notification and reporting of "weather modification" activities, neither U.S. nor international law provides readily useable authority to prohibit, regulate, or report on the conduct of SRM research or field experiments. Our recommendation is to develop and implement a voluntary research code before attempting to impose any regulatory mandates with respect to SRM research, for two reasons. First, a voluntary code can address and work out the various definitional and policy questions we discuss below. Second, a clumsy U.S. attempt to require notice and reporting of SRM research may simply delay or drive that research abroad, frustrating the ultimate objective of open access to responsibly conducted SRM research. A voluntary code, in our view, is the most sensible first step. The United States should take the lead by developing and implementing a code of best SRM research practices and a set of rules governing federally funded SRM research. After doing that, it should then undertake formal governmental steps and informal steps through scientific channels to urge other international players to promptly do the same.

A key component of a significant SRM research program is to develop a fully articulated research agenda. This might be done under the auspices of the U.S. National Academies, drawing on researchers from major universities, national laboratories, and federal agencies, with input from the international research community.

Code of Best Practices

In parallel with, or even before, developing a full research agenda, there is a pressing need to develop what we will call a code of best SRM research practices. This code will need three components. The first would comprise guidelines to provide open access to SRM knowledge by making research results available to decisionmakers and the public. The second would be the delineation of categories of field experiments that are unlikely to have adverse impacts on health, safety, or the environment (that is, experiments conducted within an agreed-upon "allowed zone" of experimental parameters and expected effects on the stratosphere.) The third component would be agreement that any field research to be conducted outside the allowed zone will not be undertaken before a clear national and international governance framework has been developed.

The development of this code will require a convening entity and sufficient resources to support activities. Federal funding through an Executive Branch agency might be secured for such an undertaking. For example, Congress could fund a National Research Council study to develop a set of clear definitions and research norms. Perhaps a faster way to get this done would be to persuade a well-respected private foundation to provide the necessary resources. The National Academies or the National Research Council would be appropriate organizations to convene the effort. Alternatively, the American Geophysical Union might do this as part of its recently expanded set of activities in public policy.

Formulating guidelines for SRM research and a policy to advance open access to SRM research must address a set of key issues of definition and scope:

- First we need to define what counts as SRM. Is the technology to be deployed only for SRM, such as a specific type of specially engineered reflective particle, or does it also include multiuse technology, such as high-altitude aircraft designed to deliver mass to the stratosphere but also capable of performing a variety of other missions that are completely unrelated to SRM? To the extent that SRM overlaps with fields of use that do not raise concerns, non-SRM commercial activity might be affected by efforts to single out SRM activity for special attention. What about research on "incidental" SRM? Such current or proposed research might include, for example, geophysical studies of future volcanic eruptions; studies of the atmospheric effects of "black carbon," the strongly light-absorbing particulate matter emitted by the incomplete combustion of fossil fuels; and studies of the behavior of sulfur dioxide emitted from stationary industrial sources. Any SRM open-access program must define SRM in order, among other things, to minimize its impact on related but uncontroversial commercial activity.
- Next we need to agree on what constitutes SRM research. Does it include theoretical research, literature searches, term papers, and legal memoranda, or should it be limited to experimental research, and if so, does it extend to laboratory research or should it be limited to only field experiments? If the focus is limited to field experiments, how should (and could) basic studies in atmospheric science be differentiated from studies that are more specifically focused on improved understanding of SRM? Trying to make such a demarcation on the basis of experimenters' intent strikes us as deeply problematic; objective criteria will be needed.
- Activities that should be subject to a requirement of prior notification of SRM research need to be defined. At what stage of a project (planning, approval, or funding) should public notification occur, and in how much detail? Also, what medium or media (for example, a dedicated public Internet site, a Federal Register notice, or a proposal submitted to a designated governmental entity) should be used?
- Any policy respecting public access to SRM research needs to spell out the type of research it covers. Does it cover only completed peer-reviewed research? What about studies whose results are not published or that are in progress but have not reached the stage of publication? What about industry research and abandoned or unsuccessful projects? How can public access be bounded in such a way as to preserve valid commercial interests while providing the appropriate level of public disclosure?
- The allowed zone stipulated for experiments will have to be defined, based on results of existing scientific knowledge. This will include careful delineation of areas of permissible field studies and of a protocol for determining that a proposed field study lies within the allowed zone.
- Finally, there are a series of important policy questions that must be addressed. Should an open-access policy be a voluntary undertaking by researchers? Should the policy be incorporated into federal grants and contracts? is it feasible to prescribe regulations that require open access to SRM research? Do any of these policies interfere with academic freedom or intellectual property rights?

Importance of Open Access

As part of the effort to develop a code of best SRM research practices, the United States should develop strategies that ensure that the knowledge developed through SRM research is available to the general public and to national and international policymakers to support informed policy discourse and decisionmaking. The creditability and usefulness of a research program can best be advanced by providing the public with advance notice of SRM field experiments and public access to research results.

The SRM research code of best practices should include a commitment to make public the existence of all SRM research activities, perhaps through a mechanism as simple as posting to a common Web site. It should include an agreement that results from prescribed types of research will be made public (preferably through publication in refereed journals). It should provide guidance on the types of field studies that can be undertaken without any special oversight or approval. And it should express an understanding with respect to privately held intellectual property, as discuss below.

Because most federally funded research would probably already have been described in publicly assessable proposals, posting announcements with an abstract of plans to conduct specific field studies on a common public Web site is not likely to present a significant problem for most investigators. However, asking investigators to post preliminary findings on such a site could be more problematic. This is because some leading journals adopt a strict interpretation with respect to the definition of "prior publication." We believe that in the interests of promoting open access to SRM knowledge, an effort should be made to induce several top journals to adopt a more lenient policy in the case of work related to SRM.

In developing a voluntary code for research conduct, comment and advice should be sought from federal agencies, universities and other research institutions, and nongovernmental organizations and companies likely to conduct SRM research. To maximize its acceptance, the code should probably draw a line between research results that are to be publicly disclosed and those that do not need to be publicly disclosed so as to protect the commercial interests of technologies with multiple non-SRM uses. The expectation is that once the code is finalized, its recommendation could be incorporated into approval requirements in government and private nonprofit funding arrangements for SRM research and promoted as a model for industrial researchers and non-U.S. researchers.

U.S. Government Support

Although there has already been some modest support of SRM research from private sources, if a concerted SRM research program is undertaken in the United States, it most likely will involve funding by the federal government as well as some use of the unique capabilities of federal equipment and laboratories. Federal research activities that meet the definition of SRM research should include provisions requiring that an abstract describing the research to be performed be made publicly available upon execution of the underlying agreement. In the case of research involving field experiments, the National Environmental Policy Act may require an Environmental Impact Assessment, unless the proposed project fits into a category excused from such assessment. If an assessment if required and prepared, the public will have ample notice and opportunity for comment.

Federal research agreements should include provisions requiring delivery to the government of publicly releasable research results, commensurate with the SRM research code of best practice. Federal agencies have experience in negotiating lists in each of their research agreements of specifically identified publicly releasable data that would meet the standards set by the SRM code while at the same time, in appropriate agreements, excluding data whose restriction on public release would not be inconsistent with the SRM research code.

Federal research agreements also typically include a patent rights clause that usually provides that the agreement awardee has the option to elect to retain title to its new inventions made under the agreement. In order to lessen the incentive for private commercial interests to influence the direction of the pursuit of SRM, it would be desirable to restrict the assertion of such private intellectual property rights to technical fields other than SRM. Federal agencies already have statutory authority to take prescribed action to restrict or partially restrict the patent rights of awardees. For example, in order to control commercialization, the Department of Energy has provided for federal government ownership of inventions made by its research contractors in the field of uranium enrichment.

A uniform standard can be applied across transactions involving multiple agencies, through mechanisms such as Federal Acquisition Regulations, Office of Management and Budget circulars, and presidential executive orders. Because the promulgation of government-wide guidance may take some time, individual agencies can act on their own initiative if they feel that their mission justifies such action. Individual agency action may lay the groundwork for broader action across the government. If a lead agency is identified to conduct SRM research, that agency should take such an initiative, in the same way that the National Institutes of Health required that investigators who received its support to conduct analysis of genetic variation in a study population submit descriptive information about their studies to a publicly accessible database. The United States could also use international cooperative research agreements as a means to encourage other countries to follow the code of best SRM research practices.

Action by the U.S. government would set a powerful precedent by a major player in the world economy and world research community, giving the nation better standing to advocate for international action in SRM research. Specific U.S. action, developed with input from stakeholders including public interest groups, would establish a model that ensures appropriate public availability of information without unnecessarily affecting commercial interests.

Understand Before Regulating

The approach we have advocated would have the United States take the lead in developing a set of norms for good research practice for SRM. We have proposed that once developed, these norms should be adopted by federal research programs and urged upon all privately funded research. Once the norms are developed and implemented, it should be possible to persuade others across the international research community to adopt similar norms. Organizations such as the International Council of Scientific Unions and the national academies of science in various countries are well positioned to promote such adoption.

As we noted above, the U.S. National Weather Modification Reporting Act provides a statutory framework for making an SRM open-access research policy mandatory in the United States, at least insofar as the research entails field experiments that are conducted domestically and are of such a scale that they could actually affect climate or weather. Our recommendation, however, is to develop and implement a voluntary research code before attempting to use this authority to implement federal rules governing SRM research.

There is also the question of whether considerations should attempt to go beyond open-access policies for SRM research (that is, notice and reporting) and impose substantive regulation, such as permit requirements or performance or work practice standards. We believe that it is premature today to embark on the development and implementation of substantive regulatory requirements. But as the prospect of large-scale field studies—or actual implementation—of SRM becomes more real, the need for and pressure to develop such regulation will grow. Because future regulations should be based on solid well-developed science, the creation of a serious program of SRM research, combined with procedures to ensure open access to SRM knowledge, is now urgent.

M. Granger Morgan is Lord Chair Professor and head of the Department of Engineering and Public Policy at Carnegie Mellon University.

Robert R. Nordhaus is a partner in the Van Ness Feldman law firm. He was formerly general counsel of the U.S. Department of Energy and of the Federal Energy Regulatory Commission.

Paul Gottlieb is a business consultant. He was formerly the assistant general counsel for technology transfer and intellectual property for the U.S. Department of Energy.

Jane C. S. Long and Dane Scott

NO

Vested Interests and Geoengineering Research

Much remains uncertain about geoengineering, which may offer important benefits—or risks. In moving ahead, there is a set of guidelines that should prove valuable.

On March 11, 2011, Japan suffered one of the most devastating earthquakes in its history, followed by a massive tsunami that engulfed reactors at the Fukushima Daiichi nuclear power plant located near the coast. In Japan, the government body that regulates nuclear power is not highly independent of the utilities it oversees, and regulators had failed to address known safety issues with the reactors. After the crisis, Japan lurched toward a nuclear-free ideology. How can you blame them?

But the catastrophe was not fundamentally caused by a lack of technical information or know-how. Reviewers of the incident found that during the crisis, regulators and company officials made some highly questionable management decisions that were influenced by fears of financial loss and of losing face. Indeed, the catastrophe could have been avoided if good decisions had been made based on available data without the influence of vested interests. As a result, Japan's energy future has been delimited by human foibles and the resulting breakdown of trust in nuclear energy.

If the tsunami in Japan flooded one coastline and several nuclear reactors, climate change may flood all coastlines and cause worldwide dislocations of people, failures of agriculture, and destruction of industries. The likelihood of these impacts has lent legitimacy to the investigation of intentional climate management, or "geoengineering." Society may, at some future time, attempt geoengineering in order to stave off the worst, most unbearable effects of climate change. The technical challenge alone is enormous, but Fukushima provides a cautionary tale for managing the endeavor. Is it possible to develop the trustworthy capacity to manage the climate of Earth?

Incentives for Manipulation

The potential opportunities, benefits, harms, and risks of geoengineering the climate will almost certainly create incentives to manipulate geoengineering choices, and the stakes will be enormous. Societies globally would be wise to face these potential vested interests as they begin to consider researching geoengineering.

Vested interests, in this realm, relate to fortune, fear, fame, and fanaticism, and what to do about them. In moderation, seeking fortune or fame, exercising caution, or being guided by philosophy are appropriate and can lead to innovation and good decisions. However, these attributes may become liabilities when nations, institutions, or individuals seek to manipulate the decisionmaking process to make money, enhance stature, save face, or influence decisions based on fanatical ideology. Society can and should expect people to act with honesty and integrity, but should also plan for dealing with vested interests.

Before moving to planning, it is first worthwhile to examine the forces at work.

Fortune. Parties who stand to gain or lose fortunes by promoting or opposing a geoengineering decision have a vested interest in manipulating that decisionmaking processes. Researchers or companies with a financial stake in experiments or possible deployments may seek to push research or deployment in a direction that is ill-advised for society as a whole. Recently, for example, a company desiring to sell carbon credits for sequestering carbon in the ocean conducted a rogue experiment on iron fertilization (the Haida experiment) off the west coast of Canada without obtaining permission or giving due consideration to potential environmental impacts. At this time, there is no legal framework in place to protect society's interests from a financially motivated company attempting such a geoengineering experiment. In the history of environmental remediation, companies that made money from remediation activities have at times fought changes in regulation that would obviate the need for remediation. For example, California used to require the excavation of soil that had been contaminated by leaking gasoline tanks, until researchers documented that naturally occurring soil bacteria would eventually consume the leaked gasoline, thereby obviating expensive excavation. Companies that stood to make a profit from excavation fought this change in regulation. Similarly, a company with contracts to perform geoengineering would have a vested interest in continued deployment.

Countries that produce fossil fuels and companies comprising the fossil fuel industry may view geoengineering as a way to delay or distract attention from mitigation efforts and thus promote the technology to protect their interests. The chief executive officer of Exxon Corporation, Rex Tillerson, articulated his opinion about climate change, glibly commenting: ". . . we'll adapt to that. It's an engineering problem and it has engineering solutions." The opinion espoused by Tillerson reflects his company's vested interests. Investigators have documented cases where companies with vested financial interests have bought studies to suppress or manipulate data related to climate change, smoking, and pharmaceuticals in order to obtain favorable opinions, decrease funding, or delay the publication of research. In *Merchants of Doubt,* Naomi Oreskis, a professor of history and science studies at the University of California, San Diego, described what she saw as the fossil fuel industry's efforts to manipulate the scientific process and conduct extensive misinformation campaigns related to climate science. These lessons reinforce the idea that the design of a geoengineering enterprise should limit the influence of financial incentives.

Fear. The idea that humans can control the climate is fundamentally hubristic. Individuals involved in geoengineering should be appropriately fearful of this technology and should have great humility and healthy self-doubt that they can control the consequences of intervention.

But there are inappropriate fears that should be avoided. Those involved in geoengineering should not fear losing face when they point out problems or discover negative results. Scientific journals should publish negative results, which for geoengineering are equally as important as positive results. Society surely needs to know if a proposed technology is ineffective or inadvisable.

An institution charged solely with managing geoengineering research would have a vested interest in having geoengineering accepted and deployed, because its continued existence would depend on the approach under consideration being a viable course of action. The institution might be tempted to overstate the benefits of the technologies if it fears losing funding. An institution whose focus is on geoengineering might not want to listen to minority opinions that could slow the momentum of research funding.

As a case in point drawn from recent events, during the economic collapse, there were minority positions within the Bush administration that could have saved the national economy from disaster. For example, the chief of the Commodity Futures Trading Commission, Brooksley Born, repeatedly warned of the dangers of the unregulated derivative market. Her prescient minority voice was suppressed by powerful groupthink within the administration that was vested in economic growth, and she eventually resigned. One cannot help but wonder how many minority voices were suppressed out of fear in light of Born's experiences. People who are in the minority and sense problems or dangers must not be afraid to speak against the majority or powerful figures who might become invested in the success of geoengineering research.

Fear is a powerful human motivator and often drives institutional culture. It would be a grave mistake to create institutions and power structures in which people are motivated to become overconfident about their ability to control the climate or fear speaking out when they represent minority opinions or are bearers of bad news.

Fame. Perhaps universally, humans have a desire for recognition. Scientists and engineers and other advocates are not immune from wanting to become a Nobel Prize winner, or be called on by the media, or even just have an enviable publication record. The desire for recognition can become a vested interest that leads to a loss of perspective.

Individuals developing geoengineering concepts are likely to know more about the subject than anyone else, and their expertise has tremendous value for society. However, it is always better to have a fresh pair of eyes on a difficult and consequential subject. Society should not depend solely on the developers of technology to assess the effectiveness and advisability of their proposals.

Fanaticism. Unlike climate change, geoengineering is not yet an ideologically polarized partisan issue, but it could become so. Society would clearly benefit from a debate over geoengineering that is grounded in quality information and reasonable dialogue. Fanaticism would polarize and distort the debate and the sound decision-making that society requires.

A reasonable ideological position drifts into fanaticism when it hardens into a rigid devotion. Most people have ideological positions on matters of importance, but human philosophies are incomplete and imperfect. For example, in a moment of surprising candor in the aftermath of the 2008 financial crisis, the former chairman of the Federal Reserve Board, Alan Greenspan, famously testified that there was a flaw in his free-market ideology, and that the flaw helped cause the crisis. The tendency to adhere too rigidly to one's worldview can put one in danger of sliding into fanaticism. Fanatics often use unreasonable and unscrupulous means to promote their causes. To state the tragically obvious: Fanatics can sincerely do much harm.

Many groups and people will oppose the very idea of geoengineering for legitimate philosophical reasons and use honest means to argue against such research. They will raise important issues that need to be debated. However, motivated segments with a vested interest in their ideology or world-view can behave like fanatics, ignoring or misrepresenting factual information and using questionable techniques to create distrust, a situation that could in turn lead to an inability to act strategically in face of climate catastrophes.

On the right side of the political spectrum, for example, an individualistic free-market ideology might lead to fanatical positions that see geoengineering as an alternative to "heavy-handed" government regulations to mitigate greenhouse gases. For example, Larry Bell, an endowed professor at the University of Houston and frequent commenter on energy-related matters, remarked in his latest book, *Climate Corruption,* that for many on the right, climate change "has little to do with the state of the environment and much to do with shackling capitalism and transforming the American way of life in the interests of global wealth redistribution." Their vested position, aligned with Exxon's, could be "we will just engineer our way out of this problem."

On the left, rigid environmental or antitechnology ideologies might lead some groups to oppose any discussion of geoengineering. Geoengineering is born out of a fundamental concern for global environmental health, but as with the climate problem in general, it has conflicts with an environmental ideology that narrowly focuses on species preservation, regional conservation, and what is called the precautionary principle. (One version of the precautionary principle states: "When an activity raises threats of harm to human health or the environment, precautionary measures should be taken even if some cause and effect relationships are not fully established scientifically.") Based on an ideology that centers on species preservation, some environmental groups oppose the development of renewable power plants that are designed to help provide energy without emissions but that could cause climate change that could wipe out many species around the globe. In the case of geoengineering, there are environmental groups, such as ETC, that cite the precautionary principle as grounds for banning all geoengineering research, which it sees as a threat to biodiversity. In an ironic twist, rigid antitechnology ideology might become a wedge used by some environmental groups to reject any consideration of geoengineering, even when research is motivated by a desire to preserve biodiversity.

Addressing the Four F's

Moderating the corrupting effects of fortune, fear, fame, and fanaticism should be integral to the development of future geoengineering choices. Society can pay attention to institutional and policy issues that would prevent vested interests from doing harm and provide a counterbalance to human foibles. In this spirit, we offer some guidance for transparency, institutional design, research management, public deliberation, and independent advisory functions. Our suggestions reflect and expand on ideas presented in the Oxford Principles, issued in 2011 by a team of scholars in the United Kingdom as a first effort at producing a code of ethics to guide geoengineering research, and in a report on geoengineering and climate remediation research published in 2011 by the Bipartisan Policy Center, an independent think tank based in Washington, DC. These overlapping strategies each deal with more than one vested interest and could help build genuine trust among scientists, policymakers, and the public.

Transparency. U.S. Supreme Court Justice Louis Brandeis famously said, "Sunlight is the best disinfectant." When all parties present accurate information clearly and forthrightly, vested interests become less influential. To enable effective public accountability and deliberation, information must be transmitted in a way that is comprehensive, but useful to the lay public. Information users need an accurate understanding of such things as funding priorities, research results, limitations, predictions, plans, and errors. This can be referred to as "functional" transparency, to emphasize that the meaning and significance of the information made transparent should also be transparent, not obfuscated in a blizzard of data.

Functional transparency presents challenges. Scientists use many specialized caveats to express what is known about the climate that are understood by and important for scientists, but can obscure the significance of information and be misleading to nonspecialists. For example, climate scientists have had a difficult time articulating the connections between extreme weather events, such as storms Irene and Sandy, and global climate change. The relationship between weather and climate is complex, and scientists know that such extreme storms have a finite likelihood of occurring with or without climate change. Yet understanding the connections between extreme weather events and climate change is important for effective public deliberations on climate mitigation and adaptation. Scientists' need for cautious, complex caveats often clouds the issue in public deliberations.

Also, the public is more likely than the scientific community to focus on the context for research. For example, public discourse on geoengineering research, especially outdoor research, is likely to focus on the purpose of the experiment (in fact, some public deliberation never gets beyond this issue), on alternatives to the experiment, on the potential benefits of the methods being researched, and on the potential risks of the experiments being used. This may be especially true whenever there is the possibility that vested interests may be involved, in which case people are wisely concerned about the motives and goals of research. As a case in point drawn from agricultural biotechnology, the debate has largely centered on the motives and goals of research. Proponents of biotechnology often claim that their goals are to address the problems of world hunger and agricultural sustainability. Opponents question these motives, charging that the real goal is a singular focus on increasing the wealth of researchers and their corporate sponsors.

Scientists, however, do not always make the purpose of research completely transparent. For example, some highly legitimate and important climate science research—say, on cloud behavior—simultaneously informs geoengineering concepts. This research spawns the publication of geoengineering analyses, even though geoengineering is not explicitly named as a purpose of the research. investigators can and do purposely downplay or obfuscate geoengineering as a purpose of research, because this topic is controversial. Just as in the debate about biotechnology, the lack of transparency about the purpose of the research may eventually erode trust and undermine public deliberation about geoengineering. Norms for research transparency should include forthright statements about the purpose of research. There should be clear and understandable assessments of the scope and state of knowledge and expected gains in understanding that could come from research. The transparent release of research information should be designed to inform public deliberation.

As a good example of bridging the divide between scientific discourses and public deliberations, Sweden's nuclear waste program conducted a study, called a "safety case," of a proposed repository for nuclear wastes. The study proved a primary tool in developing a public dialogue on the topic, and the process resulted in a publicly approved, licensed facility. The safety case communicated in lay language the technical arguments about why the proposed repository was thought to be safe. It also described the quality of the information used in the argument; that is, how well the factors contributing to safety were understood. The document laid out future plans about what would be done to improve understanding, the expected outcome of these efforts, and how previous efforts to improve understanding performed as expected or not. At a follow-up iteration of the safety case, the results of recent experiments were compared with previously predicted results. Over time, the transparency of this process enabled everyone, including the public, to see that the scientists investigating the future behavior of the proposed repository had an increasingly accurate understanding of its performance.

What lesson does this experience hold for geoengineering? Whereas the goal of this nuclear waste research was to build a successful repository, the goal of geoengineering research is not to successfully deploy geoengineering but rather to provide the best information possible to a decision process about whether to deploy. Nevertheless, the safety case provides a useful example for satisfying the norm of transparency required for effective public deliberations on scientific issues.

There is reason to hope that the propensity for ideological decisionmaking can be limited by transparency in geoengineering research. The experience at Fukushima, however, suggests that the opposite is true: Vested interests can drive nontransparent and poor management decisions that destroy public trust and encourage more extreme, fanatical responses. To engender trust, the people or groups conducting or managing research should explain clearly what they are trying to accomplish, what they know and do not know, and the quality of the information they have. They should reveal intentions, point out vested interests, and admit mistakes, and do all of this in a way that is frank and understandable—all examples of actions that enhance trust. Any subsequent modifications of plans and processes should be transparent and informed by independent assessments of purpose, data, processes, analyses, results, and conclusions.

Institutional design. Institutional design can foster standards of practice and appropriate regulations that will counteract many vested interests. Public funding of research is the first act of research governance, as it implies a public decision to do research in the first place. If research is publicly funded, then democratically elected officials can be held accountable for it. Although public funding would not by itself prevent privately funded research, it would fill a vacuum that private money has so far filled. Furthermore, publicly funded research should not lead to patenting that would produce financial vested interests. Geoengineering should be managed as a public good in the public interest.

Governments should charter the institutions charged with developing geoengineering research to be rewarded for exposing methods that are bad ideas as well as good. One way to obviate institutional vested interest in the success of a method would be to create institutions responsible for a wide spectrum of climate strategies. If an institution investigates an array of alternatives, it would have great freedom to reject inferior choices. In an ideal world, institutions would be created to develop technical strategies for dealing with climate change in general, the defining problem of our time, and these institutions would be given broad purview over mitigation efforts, adaption requirements, and the evaluation of geoengineering.

Just as institutions should not be punished for admitting to failed concepts, individual scientists involved in geoengineering research should not have their careers depend on positive versus negative results. If they discover adverse information, it should be valued appropriately as adding to overall understanding. Organizations that fund research and universities and laboratories that conduct research should publicize and reward research results demonstrating the ineffectiveness, inadvisability, or implausibility of a geoengineering idea. Just as NASA scientists in the early years applauded when a rocket (unmanned, of course) blew up, institutions should reward curiosity and courage in the face of failures.

Research management. Most research in the United States today is "investigator-driven," in which funding agencies, such as the National Science Foundation, may design a general call for proposals, but the investigators generate the research topics. Funding agencies may convene workshops to explore strategic research needs that subsequently become part of a programmatic call for research proposals. Workshops help to illuminate research that will contribute to an overall goal, but this process does not organize research to achieve a mission per se. There are important previous instances when research with a large-scale public goal was conducted in a collaborative "mission-driven" manner. Now the nation rarely uses this model, and investigator-driven research is the norm.

Geoengineering research (and climate research in general) might benefit from rediscovering, and perhaps reinventing, collaborative mission-driven research modes that focus on a structured investigation of all interconnected parts of the Earth-human-biosphere systems of interest. Interconnections, key failure modes, and critical information needs would be among critical factors to be systematically identified and addressed. The complex, potentially powerful, and intricate problem of intentional management of the climate requires a systems approach. As well, collaborative mission-driven research management would serve to balance the motivation of individuals by rewarding success in meeting the overall goals of research and would compensate for the somewhat random focus of investigator-driven research.

Initial reactions to this suggestion may tend toward the negative, given how mission-driven research was conducted during the Cold War. In the United States and the former Soviet Union, this style of research resulted in massive radioactive releases into the environment, causing extensive contamination of soil, sediments, and surface- and groundwater throughout weapons complexes. Learning from this experience, and using the suggestions offered here, could lead to a reinvention of mission research for geoengineering that would be open, transparent, publically accountable, and environmentally motivated.

There also may be a need to revise the current method, peer review, for assessing the outcomes of research. Peer review will remain necessary—in part, to help balance the exuberance of individual scientists—but by itself will probably be inadequate. Peer review of journal articles would cover geoengineering projects in pieces, without taking into consideration their tight connection to the context and the entirety of the system problem. There is a potentially useful alternative method that was developed for assessing the results of research on nuclear weapons systems that could not be published for security reasons. With severe limitations on access to peer review, laboratories conducting the research pitted two teams against each other to provide checks and scrutiny on research results. In this "red team/blue team" model, one team develops the research, and the other tries to ferret out all the problems. This approach balances a team that might represent institutional and personal vested interests in promoting a technology with a team whose vested interest is in finding out what is wrong with the idea. For evaluating geoengineering research and results, the red team/blue team approach could be considered a more systematic form of peer review.

Public deliberation. Effective public deliberation of the issues, benefits, risks, liabilities, ethics, costs, and other relevant issues will expose and help to neutralize any vested interests that might be in play. Public deliberation can highlight inappropriate profit-making concerns, point out unbalanced scientific positions, call attention to hubris and institutional bias, and counter the influence of partisan positioning on decisionmaking. Public deliberation will be enhanced and facilitated by research that is conducted transparently in trusted institutions that are managed to produce outcomes in the public interest; that is, through all of the suggestions described here. Public deliberation is perhaps one of the few approaches that can help expose ideologies for what they are, whether they come from the political right, which often obfuscates and denies climate science, or from extreme environmentalism, which often uses scare tactics to stop any technological choice anywhere, anytime. No group or individual should get a pass for mendacity in the face of the choices the nation will have to make regarding climate. Public discourse and deliberation will help prevent manipulative dialogue sponsored by ideologues from becoming decisive.

Deliberative dialogue facilitates real-life decisions about setting and prioritizing research goals and selecting the most appropriate means to achieve those goals. For geoengineering, society needs discussions that characterize ethical and social goals; examine competing alternatives; discuss practical obstacles; consider unwanted side effects; assess the technology, including its effectiveness and advisability; and ultimately produce policy recommendations. The deliberative process requires placing scientific research and technological developments in a larger social and ethical context, using this analysis to select intelligent and ethical goals, and identifying appropriate and effective means to achieve those goals.

A recent project in the United Kingdom is a successful example of effective public deliberation on geoengineering. In 2011, a team of researchers planned an experiment to investigate the feasibility of using tethered balloons to release small aerosol particles into the atmosphere that might reflect a few percent of incoming solar radiation and thereby cool things down a bit. The field test would be part of a larger research project, called Stratospheric Particle Injection for Climate Engineering, or SPICE, that involved laboratory and computer analysis of several geoengineering techniques. Although the proposed experiment was nearly risk-free—the plan was to spray a small amount of water into the air—public deliberation about the plans revealed that this work looked like a "dash to deployment" for an immature solar radiation management technology. Research on deployment was not deemed to be necessary or important at this stage. Deliberation also exposed the fact that one of the investigators had intellectual property interests in the balloon technology, and this seemed to violate the principle that geoengineering should be conducted as a public good. Consequently, the investigators themselves stopped the experiment. This honest response helped the investigators accrue credibility and build trust, because their decision responded appropriately to public deliberation.

Independent advisory functions. An independent, broadly based advisory group would facilitate all of these suggested strategies for addressing vested interests. Such a group could help develop standards and norms for transparency, assess and evaluate institutional design, help to develop norms for research management, and lead the way in developing modes and norms of public deliberation. Because the issues raised by geoengineering go far beyond science, an advisory body should also be able to address a variety of broader issues, such as ethics, public deliberation, and international implications. This expanded charge implies that a board's membership should also go beyond scientific expertise.

Forming independent advisory boards will face a number of barriers. Indeed, the need for an advisory function highlights the inherent controversial nature of geoengineering research, a fact that can make the political choice to start research even more difficult. In the United States, a public board of this type would probably have to meet the standards of the Federal Advisory Committee Act, which is intended to ensure that advisory committees are objective and transparent to the public. Ironically, the act's requirements effectively inhibit the formation of advisory committees, because they require funding, which is now scarce. There are other potential problems as well. Much current research on geoengineering is very preliminary, and perhaps all of the techniques identified so far will be ineffective, will have unacceptable side effects, or will be impossible to deploy under real-world conditions. Some people in the geoengineering field are concerned that having an advisory board to oversee research might interfere with the research before it has demonstrated that there is anything—positive or negative—that is worthy of oversight. Also, it is not clear what agency or person in the government should form such a board and to whom it should report.

As a practical example of how an advisory body might prove useful, consider again the SPICE balloon/aerosol experiment in the United Kingdom. If there had been an advisory board in place, it might well have recommended that the government cancel the experiment. Such a recommendation would have facilitated government action to stop the experiment, rather than leaving the decision up to the scientists involved, and this step would have given a rather different message to the public about managing controversial research.

The potential value of advisory boards also has been backed up by the research community itself. At a 2011 workshop on geoengineering governance sponsored by the Solar Radiation Management Initiative (an international project supported by the Royal Society in the United Kingdom, the Environmental Defense Fund, and the Third World Academies of Science), participants were asked to consider various forms of organizing geoengineering research. All of them favored a requirement for an independent advisory group, perhaps the only conclusion of this meeting that had unanimous agreement.

In practical terms, consideration of such advisory boards will give rise to many questions about their membership, scope, and authority. To whom should a board report, and how should a national advisory board relate to the international community? How should an advisory board relate to the many governmental and intergovernmental agencies that would almost surely be involved in geoengineering research of one kind or another? Review boards that deal with research involving human subjects cannot actually authorize such research, but they do have the authority to stop research deemed unethical. Should a similar authority be developed for advisory boards on geoengineering research? Answers to these questions should evolve over time, perhaps starting with informal, nonbinding discussions among the various agencies involved.

Just as scientists do not yet know very much about the effectiveness, advisability, and practicality of possible geoengineering technologies, society also does not know very much about how to manage knowledge as it emerges from geoengineering research. If society is to govern this effort without the ill effects of vested interests, it will be necessary to learn how to govern at the same time as researchers are gathering information about the science and engineering of the various concepts. So the early formation of advisory boards or commissions to guide the development of governance is perhaps the first and most important action in countering the potential adverse effects of vested interests and in ensuring that any decisions to pursue or not pursue geoengineering remain legitimate societal choices.

Preparing in Advance

Although the future of geoengineering remains uncertain although tantalizing, one thing is clear. It is not too early to begin the conversation about the human weaknesses, vested interests, and frightening possibilities of mismanaging geoengineering. The Fukushima disaster is just one in a long list of reminders of the consequences of not anticipating and moderating the effects of such all too human foibles as fortune, fear, fame, and fanaticism. It is unthinkable that geoengineering should be added to this list of human-caused technological tragedies.

And though much remains to be learned, it is also clear that a number of approaches are already available to moderate the corrupting effects of vested interests: norms for transparency, institutions designed for honest evaluation, management of research in the public interest, public deliberation to expose vested interests and counter fanaticism, and independent advisory boards to highlight and recommend specifics in all of these areas.

The challenge, then, is to get started. Earth is facing ever greater climate threats. Solutions need to be identified and implemented, with all appropriate speed. For many people, geoengineering may offer important help—if the nation, and the world, proceed in a deliberate, thoughtful manner in conducting research and applying the lessons learned.

Jane C. S. Long is the principle associate director at large and fellow in the LLNL Center for Global Strategic Research for Lawrence Livermore National Laboratory.

Dane Scott is the director of the Mansfield Ethics and Public Affairs Program at the University of Montana.

EXPLORING THE ISSUE

Do We Need Research Guidelines for Geoengineering?

Critical Thinking and Reflection

1. Which "vested interests" seem most likely to interfere with progress in geoengineering or solar radiation management? Least likely?
2. In what sense is dealing with climate change a matter of ethics?
3. What measures should be taken in the near future to best prepare for the long-term impacts of global warming?
4. Should geoengineering or solar radiation management be reserved for use as a last resort?

Is There Common Ground?

Both sides in this issue agree that geoengineering holds promise and that research efforts are appropriate in advance of actual use of the technique. They differ in their views of what form the first of those efforts should take.

1. Can technological tragedies be prevented by efforts to anticipate human weaknesses, vested interests, and mismanagement?
2. Are there other areas of society where similar efforts would be appropriate before action is taken?
3. Morgan, Nordhaus, and Gottlieb mention that possible regulation of geoengineering or solar radiation management must be based on solid science. In what sense is regulation an effort to deal with human weaknesses, vested interests, and mismanagement?

Create Central

www.mhhe.com/createcentral

Additional Resources

Scott G. Bergerson, "Arctic Meltdown: The Economic and Security Implications of Global Warming," *Foreign Affairs* (March/April 2008).

K. A. Brent and J. McGee, "The Regulation of Geoengineering: A Gathering Storm for International Climate Change Policy?" *Journal of Air Quality and Climate Change* (November 2012).

Constance Holden, "Higher Temperatures Seen Reducing Global Harvests," *Science*, (January 9, 2009).

Robert B. Jackson and James Salzman, "Pursuing Geoengineering for Atmospheric Restoration," *Issues in Science and Technology* (Summer 2010).

Richard A. Kerr, "Humans Are Driving Extreme Weather; Time to Prepare," *Science*, (November 25, 2011).

Michael T. Klare, "Global Warming Battlefields: How Climate Change Threatens Security," *Current History* (November 2007).

Alex de Sherbinin, Koko Warner, and Charles Erhart, "Casualties of Climate Change," *Scientific American* (January 2011).

Internet References . . .

University Corporation for Atmospheric Research

The University Corporation for Atmospheric Research and the National Center for Atmospheric Research are part of a collaborative community dedicated to understanding the atmosphere—the air around us—and the interconnected processes that make up the Earth system, from the ocean floor to the Sun's core. The *UCAR Quarterly* is a journal that presents reports on many issues, including geoengineering (e.g., www.ucar.edu/communications/quarterly/fall06/bigfix.jsp).

www.ucar.edu/

Global Warming

The Environmental Protection Agency maintains this site to summarize the current state of knowledge about global warming.

www.epa.gov/climatechange/index.html

Intergovernmental Panel on Climate Change

The Intergovernmental Panel on Climate Change (IPCC) was formed by the World Meteorological Organization (WMO) and the United Nations Environment Programme (UNEP) to assess any scientific, technical, and socioeconomic information that is relevant to the understanding of the risk of human-induced climate change.

www.ipcc.ch

Selected, Edited, and with Issue Framing Material by:
Thomas A. Easton, *Thomas College*

ISSUE

Is Hydropower a Sound Choice for Renewable Energy?

YES: Steve Blankinship, from "Hydroelectricity: The Versatile Renewable," *Power Engineering* (June 2009)

NO: Mike Ives, from "Dam Bad," *Earth Island Journal* (Autumn 2011)

Learning Outcomes

After studying this issue, students will be able to:

- Describe three advantages offered by hydroelectric power.
- Describe three environmental drawbacks of hydroelectric power.
- Explain how energy can be obtained from water without building dams.
- Describe how water can be used to store energy (as "pumped storage").

ISSUE SUMMARY

YES: Steve Blankinship argues that hydroelectric power is efficient, cheap, reliable, and flexible. It can serve as baseload electricity, backup for wind farms, and even as energy storage, and there is significant room for expansion, including using new technology that does not require dams. It is therefore drawing increasing interest as a way of dealing with rising demand and ever more expensive fossil fuels.

NO: Mike Ives argues that hydroelectric dams such as one proposed for the Mekong River in Laos pose flooding risks, threaten the livelihoods of farmers and fishers, and may be vulnerable to earthquakes. Decisions to build them (or not) are guided by politics, not environmental and social impacts.

Dams have long been an icon of civilization. Building dams of all sizes, from those that hold back village mill ponds to the giant Hoover Dam, was a crucial step in the settling and development of America. They supplied mills with the mechanical power generated when flowing water spun waterwheels. Combined with locks and canals, dams improved the navigability of waterways in the days before railroads. They provided water for irrigation, reduced flooding, and generated electricity. In other parts of the world, building dams for these benefits has been an important step in moving from "undeveloped" to "developing" to "developed" status. See, for example, Ibrahim Yuksel, "Hydropower in Turkey for a Clean and Sustainable Energy Future," *Renewable & Sustainable Energy Reviews* (August 2008). However, hydropower does have its critics. American Rivers, a nonprofit organization dedicated to the protection and restoration of North America's rivers, argues in "Hydropower: Not the Answer to Preventing Climate Change" (2007) that suggesting that hydropower is the answer to global warming hurts opportunities for alternative renewable energy technologies such as solar and wind and distracts from the most promising solution, energy efficiency. Aviva Imhof and Guy R. Lanza, "Greenwashing Hydropower," *World Watch* (January/February 2010), stress hydropower's drawbacks and argue that "the industry's attempt to repackage hydropower as a green, renewable technology is both misleading and unsupported by the facts, and alternatives are often preferable. In general, the cheapest, cleanest, and fastest solution is to invest in energy efficiency."

In the United States, the Army Corps of Engineers (ACE) built almost all hydroelectric power systems until the late 1970s. Today, according to the ACE pamphlet, "Hydropower: Value to the Nation" (www.vtn.iwr.usace.army.mil/pdfs/Hydropower.pdf), the ACE is the single largest owner and operator of hydroelectric power plants in the country and one of the largest in the world. Its 75 power plants produce nearly 100 billion kilowatt-hours of electricity per year. Hydroelectric power is renewable, efficient, and clean. It does not generate air or water pollution, and it emits no greenhouse gases to contribute to global warming. According to Matt Lucky ("Global Hydropower Installed Capacity and Use Increase," in *Vital Signs 2012* (Island Press, 2012)), global use of hydropower has been steadily increasing for years. In 2010, it "accounted for 16.1 percent of electricity use and 3.4 percent of energy use worldwide." North America accounts for about a fifth of global hydropower production, the Asia-Pacific region almost a third, Eurasia a quarter, and South and Central America a fifth. R. Bakis, "The Current Status and Future Opportunities of Hydroelectricity," *Energy Sources: Part B: Economics, Planning, and Policy* (vol. 2, no. 3, 2007), finds that hydropower has unique benefits (some of which are associated with reservoir development), is clean and affordable, and has an important role to play in the future.

In the United States, most good sites for large hydropower plants have already been developed. In the rest of the world, the best sites, such as China's Three Gorges project, are rapidly being developed. Unfortunately, many people see problems in these projects. Mara Hvistendahl's "China's Three Gorges Dam: An Environmental Catastrophe?" *Scientific American* online (March 25, 2008) (www.sciam.com/article.cfm?id=chinas-three-gorges-dam-disaster) is indicative. In Chile, the need for electricity versus the risks to the environment is still being debated; see Gaia Vice, "Dams for Patagonia," *Science* (July 23, 2010); Patrick Symmes, "The Beautiful & the Dammed," *Outside* (June 2010), finds the Patagonian landscape far too beautiful to spoil with dams and powerlines (as well as too vulnerable to volcanic eruptions and earthquakes), but the CEO of HidroAysen—the company that proposes to build five large dams on Patagonian rivers—says other renewables (solar and wind) just can't meet the energy demand; see Aaron Nelsen, "CEO of Chilean Energy Company Defends Project to Dam Patagonia," *Global Spin* (a *Time* blog) (May 20, 2011) (http://globalspin.blogs.time.com/2011/05/20/ceo-of-chilean-energy-company-defends-project-to-dam-patagonia/). In Southeast Asia, at issue are the Mekong River and its tributaries, which offer huge potential for hydropower. Unfortunately, as David Fullbrook, "Dams It Is!" *The World Today* (June 2008), notes, millions of farmers and fishers depend on the Mekong for food and livelihoods, and they are threatened by proposals to meet energy demand—both locally and in neighboring countries such as China—with hydropower. See also Richard Stone, "Mayhem on the Mekong," *Science* (August 12, 2011). In 2012, Laos approved construction of the Xayaburi dam on the lower Mekong ("Megadam Gets Green Light," *Science* (November 9, 2012)). In India, there is a major effort to dam rivers draining from the Himalayan mountains to provide power to some 400 million people; critics are concerned about effects on ecosystems and human settlements, both inside India and in neighboring nations; see R. Edward Grumbine and Maharaj K. Pandit, "Threats from India's Himalaya Dams," *Science* (January 4, 2013).

Because dams flood the land behind them, they destroy forests, farmland, and villages and displace thousands—even millions—of people. Species decline and vanish. Sediment trapped behind the dam no longer reaches the sea to nourish fisheries. River flow is altered. Diseases change their patterns. When a dam breaks, the resulting sudden, immense flood can do colossal damage downstream. There is therefore pressure to remove dams in order to restore fish populations; see Robert F. Service, "Will Busting Dams Boost Salmon?" *Science* (November 18, 2011). The destruction of forests also means that even though hydropower itself does not release greenhouse gases, displaced forests are no longer removing carbon dioxide from the air. According to the International Hydropower Association (http://hydropower.org), the lakes behind dams also emit greenhouse gases, and lake sediments can store large amounts of organic matter. The real issue is the *net* effect, which is ignored by those who wish to discredit hydroelectric power, who also focus on the worst cases, which tend to be in tropical environments. The net emissions of greenhouse gases from hydropower impoundments is an area of ongoing research. See Alain Tremblay, Louis Varfalvy, Charlotte Roehm, and Michelle Garneau, *Greenhouse Gas Emissions—Fluxes and Processes: Hydroelectric Reservoirs and Natural Environments* (Springer, 2005). The tension between the real benefits and the real drawbacks of hydropower is discussed by R. Sternberg in "Hydropower: Dimensions of Social and Environmental Coexistence," *Renewable & Sustainable Energy Reviews* (August 2008).

Fortunately, it is possible to get energy from water without building traditional dam-and-reservoir hydroelectric systems. Tidal power requires dams across estuaries; at high tide, water flows upstream through turbines; at low tide, the turbines are reversed to extract energy as the water flows back to the sea. Turbines can also be placed on the sea floor to take advantage of tidal (and other) currents and in rivers to use "run of the river" flows. See Jonathon Porritt, "Catch the Tide," *Green Futures* (January 2008), and David Kerr, "Marine Energy," *Philosophical Transactions: Mathematical, Physical & Engineering Sciences* (April 2007). In North America, a number of tidal power projects are being started in the Bay of Fundy; see Colin Woodard, "On US Border, a Surge in Tidal-Power Projects," *Christian Science Monitor* (August 15, 2007). Zafer Defne, et al., "National Geodatabase of Tidal Stream Power Resource in USA," *Renewable & Sustainable Energy Reviews* (June 2012), find the greatest numbers of tidal power "hotspots" in Alaska and Maine. See also the U.S. Department of Energy's Marine and Hydrokinetic Technology Database at www1.eere.energy.gov/water/hydrokinetic/default.aspx.

There is also wave power, which uses the motion of waves to work special arrangements of pistons, levers, and air chambers to extract energy. See Ewen Callaway, "To Catch a Wave," *Nature* (November 8, 2007), David C. Holzman, "Blue Power: Turning Tides into Electricity," *Environmental Health Perspectives* (December 2007), and Elisabeth Jeffries, "Ocean Motion Power," *World Watch* (July/August 2008). Yet even this can draw attention from environmentalists, who fear that the equipment may interfere with marine animals and that associated electromagnetic fields may harm sensitive species such as sharks and salmon; see Stiv J. Wilson, "Wave Power," *E Magazine* (May/June 2008). However, Urban Henfridsson, et al., "Wave Energy Potential in the Baltic Sea and the Danish Part of the North Sea, with Reflections on the Skagerrak," *Renewable Energy: An International Journal* (October 2007), note that the potential contribution of wave energy to civilization's needs is large. To take advantage of that potential requires "Sound engineering, in combination with producer, consumer and broad societal perspective." See also Kester Gunn and Clym Stock-Williams, "Quantifying the Global Wave Power Resource," *Renewable Energy: An International Journal* (August 2012).

In the YES selection, Steve Blankinship argues that hydroelectric power is efficient, cheap, reliable, and flexible. It can serve as baseload electricity, backup for wind farms, and even as energy storage, and there is significant room for expansion, including using new technology that does not require dams. It is therefore drawing increasing interest as a way of dealing with rising demand and ever more expensive fossil fuels. In the NO selection, Mike Ives argues that hydroelectric dams such as one proposed for the Mekong River in Laos pose flooding risks, threaten the livelihoods of farmers and fishers, and may be vulnerable to earthquakes. Decisions to build them (or not) are guided by politics, not environmental and social impacts.

YES

Steve Blankinship

Hydroelectricity: The Versatile Renewable

As one of the earliest and most elementary forms of power generation, hydropower remains by far the largest source of renewable energy in the world, including in North America.

In the early 1900s, hydropower was the dominant source of U.S. electric generation and as recently as the 1940s accounted for more than 40 percent of electricity production. By the 1950s, developers had tapped the hydro potential of the most mountainous regions in the U.S.—many in the Northwest—where steep inclines supply the strongest river flows and permit the most cost-efficient projects.

Hydropower supplies almost two-thirds of Canada's power and makes it the world's largest hydropower producer, representing 13 percent of global output. It's also the world's second largest exporter of hydro (after France). Altogether, its roughly 450 hydro plants, half of which produce less than 10 MW, account for 72,660 MW with another 1,800 MW currently under construction and an additional 12,000 MW under consideration, according to the Canadian Hydropower Association.

Today, hydro represents about 8 percent of all power in the U.S. and more than 90 of all the renewable power generated in the nation. Hydro provides more than 16 times as much energy as wind and solar power combined.

And hydro's use is increasing, both through updates to older hydro generation technology and through new technologies. Utilities are proposing more than 70 projects that would boost U.S. hydroelectric capacity by at least 11,000 MW over the next decade.

Driving a new wave of hydropower development is unprecedented demand for renewable energy and rising fossil fuel costs. The American Recovery and Reinvestment Act and other programs provide tax provisions to attract investment in incremental hydropower, hydro at non-powered dams, ocean, tidal and in-stream hydrokinetic technologies.

Upgrades and New Builds

AMP-Ohio, which owns and operates power production facilities for 126 member entities in Ohio, Pennsylvania, Michigan, Virginia, West Virginia and Kentucky, is developing multiple hydroelectric projects, representing one of the largest deployments of hydroelectric generation in the U.S. The projects are run-of-the-river hydroelectric facilities to be installed on existing dams on the Ohio River and the New River in West Virginia. Combined, these six projects would add more than 380 MW of new generation at an estimated construction cost of just over $1.5 billion.

As part of the project, AMP-Ohio signed a contract worth more than $300 million with Voith Siemens to manufacture turbines and generators for the first three of these projects at the Smithland, Cannelton and Willow Island locks and dams. A fourth Ohio River project will be at the Meldahl locks and dam. In addition, AMP-Ohio is pursuing a project at the R.C. Byrd locks and dam on the Ohio River and performing a feasibility study for a project at the Bluestone dam on the New River.

PPL Corp. recently filed a request with the Federal Energy Regulatory Commission for a 125 MW expansion at its Holtwood hydroelectric plant on the Susquehanna River in Pennsylvania. Holtwood currently is rated at 108 MW and has generated power since 1910. The estimated $440 million project is subject to availability of stimulus funding. Construction could start early next year.

"The hydro business is so robust right now that the contractors only go after big projects, leaving lots of room for smaller players to stay busy with medium and smaller projects," said Norm Bishop, vice president for the hydro dams market sector of MWH, a Colorado-based firm that helps develop new hydro projects and update existing ones.

In addition to the demand for renewables and the rising costs of fossil fuels, Bishop cites hydro's flexibility that allows it to meet today's power market demands, including ancillary grid support, which is especially critical in places with increasingly high penetrations of wind farms.

And the potential to make cheap power from water has barely been tapped. Of the existing dams in the U.S., 3 percent (or around 2,400) are equipped to produce power and annually generate 270,000 GWh, according to the U.S. Department of Energy. DOE estimates another 30,000 MW of capacity could be developed, including 17,000 MW at existing dams.

Pump It Up

After decades of little or no development, U.S. hydro pumped storage (by which water is pumped uphill during off peak demand periods and released to flow down hill to spin generating turbines on peak) is seeing renewed attention. In the past two years, FERC has approved 21 preliminary permits for pumped-storage projects totaling more than 12,000 MW.

Earlier this year, Energy Secretary Steven Chu said hydro pumped storage must be a part of a national plan to expand clean-energy resources and integrate variable renewable energy resources into the transmission grid. Chu said the U.S. has limited existing resources for storing energy and most of what it does have comes from the 20,355 MW of pumped-storage capacity now in service.

National Hydropower Association (NHA) Executive Director Linda Church-Ciocci said that expanding hydro pumped storage capacity will be a high priority for her association's new pumped storage council.

"Right now, the federal government has no program to spur expansion of U.S. pumped storage," she said. "We advocate investment tax credits or other similar measures that can incentivize pumped storage development immediately."

A benefit could be changes to the licensing process, an initiative NHA has worked on for a number of years. The new process focuses on collaboration among agencies, which should reduce the amount of time required for a new or renewed license from 15 years to as little as three or four years.

Relicensing is hot right now as owners hope to eke even 2 or 3 percent improvements for a price tag that can be as low as $200/kW in some cases.

"There's a tremendous opportunity to repower and upgrade the mechanical aspects of existing facilities to increase output," said Don Erpenbeck, another MWH vice president. He's particularly upbeat with some new technologies that include ultra low head hydro and emerging technologies such as hydrokinetic.

"If a project is 20 years old there's a good chance today's technology can eke out more power at a very small cost per kW."

Water to Wire = Ultimate Efficiency

Hydro power has always had high availability and quick ramp rates. It also enjoys an overall efficiency unmatched by any other power source. No fuel is needed, just the volume and motion of the water. Mechanical efficiency is high and the only true efficiency losses are limited to line loss.

"Availability is pushing 90 percent with hydro and on the mechanical side we hit 95 percent efficiency," said Erpenbeck. But some plants have lost as much as 10 percent of their efficiency due to the age of their turbine/generators. New technology can not only reclaim that efficiency, but increase output above previous levels.

"You could be looking at up to 20 percent efficiency increases if the existing machines are in bad shape," he said.

Hydro's ability to ramp quickly enhances its attractiveness as a power portfolio asset. New technology can expand that flexibility. "We can make the efficiency curve flatter," said Erpenbeck, "so hydro is more efficient running off peak. We can now run with even greater flexibility and respond to market conditions across a wider range of megawatts in terms of cycling, load following and turn down."

Erpenbeck said hydropower can routinely operate at 55 to 100 percent of rated load and back off to 20 to 40 percent as needed.

Increases to operating range provide prime quality spinning reserve for grid support, which is more important today than ever before. The increases are achieved through the ability to run in condensing mode where the generator is synchronized and motoring while the turbine spins air, or synchronized at low power (20 to 40 percent of rated load) going to full power in seconds. "With all the wind power coming onto the grid this is being used much more," said Bishop. "Modern hydro's ramp rate is fast."

Hydro also provides high-quality ancillary grid support. For example, Grand Coulee Dam on the Columbia River in Washington State can go from low load to full load (about 800 MW) in matter of seconds.

Technology Improvements

Improvements to conventional hydro technology provide a variety of upgrades that help hydropower remain low cost while offering environmental benefits.

Grant County Public Utility District, part of the Mid-Columbia System, is installing 10, $15 million fish-friendly turbines at Wanapum Dam and plans to replace another 10 turbines at Priest Rapids. The old turbines are being replaced with models that use six smaller blades instead of five. When completed in 2012, the project is expected to improve each turbines' efficiency by 3 percent and the facility's overall capacity by 15 percent.

Recent upgrades to the Sacramento Municipal Utility District's Jaybird and Loon Lake hydroelectric powerhouses have led to still more efficiency gains. Installing new computerized controllers to better regulate water flow to the turbines has increased output by 15 MW for the same amount of water when running at low power levels. The new governor control system automatically regulates the amount of water that shoots out of six high-pressure nozzles and onto a wheel that spins the generator.

With the old equipment, the controller opened all six needles at once, boosting water flow to the turbine as electricity demand rose. When the unit was at low load, it required less water. But this fanned out of the needles similar to a garden hose set to a wide spray pattern and caused most of the water to miss the turbine wheel.

The new equipment opens two needles initially and adds others as demand for power rises. By moving the same volume of water through two needles instead of six, the water stream is more tightly focused and hits the turbine wheel more directly. This results in significant water savings for the same amount of power generation. Based on current short-term power price forecasts, the utility estimates the equipment will save it $130,000 a year.

Canada's two largest hydro utilities—Ontario Hydro and Hydro Quebec—continue to expand capacity. Hydro

Quebec will announce this summer a revised hydro expansion schedule. But current expansion plans include completing the last generating units at the Péribonka development and the first units at Chute-Allard and Rapides-des-Coeurs.

Work also proceeded at the Eastmain-1-A/Sarcelle/Rupert jobsite. The project will divert a portion of the flow from the Rupert River watershed into the Eastmain River watershed. That will involve four dams, a spillway on the Rupert River, 74 dikes, two diversion bays, construction of a 1.8-mile-long tunnel and a network of canals and hydraulic structures on the Rupert River to maintain post-diversion water levels along half of the river's length.

Ontario Hydro's Niagara tunnel project will increase the amount of water flowing to turbines at the Sir Adam Beck generating stations at Niagara Falls, allowing them to better use available water. Upon completion of the 6.5-mile-long tunnel, average annual generation from the Beck stations is expected to increase by about 1.6 TWh. Ontario Power also recently completed a 12.5 MW hydroelectric generating station on the English River. The new Lac Seul generating station uses most of the spill currently passing the existing Ear Falls generating station, thus increasing overall efficiency, capacity and energy generated from the plant. The project is expected to be inservice later this year.

Ontario Power is proceeding with the definition phase for a 450 MW development on the Lower Mattagami River, including replacing the Smoky Falls station and expanding the Little Long, Harmon and Kipling stations. The company also approved redeveloping four existing stations, which otherwise would have been removed from service.

New Wave for Hydropower

The tremendous force of moving water is obvious to anyone who has stood in breaking ocean waves or swum against a river's current. Hydrokinetic—or kinetic hydro—technologies generate electricity from waves or directly from the flow of water in ocean currents, tides or inland waterways and is gaining increased attention.

Hydrokinetic technology uses stream flow to make power and requires a steady three to five knots of flow to operate. Hydrokinetic water turbines (HUTs) can be placed where there is no dam; for example, they may be attached to bridges or to frames on the river bottom. Hydrokinetic boosts potential capacity far beyond conventional hydro power. As one example, thousands of miles of canals in California are designed primarily for irrigation, but could also host kinetic turbines.

HUTs are smaller than wind turbines because water is about 800 times denser than air. Ocean tidal current can deliver predictable 20 hours per day energy and a HUT can produce up to four times more energy than a wind turbine on a good day. Venturi and centrifugal designs can accelerate water speed through the turbine and double the energy produced. Current project proposals suggest that kinetic hydro produced by U.S. waves, tides and rivers, could produce 13,000 MW by 2025.

FERC has approved the nation's first commercially-operational hydrokinetic power station in Hastings, Minn. The 4.4 MW run-of-river hydropower plant will use two hydrokinetic units, each with a nameplate capacity of 100 kW.

Near and off-shore ocean waves might have the greatest hydrokinetic potential. Extracting just 15 percent of the energy in U.S. coastal waves would generate as much electricity as is currently produced at conventional hydro dams. Much of this wave potential is along the Pacific Coast and close to population centers.

Beyond the sheer size of the resource, hydrokinetics are attractive for their predictability. Wave patterns can be predicted days in advance. Since the kinetic energy held in a stream is related to its speed cubed, extracting the most electricity from each hydrokinetic project will depend heavily on site selection. Energy output increases eight times with only twice as much water current speed.

State and federal policymakers across the U.S. have taken notice of the potential of hydrokinetic energy and have begun to support its development through legislative and monetary means. Ocean energy is eligible for credit under renewable electricity standards in 16 states and for federal renewable production tax credits, as expanded in the Energy Policy Act of 2005. Furthermore, hydrokinetic energy development was marked for increased research funding appropriations in the 2007 Energy Independence and Security Act.

Overcoming Environmental Opposition

Hydro has all but disappeared from the renewable energy options usually cited by renewable energy advocates. Many environmentalists have long opposed hydroelectric power and do not consider it "green" or renewable. Much of the opposition is based on the water diversions required by traditional hydroelectric projects and the effects on land and wildlife. Fish killed as a result of passing hydro turbines has also led to a substantial amount of environmental concern.

Because of this environmental opposition, some states restrict the extent to which hydroelectric projects may qualify under renewable portfolio standards.

"Policy makers at the federal and state level have a difficult task of designing regulations and incentives that recognize the fact that an existing renewable source like hydropower can be further developed with the right incentives," said Michael Cutter, vice president of engineering and development for Brookfield Renewable Power (BRP). The company has developed, owned and operated hydro power facilities for more than 100 years and has 100 hydropower facilities totaling nearly 2,000 MW in nine U.S. states.

Cutter said opportunities exist throughout the U.S. for continued development of hydro electric generation. "Recent studies show the amount of hydropower could double from the current amount of installed hydro generating capacity by 2030 if the country could upgrade existing hydropower, add hydropower at non power dams and develop some of the new technologies," he said. "To reach hydropower's potential it is important to continue to strengthen federal and state energy policies and educate the public on hydropower's role as an indigenous, renewable energy source."

Steve Blankinship is an associate editor of *Power Engineering* magazine.

Mike Ives

NO

Dam Bad

Laos' Plans to Dam the Mekong Could Open the Floodgates to Further Dams on the River

Sathian Megboon is a DJ for 94.5 FM, a radio station in northeast Thailand. It's a fun gig, he says, because the station broadcasts across the Mekong River to Vientiane, the tiny capital of the Lao People's Democratic Republic, which gives him the chance to take requests from listeners in two countries. Last year, listeners started calling more than usual, but not to ask for the folk songs Sathian likes to play. They wanted to know what he thought of reports that a Thai company was planning to build a \$3.5 billion dam a few hundred kilometers upstream on the Lao–Thai border in a remote and impoverished mountain area.

Sathian's Vientiane listeners may have read about the proposed Xayaburi dam in The Vientiane Times, a mouthpiece for the secretive Lao Communist Party. But they wanted the real story: Namely, how would a hydropower dam in Xayaburi Province affect them?

The DJ said he wasn't sure, because he isn't a politician or hydropower expert. But building dams on the Mekong—the world's tenth-longest river—seemed to him a terrible idea. China, which borders northern Laos, built four hydroelectric dams on the upper Mekong between 1986 and 2009. Sathian and his neighbors say those dams have changed the Mekong's "flood pulse," the seasonal ebb and flow that regulates, agriculture and fishing and feeds the Lower Mekong Basin's 60 million residents. According to elder farmers who grew up beside the Mekong, erratic flow patterns that appeared in the 1990s have made it harder to grow staple crops such as chili peppers, eggplants, and corn. They say they cannot imagine how additional dams would improve the situation.

Sathian and his neighbors claim that, in 2007, Chinese dams triggered violent flooding. "It happened very fast, and we didn't have any warning," Sathian, who is 63 and generously tattooed, told me on a lethargic mid-April afternoon. "It wasn't raining, but the river flooded for seven days! If they build a new dam in Xayaburi, I'm afraid the next flood could be like a tsunami."

We were standing on the banks of the Mekong under a white banner that said NO. MEKONG DAMS in English. Looking across the river, I saw monks in orange robes bathing against the backdrop of Vientiane's unassuming skyline. Fishing skiffs were gliding downstream, and the air felt sticky and stagnant. It was hard to imagine that a planned hydropower dam hundreds of miles upstream, in the mountains of landlocked Laos, had caused such fear. But a few weeks earlier, 263 nongovernmental organizations from 51 countries had written to the Lao prime minister and urged him to cancel the project. Apparently Xayaburi was kind of a big deal.

Hydropower dams are common in Southeast Asia and have already been constructed on some of Mekong's tributaries. But the 1,280-megawatt Xayaburi dam, which Laos proposed last September, would be the first of 11 dams planned for the river's mainstream. Nine would be sited in Laos, the other two in Cambodia. Along with a proposed "river diversion" project in Laos, the dams could supply about 65 terawatt hours of electricity per year—up to 8 percent of the Mekong region's projected 2025 electricity demand and slightly less energy than Americans use each year to power their televisions. About 90 percent of the power would go to Vietnam and Thailand.

Environmental activists and civil society groups across Southeast Asia say that if the Xayaburi dam is built, it will lay the political groundwork for the other dams, which they fear would have devastating cumulative impacts on ecosystems and livelihoods. They also worry that hydropower developers are ignoring climate change, which, according to scientists, will affect Mekong hydrology this century. The activists have rallied behind a 2010 study by the International Centre for Environmental Management (ICEM) that recommended a ten-year moratorium on new Mekong dams because the dams, if built, would provoke "permanent and irreversible" social and environmental consequences.

"We need food, not electricity," says Mu Panmeesri, a 27-year-old schoolteacher who lives downstream of Sathian Megboon and organizes anti-Xayaburi rallies in his town. "We can't eat electricity."

The Lao PDR, a former French colony that declared independence in 1945, has been governed by one political party for the last 36 years. Usually, if Lao officials want to build something, a road, a bridge, or a massive dam, it would probably be built. But last year's Xayaburi proposal triggered a review process moderated by the Mekong River Commission (MRC), an advisory body formed in 1995 by the four lower Mekong countries—Laos, Thailand, Vietnam, and Cambodia—to promote sustainable development in the Lower Mekong Basin.

Encouraging sustainable development is no small task in Southeast Asia, where environmental regulations are thin and civil society has little or no voice. Powerful governments often approve energy projects without consulting their citizens or requiring detailed environmental impact assessments. But the four lower Mekong countries agreed in 1995 to initiate a multilateral MRC review if one of them ever proposed a dam on the river's mainstream. So environmental groups and local dam opponents are relying on this untested international body to stop the Xayaburi project.

Xayaburi is the first mainstream dam proposed for the lower Mekong since 1995, and the MRC review that began last fall is the first of its kind. MRC member countries can't legally stop Laos from damming the Mekong, but they can commission feasibility studies and draft statements recommending the best course of action. The MRC review process for the Xayaburi dam was supposed to end in April, but as I write these words in August, analysts aren't sure when the process will end or whether Laos will heed its neighbors' recommendations. Regardless, it's clear that the MRC process has sparked an important public debate about energy, ecology, and food security in Southeast Asia—an achievement in itself for a region plagued by poverty, corruption, and the legacy of war.

Xayaburi appears to be a bellwether of regional environmental diplomacy. Decisions made in the coming months on Xayaburi and other dams will affect millions of people, perhaps for generations. In 50 years, will people who live near the Mekong have enough to water to drink and food to eat? Will Mekong countries establish procedures for sharing their river resources, or will diplomatic scuffles escalate to armed stand-offs? How best can poor countries' demands for energy be balanced with the interests of riverine communities?

These questions invite speculation about whether dams are the best way to meet the region's rising electricity demand, which is predicted to increase each year until 2025. The region has what ICEM calls a "massive potential for hydropower," but sediment buildup in dam reservoirs can hinder medium-and long-term capacity; sedimentation at the Xayaburi dam, according to the MRC, would decrease the dam's output by up to 60 percent in 30 years. Critics charge that the electricity from Mekong dams wouldn't justify the negative impacts the dams would have on watersheds, fisheries, and food production. Rather than dam the Mekong, they say, Mekong countries should promote wind turbines and solar panels.

Laos counters that Mekong dams, in addition to providing energy for the regional grid, would help lift Laotians out of poverty. While many rural development experts say Laos should temporarily or permanently postpone Mekong dams, others suggest the dams, though imperfect, may be a reasonable way for Laos—which was heavily bombed during the Vietnam War and remains one of the world's poorest countries—to achieve its goal of escaping from UN-designated "Least Developed Country" status. Lao officials say they want their country to be the "battery of Southeast Asia."

Dams on the Mekong's mainstream would surely have negative impacts on downstream communities and ecosystems, says Stuart Ling, who directs the Lao office of a Belgian NGO called VECO. "But the Lao government has GDP targets, and these dams that are going ahead were in the system a long time ago because Laos is trying to develop. If Laos doesn't get its revenue from generating hydropower, how will it get its revenue?"

Dams were first proposed for the Mekong in the 1950s, but the Cold War put them on hold. By the time they were re-proposed in the 1990s, writes Philip Hirsch, a Mekong expert at the University of Sydney, resistance from environmental groups made them "unpalatable." Renewed interest in developing hydropower in the Lower Mekong Basin has escalated since 2006 in tandem with rising private investment in power infrastructure. Privately owned hydropower companies are filling a void left by multilateral institutions like the World Bank and the International Monetary Fund, which are less eager than they once were to fund hydropower projects. One reason is that a 2000 report by the World Commission on Dams found dams had displaced 40 to 80 million people worldwide, and that "in too many cases," the associated social and environmental costs were "unacceptable and often unnecessary."

Private developers aren't held to the same environmental regulations that multilateral institutions would be. But the financiers and developers do have to weather criticism from environmental groups—particularly the Berkeley-based NGO International Rivers, which employs a full-time "Mekong Campaigner."

Resistance to Xayaburi raises the question: If the idea of damming the Mekong is unpalatable to so many people, why are developers—and the Lao and Cambodian governments—willing to risk drawing flak?

One explanation is China. The four Mekong dams the Chinese built pump more water downstream in the dry season than the river would otherwise supply. By suppressing the Mekong's flood pulse, they have created an economic incentive for downstream developers, who at the moment have access to a steadier water supply. China has become a hydropower "role model" for downstream neighbors, says Prescott College Professor Ed Grumbine: Southeast Asian countries are thinking, "If China is using the river as a resource and gaining greatly from it, then why can't we do the same thing?"

Indeed, why not? Yes, you can make a case—as developers have and will—that hydropower is a "green" alternative to coal and nuclear power. But it is hard to argue that dams in Laos promote environmental sustainability or benefit the communities they displace. Since the Lao Communist Party seized power in 1975 after a protracted civil war, its primary development strategy has been to sell timber, rubber, mineral, and hydropower rights to foreign bidders.

"The combination of neoliberal economic policies, foreign direct investment, and a nontransparent, nepotistic kind of government [in Laos] is a real toxic mix," says Ian Baird, an environmental expert who has worked there for years. Earnings are not trickling down to everyday Laotians. Vientiane may have fancy hotels and restaurants, but a typical Lao village is a smattering of bamboo huts. According to the United Nations, food insecurity is "widespread" across the country—"alarmingly high" in rural areas—and half of all children under five in Laos are "chronically malnourished."

Baird, a geography professor at the University of Wisconsin-Madison, has seen how hydropower affects Lao communities, and he's not impressed. This spring, as Baird monitored the Xayaburi dam controversy, he was also analyzing a proposal to dam Khone Falls, the only large waterfall on the lower and middle Mekong. He says the project would negatively affect the nutrition of hundreds of thousands of people.

"I'm not an unreasonable person," Baird told me. "If you're building a dam, you should really cost it out in terms of environmental and social impacts and compensate people for the life of the project. But to be honest, I can't tell you about a hydropower project in Laos where they've done a good job."

Environmental activists say a wild Mekong is worth fighting for. The river has the world's most productive inland fishery and is a major source of livelihood for millions of people. The Xayaburi dam would threaten at least 41 of the Mekong's 1,300 fish species and cause $476 million in direct losses through reduced fish harvests—an estimate that doesn't account for fisheries in Vietnam's fertile Mekong River Delta.

Proponents of the dam say it would have "fish ladders" and other fish-friendly technologies, but aquaculture experts say those technologies wouldn't prevent fish extinctions. A study by the World Wildlife Fund and other groups noted that the ladders would be "challenging" even for strong Northern Hemisphere salmon. "If fish can't migrate, they don't breed," explains Stuart Chapman, WWF's Greater Mekong Program manager. "This will lead to a collapse of the fishery."

The dams would also disrupt the production of rice and other crops along Mekong's banks. Thailand and Vietnam are the world's first and second-largest rice exporters, respectively, and farmers in the Mekong River Basin depend on the river to irrigate 6.6 million hectares of farmland. According to ICEM's 2010 study, the dams would destroy about half of the Mekong's riverbank gardens and cost about $25 million per year in lost agricultural land.

How about earthquakes? The concerned residents I met in Thailand worry earthquakes would destroy Mekong dams and cause catastrophic floods worse than the flood that scared them in 2007. After the disastrous March earthquake and tsunami in Japan, two Chinese earthquake experts wrote to the Chinese premier, Wen Jiabao, to warn that building dams in Southwest China on the Mekong and two other rivers (the Salween or Nu and the Yangtze), was ludicrous because the region lies on an active fault line. If an earthquake were to destroy a dam on a river that has other dams, they predicted a torrent of water, mud, and rocks could careen downstream and set off a "chain reaction" of devastation.

And then there is climate change. The Mekong River begins in the Himalayas and flows 4,180 kilometers to the Vietnamese coast. Emerging research suggests that increased glacial melting in mountainous Central Asia will likely increase downstream river flows for a few decades but ultimately cause late-summer water shortages. "Climate change will exacerbate the impact of hydropower dams on the downstream Mekong Delta, but there's a lot we don't know," says Dr. Kien Tran-Mai, the MRC's climate change program officer. Because not enough research has been done on the cumulative impacts of climate change on the Mekong, Dr. Kien told me, the MRC doesn't require developers to plan for climate change in their proposals. The commission is not ignoring climate change, he insists, but as a mere advisory body it cannot require hydropower developers to create proposals based on climate modeling that doesn't yet exist.

Hydropower proponents argue that when climate change alters the Mekong's flow patterns, dam operators could simply increase water flow during dry periods and reduce it when water levels are too high. The argument sounds logical, Dr. Kien says, but it doesn't make him feel better, because dam operators are primarily concerned with "economic benefit and electricity generation."

Sathian Megboon and other concerned citizens in Thailand say they don't believe dam operators will ever look out for their best interests. "We're controlled by China," Somphong Paratphom, a village chief, said in April as he drove me across a Mekong sandbar in his pickup truck. "If the Chinese wanted to kill us, they could just open the dam's gates. And the danger from Xayaburi is twice as high as it was in China, because China is farther away! If they build a dam in Xayaburi, why wouldn't flooding happen again?"

On April 19, as resistance to Xayaburi was building, diplomats from the four lower Mekong countries met at the MRC headquarters in Vientiane to draft their final recommendation. But the leaders couldn't reach a consensus. Instead, they agreed on a follow-up meeting at an unspecified date. Thailand, Cambodia, and Vietnam issued separate statements saying more study was needed on the Xayaburi dam's "transboundary impacts." Vietnam issued the strongest statement, calling for a ten-year moratorium on new Mekong dams. Laos directed the dam's Thai developer, Ch. Karnchang, to fund a new study of the dam's potential environmental impacts.

One thing, Professor Ed Grumbine said, was clear: The decision over whether to build the dam would be based not on science, but politics.

Would Laos really allow a Bangkok developer to build the Xayaburi dam without waiting for the MRC process to formally conclude? Despite a swirl of rumors on the business pages of Thai newspapers suggesting that the dam was still moving forward, it seemed unlikely to some Laos experts that Laos would build the dam over Vietnam's objection. "I think there's a good chance this project is dead," said Baird, the University of Wisconsin professor, noting it was "unprecedented" since 1975 for Vietnam to publicly disagree with Laos, a close ally. "Considering the loss of face, what Lao politician would be willing to put his neck on the line and propose this project again?"

The plot twisted again in late June, when International Rivers released two leaked letters suggesting Laos was indeed moving forward with the project. In the first letter, dated June 8, an official from Laos's Ministry of Energy and Mines informs the Xayaburi Power Company—a subsidiary of Ch. Karnchang—that a consulting firm has reviewed the company's Xayaburi dam proposal and concluded that Laos has "taken all legitimate concerns from member countries into consideration." (A spokesperson for Ch. Karnchang declined to comment for this article.) In the second letter, dated June 9, the chairman of the company's board of directors writes to the governor of the Electricity Generating Authority of Thailand and says the company is ready to execute a power of purchase agreement at the Thai government's earliest convenience.

On August 4, International Rivers reported that a "substantial construction camp" with "at least a few hundred workers" had been established near the dam site. It seemed that the Lao Communist Party was prepared to defy Vietnam, its longtime political ally.

It's hard to get around in Laos. The countryside is mountainous, and the roads are in deplorable shape. To get near the site of the Xayaburi dam, you have to take a rickety school bus from Luang Prabang, the ancient Lao capital, toward Xayaburi City. Thirty minutes into the ride, the bus is traversing mountain passes and barreling past fields of upland sticky rice. When the road turns to dirt, windows shake as the wheels slam into potholes.

I made the journey in late April with a Lao friend. After bumping along for a few hours, the bus crossed the Mekong in a ferry, and a few minutes later it left us in a dusty roadside village about fifteen kilometers north of Xayaburi City. We approached a group of people sitting on the porch of a simple concrete house. The dam site was nearby, they said, but in order to visit we had to get permission from the police.

The police station was across the street, and we approached warily. Inside, two officers sat at a wooden table in a bare room. They didn't look happy to see us, and they asked for my passport. When I refused, they said we couldn't visit the site.

We returned to the village and paid two men to drive us back to the Mekong on their motorbikes. Then we paid a few Lao villagers to take us downriver in their orange fishing skiff. It would take too long—about five hours—to motor all the way to the dam site, but they could introduce us to fisherman in nearby villages who would be displaced by the dam.

We climbed into the skiff and were soon lurching down the river. The skiff's 5.5 horsepower engine drowned out conversation, but it could barely keep the craft straight in the muddy Mekong's strong current. Against a mountain backdrop, we saw fishermen inspecting nets that were strung across a line of riverside boulders. Our guide recognized the men and pulled the skiff ashore.

What had they heard about the Xayaburi dam? As far as they knew, they said, it was going to be built. The fishermen said a few people representing the Thai dam developer had visited their villages and offered, as compensation for the dam, to build them new homes, plus a hospital and a school, and to give them loans—the equivalent of roughly $250 per family—to help them buy livestock. The men, who support their families on about $500 per year, said they were okay with moving to a new village and planting new gardens, so long as the company followed through on its promises.

Rural development experts tell me that Lao villagers who have been displaced by hydropower dams on Mekong tributaries usually end up worse off even if companies provide compensation. In many cases, villagers not only lose their main source of livelihood but also incur debts as they struggle to survive on their new land, which may be less productive than the parcels they left behind. Eventually, they may move to cities like Bangkok and join the ranks of the urban poor.

"The dam will be good and bad for me," said Harm, a wiry 25-year-old who stood beside a fishing net. "Good because the company will build us a school and we'll get new jobs, bad because we'll have to leave our villages, and we won't be able to fish anymore."

Harm looked at the river. He didn't look angry. "This is all going to become a big pond," he said. "But that's what the government decided, and we have to respect the government."

Mike Ives is a writer based in Hanoi. Before he moved to Vietnam in 2009, he was a staff writer at the Vermont newspaper *Seven Days*.

EXPLORING THE ISSUE

Is Hydropower a Sound Choice for Renewable Energy?

Critical Thinking and Reflection

1. Why may greenhouse gas emissions increase after the land is flooded by a reservoir?
2. In some parts of the world much of the water that rivers carry comes from melting snowpack and glaciers. In a "global warming" world, can a hydroelectric dam on such a river be said to provide "renewable" electricity?
3. How may hydroelectric development affect (for both good and bad) the lives of poor people in developing nations?

Is There Common Ground?

Many of the drawbacks of hydroelectric power have to do with constructing dams. In-stream turbines or hydrokinetic devices, such as those proposed for generating electricity from ocean currents, can also be used in rivers (though they may pose navigational problems). Research this topic (start at the Union of Concerned Scientists' Hydrokinetic Energy page at www.ucsusa.org/clean_energy/our-energy-choices/renewable-energy/how-hydrokinetic-energy-works.html) and answer the following questions:

1. Are there environmental drawbacks?
2. What can turbine operators do if a river dries up?
3. Are they affordable and practical in developing countries?

Create Central

www.mhhe.com/createcentral

Additional Resources

R. Bakis, "The Current Status and Future Opportunities of Hydroelectricity," *Energy Sources: Part B: Economics, Planning, and Policy* (vol.2, no. 3, 2007).

Kester Gunn and Clym Stock-Williams, "Quantifying the Global Wave Power Resource," *Renewable Energy: An International Journal* (August 2012).

David C. Holzman, "Blue Power: Turning Tides into Electricity," *Environmental Health Perspectives* (December 2007).

Aviva Imhof and Guy R. Lanza, "Greenwashing Hydropower," *World Watch* (January/February 2010).

Internet Reference . . .

The Federal Energy Regulatory Commission

The Federal Energy Regulatory Commission regulates over 1600 nonfederal hydropower projects at over 2500 dams pursuant to Part 1 of the Federal Power Act, or FPA. Together these projects represent 54 gigawatts of hydropower capacity, more than half of all the hydropower in the United States.

www.ferc.gov/industries/hydropower.asp

Selected, Edited, and with Issue Framing Material by:
Thomas A. Easton, *Thomas College*

ISSUE

Does a Hydrogen Economy Make Sense?

YES: John Andrews and Bahman Shabani, from "Reenvisioning the Role of Hydrogen in a Sustainable Energy Economy," *International Journal of Hydrogen Energy* (January 2012)

NO: Ulf Bossel, from "Does a Hydrogen Economy Make Sense?" *Proceedings of the IEEE* (October 2006)

Learning Outcomes

After studying this issue, students will be able to:

- Explain why hydrogen is a potential replacement for fossil fuels.
- Describe the difficulties of converting to a sustainable hydrogen economy.
- Explain why hydrogen is a less efficient form of energy than fossil fuels or electricity.

ISSUE SUMMARY

YES: John Andrews and Bahman Shabani argue that hydrogen gas can play an important role in a sustainable energy system. The key will be a hierarchy of spatially distributed hydrogen production, storage, and distribution centers that minimizes the need for expensive pipelines. Electricity will power battery-electric vehicles for short-range transportation and serve as the major long-distance energy vector.

NO: Ulf Bossel argues that although the technology for widespread use of hydrogen energy is available, generating hydrogen is a very inefficient way to use energy. A hydrogen economy will never make sense.

The 1973 "oil crisis" heightened awareness that the world—even if it was not yet running out of oil—was extraordinarily dependent on that fossil fuel (and therefore on supplier nations) for transportation, home heating, and electricity generation. Recent price increases have repeated the lesson. Since the supply of oil and other fossil fuels is clearly finite, some people worry that there will come a time when demand cannot be satisfied, and our dependence will leave us helpless. We are also acutely aware of the many unfortunate side-effects of fossil fuels, including air pollution, strip mines, oil spills, global warming, and more.

The 1970s saw the modern environmental movement gain momentum. The first Earth Day was in 1970. Numerous governmental steps were taken to deal with air pollution, water pollution, and other environmental problems. In response to the oil crisis, a great deal of public money went into developing alternative energy supplies. The emphasis was on "renewable" energy, meaning conservation, wind, solar, and fuels such as hydrogen gas (which when burned with pure oxygen produces only water vapor as exhaust). However, when the crisis passed and oil supplies were once more ample (albeit more expensive), most public funding for alternative-energy research and demonstration projects vanished. What work continued was at the hands of a few enthusiasts and those corporations that saw future opportunities. In 2001, the Worldwatch Institute published Seth Dunn's *Hydrogen Futures: Toward a Sustainable Energy System*. In 2002, MIT Press published Peter Hoffman's *Tomorrow's Energy: Hydrogen, Fuel Cells, and the Prospects for a Cleaner Planet.*

What drives the continuing interest in hydrogen and other alternative or renewable energy systems is the continuing problems associated with fossil fuels, concern about dependence and potential political instability, rising oil and gasoline prices, and the growing realization that the availability of petroleum will peak in the near future. Will that interest come to anything? There are, after all, a number of other ways to meet the need. Coal can be converted into oil and gasoline (though the air pollution and global warming problems remain). Cars can be made more efficient (and mileage efficiency is much greater than it was in the seventies despite the popularity of SUVs). Hybrid gas-electric cars are available.

Hydrogen as a fuel offers definite benefits. As Joan M. Ogden notes in "Hydrogen: The Fuel of the Future?" *Physics Today* (April 2002), the technology is available and compared to the alternatives it "offers the greatest potential environmental and energy-supply benefits." To put hydrogen to use, however, will require massive investments in facilities for generating, storing, and transporting the gas, as well as manufacturing hydrogen-burning engines and fuel cells. Currently, large amounts of hydrogen can easily be generated by "reforming" natural gas or other hydrocarbons. Hydrolysis—splitting hydrogen from water molecules with electricity—is also possible, and in the future this may use electricity from renewable sources such as wind or from nuclear power. The basic technologies are available right now. See Thammy Evans, Peter Light, and Ty Cashman, "Hydrogen—A Little PR," *Whole Earth* (Winter 2001). Daniel Sperling notes, in "Updating Automotive Research," *Issues in Science and Technology* (Spring 2002), that "Fuel cells and hydrogen show huge promise. They may indeed prove to be the Holy Grail, eventually taking vehicles out of the environmental equation," but making that happen will require research, government assistance in building a hydrogen distribution system, and incentives for both industry and car buyers. See also Piotr Tomczyk, "Fundamental Aspects of the Hydrogen Economy," *World Futures* (July 2009). M. Z. Jacobson, W. G. Colella, and D. M. Golden, "Cleaning the Air and Improving Health with Hydrogen Fuel-Cell Vehicles," *Science* (June 24, 2005), conclude that if all on road vehicles are replaced with fuel-cell vehicles using hydrogen generated by wind power, air pollution and human health impacts will both be reduced and overall costs will be less than for gasoline. Joan Ogden, "High Hopes for Hydrogen," *Scientific American* (September 2006), agrees that the potential is great but stresses that the transition to a hydrogen future will take decades. Michael K. Heiman and Barry D. Solomon, "The Hydrogen Economy and Its Alternatives," *Environment* (October 2007), argue that hydrogen may serve as a bridge to the future in some ways, but it is not likely to play much role in the transportation sector.

I. P. Jain, "Hydrogen the Fuel for 21st Century," *International Journal of Hydrogen Energy* (September 2009), believes that "the day is not far when hydrogen will take over oil." Jeremy Rifkin, "Hydrogen: Empowering the People," *Nation* (December 23, 2002), says local production of hydrogen could mean a much more decentralized energy system. He may be right, as John A. Turner makes clear in "Sustainable Hydrogen Production," *Science* (August 13, 2004), but Henry Payne and Diane Katz, "Gas and Gasbags . . . or, the Open Road and Its Enemies," *National Review* (March 25, 2002), contend that a major obstacle to hydrogen is market mechanisms that will keep fossil fuels in use for years to come, local hydrogen production is unlikely, and adequate supplies will require that society invest heavily in nuclear power. There are also technical obstacles, according to M. Balat and E. Kirtay, "Major Technical Barriers to a 'Hydrogen Economy'," *Energy Sources, Part A: Recovery, Utilization & Environmental Effects* (June 2010). Jim Motavalli, "Hijacking Hydrogen," *E—The Environmental Magazine* (January–February 2003), worries that the fossil fuel and nuclear industries will dominate the hydrogen future. The former wishes to use "reforming" to generate hydrogen from coal (which means a continuing contribution to global warming), and the latter sees hydrolysis as creating demand for nuclear power. In Iceland, Freyr Sverrisson, "Missing in Action: Iceland's Hydrogen Economy," *World Watch* (November/December 2006), notes that the demand of industry for electricity has shifted plans to develop hydrogen to the development of hydroelectric dams instead.

The difficulty of developing a hydrogen economy is underlined by Robert F. Service in "The Hydrogen Backlash," *Science* (August 13, 2004) (the lead article in a special section titled "Toward a Hydrogen Economy"). According to Paul Ekins and Nick Hughes, "The Prospects for a Hydrogen Economy (1): Hydrogen Futures," *Technology Analysis & Strategic Management* (October 2009), one major difficulty is the sheer scale of the task of replacing one mature energy industry (fossil fuels) with another. Jeff Tollefson, "Fuel of the Future?" *Nature* (April 29, 2010), sees signs of increasing interest in hydrogen-fueled vehicles but notes that whether electric or hydrogen-fueled vehicles will rule future roads is far from settled. See also Laurie Wiegler, "The Future of Hydrogen Cars," *Technology Review* (September 21, 2011) (www.technologyreview.com/energy/38647/). Nadya Anscombe, "Hydrogen: Hype or Hope?" *Engineering & Technology* (May 8–28, 2010), notes that we will not have a hydrogen economy until we first have a renewable energy economy. In Germany, the marriage of hydrogen and renewables seems well begun. The country aims to produce 80 percent of its electricity from renewable sources such as wind and solar by 2050, and the Siemens corporation is developing large-scale hydrogen production and storage systems to handle electricity supply when the sun isn't shining and the wind isn't blowing; see Kevin Bullis, "Hydrogen Storage Could Be Key to Germany's Energy Plans," *Technology Review* (March 29, 2012) (www.technologyreview.com/energy/40001/).

In the YES selection, John Andrews and Bahman Shabani argue that hydrogen gas can play an important role in a sustainable energy system. The key will be a hierarchy of spatially distributed hydrogen production, storage, and distribution centers that minimizes the need for expensive pipelines. Electricity will power battery-electric vehicles for short-range transportation and serve as the major long-distance energy vector. In the NO selection, Ulf Bossel argues that although the technology for widespread use of hydrogen energy is available, generating hydrogen is a very inefficient way to use energy. A hydrogen economy will never make sense.

YES

John Andrews and Bahman Shabani

Reenvisioning the Role of Hydrogen in a Sustainable Energy Economy

Introduction

Where does hydrogen fit into a sustainable energy economy? To the forebears of the hydrogen economy, the answer to this core question was clear. The electrochemist, John Bockris, describes the genesis of this concept of a hydrogen economy in his pioneering book *Energy: The Solar Hydrogen Alternative* first published in 1975 as follows:

> The phrase 'A Hydrogen Economy' arose for the first time in a discussion between Bockris and Triner of the General-Motors Technical Center, 3 February 1970. They had been discussing (along with others in a Group) the various fuels which could replace polluting gasoline in transportation and had come to the conclusion that hydrogen would be the eventual fuel for all types of transports. The discussion went to other applications of hydrogen in providing energy to households and industry, and it was suggested that we might live finally in what could be called 'A Hydrogen Society'. The phrase 'A Hydrogen Economy' was then used later in the same conversation.

The original vision for such a Hydrogen Economy (HE) was conceived at a time when concerns about running out of oil, natural gas, and ultimately coal in the face of exponential growth in global primary energy use, and the associated rising pollution levels, were first being raised. The seminal meeting described above took place just before the release of the Club of Rome's controversial *Limits to Growth* report, and three years before the first major oil crisis occurred leading to a major hike in the price of crude oil and risks about the security of future supplies from the Middle East. Presciently, Bockris in his 1975 book does refer to the fact that increasing coal consumption could lead to increasing carbon dioxide in the atmosphere and global warming. But it is a cursory mention, since the threat of looming climate change was then only dimly recognized, and in no way a driving force behind the transition to a HE as it is today.

In essence, Bockris' HE vision centered on the production of hydrogen by electrolysis of fresh and sea water by electricity generated by large-scale solar power stations located in hot remote parts of the world—most notably the desert regions of North Africa, Saudi Arabia, and Australia—and/or by nuclear fission reactors. The hydrogen produced would then be transmitted to distant population centers by long pipelines for consumption in all sectors of the economy.

Now that we confront the three-pronged threat of irreversible climate change, a deficit between oil demand and supply, and rising levels of pollution generally, the original HE concept needs re-envisioning. In transport applications, there have been significant developments in battery technology, with lithium ion and lithium polymer batteries becoming available with much higher gravimetric and volumetric energy densities than traditional lead acid batteries. Hence there is a major effort worldwide to commercialize electric vehicles, particularly cars and light commercial vehicles, as an alternative to conventional gasoline and diesel vehicles. If electric vehicles are to be a true zero-emission mode of transport, however, the electricity for battery charging must come from renewable energy (RE) sources of electricity (or the more problematic nuclear, or fossil fuel power stations with carbon capture and storage). Yet the very same is the case for the electricity to produce hydrogen by electrolysis, the most likely early production technology, for use in hydrogen fuel cell vehicles. Why then traverse the apparently more circuitous and energy lossy route of converting electricity to hydrogen, transporting and storing it, and then reconverting it back to electricity on board a vehicle in a fuel cell,

Abbreviation: A, Aircraft; AC, Alternating Current; AHC, Autonomous Hydrogen Center; B, Bus; BEV, Battery Electric Vehicle; C, Cycle; CCS, Carbon Capture and Storage; CHC, Coastal Hydrogen Center; DC, Direct Current; DoE, Department of Energy; EERE, Energy Efficiency and Renewable Energy; EO, Electric Overhead; EU, European Union; HE, Hydrogen Economy; HFC, Hydrogen Fuel Cell; HFCV, Hydrogen Fuel Cell Vehicle; HHV, High Heating Value; HISE, Hydrogen in a Sustainable Energy (strategy); IHC, Inland Hydrogen Center; IPCC, Intergovernmental Panel on Climate Change; JetLH, Liquid Hydrogen Jet Fuel; kWh_e, Kilowatt Hours (electrical); LHV, Low Heating Value; LPG, Liquid Petroleum Gas; NHA, National Hydrogen Association; OHC, Off-shore Hydrogen Center; PV, Photovoltaic; R, Rail; R&D, Research and Development; RE, Renewable Energy; S, Ship; T, Tram; UPT, Urban Public Transport; W, Walking; WWS, Wind, Water, and Sunlight.

Andrews, John and Shabani, Bahman. From *International Journal of Hydrogen Energy,* January 2012, excerpts pp. 1184–1187, 1192–1196, 1198–1199, 1200–1201.

rather than simply charging batteries in vehicles using grid electricity generated from renewables? With batteries, it is electricity in and electricity out directly from the one electrochemical device.

Another alternative that has emerged to hydrogen as a transport fuel is biofuel, including principally ethanol, various bio-oils and biodiesel. All such biofuels are produced from organic materials—starch, sugar or cellulosic plants, or algae—that have absorbed carbon dioxide from the atmosphere by photosynthesis during their growth phase so that on combustion the same quantity of carbon dioxide is emitted once again. Provided then the energy used to produce and distribute these biofuels is also obtained from renewable resources, they are a zero-emission option like hydrogen produced from renewables. Biofuels for transport can be used as blends with existing fuels without any modification to today's internal combustion engines, the remainder of vehicle technology, and fuel distribution, storage and delivery infrastructure, and as 100% alternatives with relatively minor changes to existing engines and fuel distribution infrastructure. To many, biofuels are thus seen as a much more readily implementable substitute for petroleum fuels than taking on the apparently herculean challenge of switching to hydrogen, which indeed would require a completely new fuel distribution, storage and dispensing infrastructure, as well as a radical change in vehicle motive power systems and associated vehicle design.

In the original HE, hydrogen further played the critical role of providing the energy storage that would allow continuous base-load electricity supply in a system relying substantially on intermittent and variable RE sources such as solar, wind and ocean power. In recent years this role for hydrogen too has come under strong challenge from a number of alternatives, including batteries, supercapacitors, thermal storage, and multiple RE inputs geographically distributed over a large-scale grid.

Over the past decade, there have been many notable and useful works that have sought to develop and modify the original vision of a hydrogen economy to reflect more recent environmental, resource, and political-economic contexts, and technological developments. In the area of more specific and quantitative scenario-based studies, the International Energy Agency researched the consequences of introducing hydrogen globally, finding that hydrogen and fuel cells could reduce carbon dioxide emissions by a further 5% (1.4 Gt/year) by 2050 compared to just deploying efficiency measures (such as petrol-electric hybrid vehicles) and alternative fuels like ethanol.

One of the most thorough studies of the potential role of hydrogen in a sustainable energy economy conducted to date has been the HyWays European hydrogen roadmap supported by the European Union (EU) and ten of its member countries. In the high policy support, fast learning, hydrogen-emphasis scenario evaluated by Hyways, the penetration of hydrogen fuel cell vehicles in passenger transport rises rapidly from 3% in 2020, to 25% in 2030, and tends towards saturation at just under 75% in 2050. The corresponding hydrogen production mix in 2030 is 31% from nuclear fission power, 27% from RE sources, 26% from steam reforming of natural gas, and 14% from coal via integrated gasification combined cycle plants and carbon capture and storage. In this scenario, transport greenhouse gas emissions in 2050 for the ten countries modelled were projected to be more than 60% lower than 2000 levels.

Drawing on the HyWays study and the earlier European Commission-supported World Energy Technology Outlook hydrogen study, Doll and Wietschel concluded that the use of hydrogen in a sustainable transport future could significantly reduce carbon dioxide emissions of the transport sector, taking into account tailpipe and upstream emissions, and importantly reduce local air pollutants by up to 80%. Possible negative impacts identified were accident risks, increased nuclear waste, and increased biomass demand (for hydrogen production alongside other sources).

The prospects for a transition to a hydrogen economy based on RE sources in Spain were discussed by Brey *et al.*, considering a short-term target of 10% of transport energy demand being met by hydrogen. This study concluded that most of the Spanish regions could be self-sufficient for supplying their energy demand via renewable sources and hydrogen, except for Madrid which would require transfer of hydrogen from nearby regions. The main barriers to a transition to hydrogen were identified as the lack of development of technologies for hydrogen production, storage, transport, and distribution, and high costs compared with the current system. Balat analyzed the potential importance of hydrogen produced from coal and natural gas (with carbon sequestration), nuclear power, and large-scale renewables as a future solution to environmental and transportation problems. Hydrogen from steam reforming of natural gas was identified as the most economical production method among the current commercial processes, yielding a unit cost of between 1.25 US$/kg for large systems to about 3.50 US$/kg for small systems with a natural gas price of 6 US$/GJ, compared to 8 US$/kg for hydrogen from electrolytic processes. The role of hydrogen in road transport in a sustainable energy system in Korea has been examined by Kim and Moon, in Austria by Ajanovic, and in all sectors of the United Arab Emirates' economy by Kazim. Carton and Olabi propose the use of hydrogen produced by electrolysers using surplus wind power to allow wind farms in Ireland to provide much more consistent electricity supply to the main grid, particularly as the problems of variability and intermittency are exacerbated as the country heads towards a target of 40% electricity from renewables by 2020. Focusing on the European Union, Bleischwitz and Bader concluded that the [then] EU policy framework neither hindered nor enhanced hydrogen development, and that the large-scale market development of hydrogen and fuel cells would require a new policy approach with technology-specific and regionally-based support.

The global potential for the production of hydrogen from multiple biomass feedstocks via a two-stage bioprocess in a cost-effective and environmentally friendly manner was reviewed by Urbaniec *et al.,* based on the preliminary results of the Hyvolution Integrated Research Project supported by the 6th Framework Programme of the European Union.

The greenhouse gas reduction benefits and costs of a large-scale transition to hydrogen in the USA were investigated by Dougherty *et al.* The hydrogen production options considered were on-site and centralised steam reforming of natural gas and electrolysis using RE, and centralised coal and biomass reforming with and without sequestration of carbon dioxide. Dougherty *et al.* concluded that a coordinated shift towards hydrogen, focussed on displacing gasoline and diesel (non-military) in cars, light trucks, heavy-duty vehicles, marine vessels, and trains, and avoiding serious economic disruption, would likely entail a several decades transition and higher costs in the short-term, but is technically feasible.

The National Hydrogen Association released a report on energy-economic modeling of a hydrogen-emphasis scenario in transport in the USA. This report found that a scenario in which hydrogen fuel cell vehicles dominated the marketplace in the USA, in conjunction with hybrids, plug-in hybrids and biofuels, could cut greenhouse gas pollution by 80% below 1990 levels by 2100; allow America to become essentially independent of petroleum fuels by the latter year; eliminate nearly all controllable urban air pollution by 2100; and reduce societal costs of transport by up to $US 600 billion per year by 2100. Hydrogen is made initially from natural gas, transitioning to hydrogen from biomass, from coal with carbon capture and storage (CCS), from natural gas with CCS, and eventually from electrolysis of water using renewable and nuclear electricity. On the other hand, McKay rejects hydrogen in his sustainable energy strategies for the UK on the grounds that converting energy to and from hydrogen can only be done inefficiently, and it has "a whole bunch of practical defects", opting instead to use primarily Battery Electric Vehicles (BEVs) with charging from low or zero-emission electricity, and their collective battery banks for energy storage on grids as the renewables input increases.

The critical issue of whether there is enough RE available to provide all the primary energy required by a global sustainable energy economy relying substantially on hydrogen for storage and as a transport energy carrier has been addressed by Kleijn and van der Voet and Jacobson and Delucchi. Both these studies answer this question in the affirmative, but with some important conditions.

It is our view that the original HE concept now needs radical re-envisioning. As in many of the strategic sustainable energy studies referred to above, and drawing on Andrews' preliminary sketch of a sustainable hydrogen economy, we argue in the present paper that, rather than seeing hydrogen as the exclusive fuel for the future, the specific roles to which it is uniquely suited in each major sector within an overall sustainable energy strategy need to be identified. With this approach we expect that hydrogen would still play a substantive and crucial role, but a role in concert rather than competition with that of electricity and technologies such as BEVs and a variety of shorter-term energy storage options for grid power.

We therefore propose six principles that could guide the role played by hydrogen in a truly sustainable energy economy based on taking energy efficiency to its economic limit and ideally using only RE sources. We elaborate on and discuss the implications of these principles in turn, in sketching a sustainable energy economy with a strong emphasis on hydrogen. The focus is thus on the potential role of hydrogen, rather than other equally-important aspects of a global sustainable energy strategy. Our intention is to keep this vision as general as possible at this stage so that it is potentially applicable to most countries and regions around the world. Inevitably, many important issues cannot be dealt with in detail in the present work, including, for example, a comparison of the relative merits of biofuels and hydrogen in various forms of land, sea and air transport.

However, our recommendation is that these principles for hydrogen deployment in the strategic context of global sustainable energy may in the future be applied in detailed and quantitative energy-economic modeling of the global economy and the economies of individual geo-political regions and nations. Evidently it will only be after the findings of such studies are assessed that any claims of the economic, environmental and social merits of the approach we propose can be verified.

Principles

The six principles we propose to guide the role played by hydrogen in sustainable energy strategies, both globally and at national levels, are the following:

1. A hierarchy of sustainable hydrogen production, storage and distribution centers relying on local RE sources producing hydrogen as required
2. Complementary use of hydrogen and electricity as energy vectors to minimize the extent of new hydrogen pipeline distribution networks
3. Production of hydrogen from a range of RE sources and feedstocks, without dependence on nuclear fission power or carbon capture and storage, but with the application of energy efficiency measures to the economic limit across all sectors of the economy
4. Recognition of the complementary roles of hydrogen and battery storage across a range of transport vehicles and transport services
5. Use of hydrogen for longer-duration energy storage on centralized grids relying extensively on RE inputs

6. Employment of bulk hydrogen storage as the strategic energy reserve to guarantee national and global energy security in a world relying increasingly on RE.

As a snapshot, the key differences between the original HE concept and the re-envisioned role for 'Hydrogen In a Sustainable Energy' (HISE) strategy presented here are the following:

HISE is set firmly in the context of a zero greenhouse gas emission economy in terms of both the production of hydrogen from renewables and consumption, rather than just as a response to depleting reserves of fossil fuel. While HE involved centralized production of hydrogen from mainly solar and wind energy occupying vast areas of generally remote land, as well as nuclear fission reactors, and hence very long distance transmission of hydrogen via pipelines to centers of consumption, HISE involves decentralized distributed production of hydrogen from a wide variety of renewables and feedstocks. In HISE, hydrogen and electricity play complementary roles as energy vectors, and hydrogen and batteries complementary roles as energy stores, in the transport sector and industrial, commercial and residential sectors—no longer is hydrogen the sole and exclusive energy carrier and store in every sector of the economy.

While HE accepted primary energy inputs from nuclear fission power, as well as in some variants from natural gas and coal too, in its ideal manifestation HISE focuses exclusively on renewables, coupled with an equally strong emphasis on energy efficiency and demand management, in an overall sustainable energy strategy akin to that espoused over many years by Amory Lovins and his coworkers. However, in a more pragmatic vein, we also briefly canvas the roles hydrogen could play in the event of a substantial shift to nuclear power, and proven economical use of carbon capture and storage to allow continued use of natural gas and coal. The six principles underlying the HISE strategy and their implications will now be elaborated in turn.

A Hierarchy of Sustainable Hydrogen Centers With

Overview of the Hierarchy

Given the spatial dispersion of RE sources, and the desirability of producing hydrogen near to where it is consumed, a hierarchy of distributed sustainable hydrogen production, storage and distribution centers would be established. These centers would draw upon a range of RE sources to produce hydrogen from a number of different feedstocks for a variety of end-use applications. While the precise structure of the hierarchy would depend on the local conditions in a particular country or region, the following principal types of center would be expected: off-shore, coastal, inland, and autonomous local. . . .

Complementary Use of Hydrogen and Electricity as Energy Vectors to Minimise the Hydrogen Pipeline Distribution Network

The complementary role of electricity and hydrogen as energy vectors is evident. Wherever practical, the long-distance transmission and distribution of the RE supply is via electricity, probably in the future increasingly by high-voltage DC transmission or even superconducting electricity transmission lines, which have much lower losses than current high-voltage AC transmission networks. The transmission of hydrogen by pipeline is restricted so far as possible from hydrogen production plants (mainly electrolyzers) near to solar, wind and wave energy sources, to the nearby cities and towns.

Clearly the construction of a new hydrogen distribution network involving compressed hydrogen gas piped from location to location, together with the required plant for pressurization, safety regulation and storage, would be an expensive piece of infrastructure investment per kilometre of pipeline. Hence an important guiding principle in the design of a sustainable hydrogen system is to seek to minimize the extent of the required hydrogen distribution network. The hierarchical network of sustainable hydrogen production, storage and distribution centers has been designed in accordance with this principle.

The central design feature to minimize the extent of the hydrogen pipeline network is to create a geographically distributed network of hydrogen production centers, so that so far as possible hydrogen is produced regionally or even locally for refueling vehicles, or energy storage for use in combined electricity and heating systems, in that same region or locality. As Dougherty *et al.* and McDowell and Eames point out, decentralized production is one way to overcome many of the infrastructural barriers to a hydrogen transition. Along the same lines, Rifkin and Sorenson proposed decentralized or on-site hydrogen production actually in residential or commercial buildings, for refueling vehicles, and via fuel cells electricity and heat as well.

Ideally, the only need for a hydrogen pipeline distribution system would be in major cities to transport hydrogen from bulk storage facilities (associated with off-shore, coastal or major inland hydrogen centers nearby) to:

- a network of medium-sized hydrogen storages from which hydrogen could be transferred on demand (most likely by road tankers initially) to a network of refueling stations for road transport vehicles—cars, commercial vehicles and trucks
- facilities for producing liquefied hydrogen for use by aircraft (probably only one or two such facilities for each major city)
- hydrogen storages at major ports for refueling ships

- hydrogen storages at major railway terminals for refueling long-distance freight and passenger trains
- fuel cell power stations for supplying electricity to the grid at periods of low RE input, or during national emergencies that resulted in disruptions to normal supplies. . . .

Production of Hydrogen from Renewable Energy Sources and Feedstocks, Without Nuclear Fission Power or Carbon Capture and Storage

The ultimate and ideal sustainable energy economy would rely solely on the earth's RE income, from solar, wind, wave, tidal, hydro, biomass and geothermal sources, and use energy to meet end-use needs in the most energy-efficient manner possible. Furthermore, hydrogen would be produced from a diverse range of RE sources ensuring zero-emissions in production, and hence no contribution to aggregate global greenhouse gas emissions from the overall system given that the consumption of hydrogen in fuel cells, internal combustion engines or simply by external combustion to deliver end-use services simply leads to water vapour. During the transition to a truly sustainable economy, some hydrogen is also likely to be produced by steam reforming of natural gas, the lowest emission fossil-fuel source and process.

The fundamental question thus arises as to whether there are sufficient RE sources available, and economically deployable, to meet global demands for the services energy can provide, taking into account forecast population growth and rises in material standards of living, particularly in developing countries. The potential resource constraints in a HE based on RE sources were investigated by Kleijn and van der Voet. They estimated that the primary energy requirements of a global economy in 2050 that were 2.5 times those in 2005 could be met entirely from potentially collectable solar radiation (80% of the total supply), wind power (15%) and other renewables (5%). However, it was pointed out that the infrastructure to harvest that amount of RE would require massive investments, and that extensive transmission networks may be necessary since optimal energy harvesting locations are often far from the centres of consumption. A highly decentralised sustainable energy economy along the lines suggested in the present work was not considered.

Jacobson and Delucchi have recently completed one of the most thorough studies to date into the potential of Wind, Water and Sunlight (WWS) energy sources to provide the primary energy required by a global sustainable energy economy in 2030. Referring to US Energy Information Administration (2008) projections, Jacobson and Delucchi base their scenarios on the current average world rate of energy consumption for all end-uses rising from 12.5 TW (10^{12} W) in 2008 to 16.9 TW in 2030 on the basis of the current range of primary fuels employed, primarily fossil fuels, nuclear and a small contribution from renewables. However, they estimate that a shift to renewable WWS sources to replace all fossil fuel and wood combustion by 2030, together with a shift to electricity and hydrogen as energy carriers, and strong energy efficiency measures in all sectors, could reduce the global demand to be met in that year to just 11.5 TW, that is, 8% less than in 2008. Jacobson and Delucchi show how this demand could be met entirely from WWS sources including wind, wave, hydro, geothermal, photovoltaic and solar thermal power technologies. The estimated total new land area—excluding land already used for renewables such as hydroelectric plants, and the space occupied by offshore wind, wave and tidal power devices—would be only 1% of the total global land area, and hence in principle potentially feasible. These authors conclude that barriers to a 100% conversion to WWS power worldwide are primarily social and political, not technological or even economic. . . .

Complementary Roles for Hydrogen and Battery Storage in Transport

To reduce transport-related greenhouse gas emissions, and effect a transition away from petroleum fuels, a number of more sustainable demand-side, primary energy resource, and technology options are being considered around the world, including:

- urban restructuring and land-use planning to reduce average trip and freight movement distances,
- modal shifts to urban public transport, high-speed intercity rail, and rail freight,
- use of hybrid petrol/gas electric vehicles
- deployment of internal combustion engine vehicles running on biofuels such as ethanol, methanol, or bio-oils produced from biomass crops
- [Battery electric vehicles (BEVs)] charged from the main electricity grid, assuming an increasing proportion of electricity supply derives from zero-emission sources
- development of hydrogen fuel cell vehicles (HFCVs) with hydrogen produced from renewables.

Clearly reducing the passenger and freight task per capita, and mode shifts that lower energy intensity are desirable and deserve full support in their own right. To the extent that they are successful, the remaining transport task to be met by the alternative fuel supply options is facilitated.

Petrol/gas hybrid vehicles are likely to be an important short to medium term option, because of their improved emission performance compared to standard petrol and diesel vehicles and compatibility with existing infrastructure. Yet they are not zero emission technologies as long as petroleum fuels are used as the primary energy input. Inevitably in the medium to longer term they will need to be replaced by BEVs or HFCVs. . . .

Both BEVs and HFCVs offer a completely zero-emission transport solution, provided the electricity to charge batteries, and electricity (or other energy source) to make the hydrogen, is also zero emission, that is, renewable, nuclear or fossil fuel with carbon capture and storage. . . .

As alternative routes for zero-emission hydrogen production, taking some of the pressure off the renewable sources of electricity. Such relief would not be available in an exclusive BEV scenario. . . .

Hydrogen storage currently has, and will probably extend in the future, a substantial advantage over batteries in gravimetric and volumetric energy densities when used in vehicles with a range similar to that of today's petrol and diesel vehicles. Other things being equal, this advantage should mean that hydrogen fuel cell vehicles will have a much greater range (two to three times) that of a comparable battery electric vehicle for a given volume and mass of the storage system.

However, the figures arrived at here are merely indicative of the general case, so that it remains essential to compare hydrogen and battery storages of particular kinds employed in specific comparable vehicles to be sure about their relative merits in each case. Moreover, technological development is continually leading to improved energy densities in both battery (especially lithium ion) and hydrogen storage systems. Consequently, any changes in relative energy densities through technological advances will need to be watched closely. Indeed a necessary condition for use of hydrogen for transport in a sustainable energy strategy is that hydrogen storage maintains a substantial advantage over battery storage in terms of gravimetric and volumetric energy densities.

The optimal energy storage system for vehicles requiring a range equivalent to today's petrol and diesel vehicles is actually likely to employ a combined hydrogen and battery system. The hydrogen system would provide the bulk energy storage, while a relatively small energy capacity battery would allow regenerative braking, meet peak power demands, and generally buffer the fuel cell against load changes to extend its lifetime. This complementary use of hydrogen and battery storage is precisely the arrangement employed by Honda in its FCX Clarity hydrogen car that is now available commercially in limited numbers.

The complementarity of hydrogen and battery storage may well be extended to the question of which type of vehicle is best across a range of transport applications. [This is] a 'horses for courses' approach to meeting the gamut of end-use transport services by a combination of hydrogen fuel cell, battery electric, hydrogen-fuelled jet engines, and electric vehicles supplied by overhead electricity, drawing entirely upon RE sources, and after implementing a number of mode shifts to preserve service levels while reducing total transport energy demand.

A mode shift to walking, cycling and urban public transport is highly desirable for urban short trips. The remaining demand for short trips (less than 100 km typically) could conveniently be met using plug-in battery-electric cars, small station wagons and commercial vehicles (that is, BEVs), to take full advantage of the relatively high round-trip energy efficiency of batteries when the period between charging is not long.

For medium to longer distance urban, regional, and intercity trips over land (>100 km), a mode shift to electric rail (supplied by overhead or power rail) would reduce the overall demand for transportable fuel. Hydrogen fuel cell cars, buses, and trains (where new overhead construction is too expensive or impractical) would meet the remaining demand for journeys of more than 100 km, with ranges of more than 450 km between refueling. HFC vehicles would usually employ a small energy capacity battery to allow regenerative braking and meet short-term maximum power demands.

BEVs are also highly suited for urban goods delivery over short distances (<100 km). For medium and long-distance road freight, hydrogen fuel cell trucks, without any battery storage, are likely to be preferable since the vehicles operate for long periods at relatively constant speeds, rapid acceleration is not so critical, and regenerative braking would not offer significant savings. The more stop-start the usage, the more the balance would tip to including a small energy capacity battery into the system as well.

Coastal and international shipping where the range required is large are also likely to employ hydrogen storage and electric drive supplied by fuel cells. A mode shift to very fast electric rail for land-based intercity travel where possible would be beneficial. For trips that still have to be undertaken by air, jet and turboprop aircraft will almost certainly have to rely on liquid hydrogen to get mass and energy densities down to at least the same order of magnitude as current aviation fuel (kerosene and aviation diesel).

Use of Hydrogen for Longer-Duration Energy Storage on Centralised Grids Relying Extensively on Renewable Energy Inputs

Just as batteries have emerged as a major competitor to hydrogen energy storage and fuel cells in the area of transport, so a number of alternatives to hydrogen are currently being mooted to allow electricity grids to maintain continuous and reliable supply as the primary energy inputs to electricity generation from inherently intermittent and variable renewables increase in order to meet greenhouse gas reduction targets. Among these means are, most notably:

- batteries,
- supercapacitors,
- thermal storage, particularly for night-time supply with solar-thermal power systems,
- geothermal power stations, which can supply power on a near continuous basis,
- a large-scale grid covering a vast geographical area with distributed RE inputs of many kinds—such as solar PV, solar thermal, wind power, and biomass power generation—so that the complementarity over time of these variable inputs can reduce the variations in aggregate supply and reduce the requirement for any other form of energy storage such as hydrogen, and
- pumped hydroelectric schemes.

The first three options—batteries, supercapacitors and thermal storage—essentially provide just short-term storage: in the order of seconds for supercapacitors, a few days to a week in the case of batteries, and from day to night for thermal storage. Such storage will undoubtedly be highly valuable on many grids, especially given the diurnal cycle of solar radiation, and hence will probably find many applications of this kind. However, in locations where there are variations in renewable input over longer cycles, in particular from season to season, a longer-term form of storage such as hydrogen will probably still be necessary for security of supply and be advantageous economically. . . .

A large-scale grid drawing on inputs from a range of different renewables that are geographically dispersed would have a reduced need for storage to meet demand continuously and reliably throughout the year. Hence it clearly makes sense to encourage this diverse range of distributed renewable inputs. However, a number of factors militate against this strategy eliminating the need altogether for a substantial capacity of some guaranteed form of energy storage such as hydrogen:

- Renewables such as solar, wind, waves and tidal stream all follow seasonal patterns of variation, so these variations will not be eliminated by taking inputs from varying locations at a given time (at least in the same hemisphere).
- Inputs from distributed renewables will vary from location to location over the whole grid, but transmission losses are likely to be very high if the entire grid has to be supplied at certain times from just a few sources located in one region.
- The installation of very high voltage DC transmission lines in place of the AC lines currently used has been suggested as one way to minimize such losses, but such an upgrading of the entire grid infrastructure would be very expensive.
- Considerable excess generating capacity would need to be installed in each area if at times the output from this area had to meet a major proportion of the total demand from the entire grid when there is a deficiency of aggregate input from the generating capacity from other areas.
- Reliance on a joint probability distribution for the supply of power from a diverse range of types and locations of RE generators, each subject to its own probability distribution over an annual period, should indeed give a greater continuity and reliability of supply than that obtainable from a small number of very large renewable power stations. However, there will remain a finite probability of low supply that is insufficient to meet the demand. This situation cannot be tolerated in modern grid systems that are usually bound by legally enforceable supply reliability and continuity contracts, not to mention consumer demands. Hence there will remain a need for a secure and totally reliable source of supply that can be relied upon with total confidence when necessary. Hydrogen storage and fuel cells can meet this requirement for a guaranteed back up supply, both to meet any deficit from renewables, and to be called upon in times of national emergency.

Pumped hydroelectric schemes in which surplus power is used to pump water to the high reservoir of a hydroelectric facility, and then allowed to run back to the lower reservoir through the turbines at times of supply shortage, offer a reasonably high roundtrip energy efficiency (above 70%). However, the global availability of additional environmentally-acceptable sites for such schemes, which require very large reservoir capacities, is generally now very limited. Even at 100% energy conversion efficiency and 100 m head the volumetric energy density of pumped hydroelectric storages is only 0.273 Wh_e/litre, compared to up to 0.47 kWh_e/L achieved with metal hydrides and fuel cells, that is, well over a thousand times lower.

For all these reasons, hydrogen energy storage is likely to have some role to play, especially for longer-term storage in most grids that rely heavily on RE inputs, often (as in transport) in concert with other forms of storage. However, the extent of this role will vary from one grid to another, and can only be investigated with any confidence through full system modeling of each grid on an annual basis, and taking into account climate variations over the longer term.

Bulk Hydrogen Storage for Energy Security When Relying on Renewable Energy

As national economies, and thus in turn the international economy, shift to relying increasingly on RE sources for both electrical power generation and transport to achieve stringent global greenhouse gas emission reduction targets over the coming decades, entirely novel challenges arise to ensure national and international energy security compared to those we face today in the fossil-fuel era. Coal, oil and natural gas resources are located in specific geographical regions and must be transported around the globe to consuming countries, most of which do not have sufficient indigenous supplies to meet their own needs. Hence energy security considerations today focus largely on guaranteeing a continuous and sufficient supply of fossil fuels to the main consuming nations, particularly the USA, the European Union, China, India and Japan, from the main fossil fuel supply nations such as the OPEC nations in the Middle East, Russia, Mexico, and Australia. By contrast, in the sustainable energy economy being sketched here, a large proportion of the primary energy input would be in the form of distributed RE sources. Each country, and indeed wherever possible each region therein, will therefore draw its energy to a large extent from local and indigenous energy sources, with much less dependence on energy imports from other countries. Since most renewables are inherently intermittent and variable both on short (hourly, daily, weekly) time scales, medium or seasonal time scales, and to some extent also on longer time scales (years and decades, especially if there is significant climate change), the challenge of energy security shifts to ensuring energy supply in the face of this inevitable variability. The reliance on a diverse range of renewables (solar, wind, biomass, waves) that are themselves geographically distributed will mitigate the effects of the variable inputs from particular sources at any time. Certain renewables such as biomass and geothermal can provide more continuous supply. Yet there will remain a need for a strategic energy reserve that is available with effective certainty to meet demand in periods of low availability of aggregate primary energy from the renewables, and in the event of any major breakdowns in supply or distribution technology, or catastrophic events such as volcanic eruptions, cyclones, bushfires, floods, droughts, or during wars or terrorist attacks.

In the sustainable energy vision proposed here, a number of bulk hydrogen storages as integral parts of offshore, coastal and inland hydrogen centers would serve as strategic energy reserves both within nations, and preferably internationally too, organized via the United Nations. This hydrogen reserve would be able to maintain supply to both the transport and electricity supply sectors in the event of unforeseen interruptions or deficiencies from the primary renewable supply sources. Hydrogen can store energy near permanently, so that bulk hydrogen storage would play a role akin to that of fossil fuels today, with one critical difference: the hydrogen storage can be regularly replenished with more hydrogen produced using the earth's RE income, while fossil fuels once used are irreversibly depleted.

Conclusions and Recommendations

In this paper we have sought to re-envision the role of hydrogen in a sustainable energy strategy broadly applicable at national and international levels, taking into account the need to confront the three-pronged challenge of irreversible climate change, uncertain oil supply, and rising pollution levels of diverse kinds, and the strong challenges to hydrogen storage that have arisen from a range of competing technologies.

We suggest that the time for proposing an exclusively HE has passed, since the sustainable energy strategy proposed here, ideally based only on RE inputs but taking energy efficiency to its economic limits, would also make extensive use of electricity, batteries and probably other storage technologies and zero-emission fuels too. But hydrogen would still have a critical and substantial role to play: in the transport sector, in road and rail vehicles requiring a range comparable to today's petrol and diesel vehicles, in coastal and international shipping, and in air transport; and in the electricity sector to provide longer-term seasonal storage on electricity grids relying exclusively on variable RE inputs.

A core difference between this vision and earlier concepts of a HE is that a hierarchy of spatially-distributed sustainable hydrogen production, storage and distribution centers relying on a range of local RE sources and feedstocks would be created. Hydrogen would be produced, stored and consumed locally so far as practical, rather than being produced at a few large-scale facilities and then transmitted via long-distance pipelines centralized to distant cities. The required hydrogen pipeline distribution system would be limited to separate distribution networks for the main metropolitan areas and regions, by complementary use of hydrogen and electricity as energy vectors. Bulk hydrogen storage would, however, provide the strategic energy reserve to guarantee national and global energy security in a world relying increasingly on RE.

This vision of a sustainable HE has intentionally been outlined in a generic form so that it is applicable to many different countries and regions. The vision remains merely a thumbnail sketch at this stage, without detailed quantification of its associated primary energy supply, storage, distribution and consumption profiles, and without a detailed comparison on triple bottom line—that is, economic, environmental (including principally greenhouse gas emissions), and social—criteria with alternative energy scenarios.

What is needed now as a next step is to apply this vision to specific countries (or groupings of nations) by conducting detailed energy-economic-environmental modeling to quantify its key characteristics in particular contexts. A quantitative scenario for a transition to a hydrogen-based sustainable energy strategy over time will need to be developed in these contexts, and an evaluation conducted into its overall economic, environmental and social benefits compared with alternative scenarios.

A number of features included tentatively in the vision presented here require in particular further investigation:

- The most suitable methods for producing hydrogen from biomass resources of various kinds including cellulosic and algal sources, and a triple bottom line comparison of these methods with direct production of biofuels for use in internal combustion engines, or aircraft jet engines.

- The magnitude of the hydrogen storage capacity needed to provide the required level of supply security on national electricity grids of various structures, and with different levels and types of variable and distributed RE input, along with the use of other types of short-duration energy storage such as supercapacitors and batteries.
- The technical feasibility, and triple bottom line evaluation, of storing hydrogen in very large quantities in subsea or subterranean depleted natural gas or oil reservoirs, or other on and off-shore geological formations, whether in their natural or artificially altered forms.
- The most appropriate methods for bulk storage of hydrogen at Coastal and Inland Hydrogen Centers prior to regional/local distribution, including high-pressure (350 or 700 bar) gas, in metal or chemical hydrides, in slurries (such as alane slurry), or in carbon-based materials. Given the enormous quantities of hydrogen and hence hydrogen storage material that will be needed in a fully-fledged HISE strategy, ultimately carbon-based storage materials would clearly be preferable from the perspective of material availability (and hence price) on a global basis.
- The development of hydrogen storage and fuel cell systems suitable for large transport vehicles, in particular, long-distance road trucks (semi-trailers and B-doubles), long-distance buses, intercapital freight and passenger trains, tractors and other heavy mobile machinery, and international and coastal ships.
- The development of liquid hydrogen fuelled jet aircraft, and associated on-board storage, and airport refueling systems. In addition, R&D to develop the most cost-efficient methods of liquefying hydrogen using just RE sources is necessary, and/or to find an alternative high-density form of hydrogen storage suitable for aircraft.

While the concept of a HE may now need re-envisioning, the role of hydrogen in a sustainable energy economy deserves full and urgent consideration in terms of policy studies, and research, development, demonstration and commercialization of the enabling technologies.

JOHN ANDREWS is an associate professor in the School of Aerospace, Mechanical and Manufacturing Engineering, RMIT University, Melbourne, Australia. He directs the school's Master of Engineering (Sustainable Energy) and RMIT-NORTH Link Greenhouse Emission Reduction programs and leads the renewable-energy hydrogen R&D group. His book *Living Better with Less* (Penguin, 1981) was one of the first works to propose sustainable development for Australia.

BAHMAN SHABANI is a lecturer in the Master of Engineering Sustainable Energy program at the School of Aerospace, Mechanical and Manufacturing Engineering, RMIT University, Melbourne, Australia.

Ulf Bossel

NO

Does a Hydrogen Economy Make Sense?

Introduction

The technology needed to establish a hydrogen economy is available or can be developed. Two comprehensive 2004 studies by the U.S. National Research Council and the American Physical Society summarize technical options and identify needs for further improvements. They are concerned with the cost of hydrogen obtained from various sources, but fail to address the key question of the overall energy balance of a hydrogen economy. Energy is needed to synthesize hydrogen and to deliver it to the user, and energy is lost when the gas is converted back to electricity by fuel cells. How much energy is needed to liberate hydrogen from water by electrolysis or high-temperature thermodynamics or by chemistry? Where does the energy come from and in which form is it harvested? Do we have enough clean water for electrolysis and steam reforming? How and where do we safely deposit the enormous amounts of carbon dioxide if hydrogen is derived from coal?

This paper extends a previous analysis of the parasitic energy needs of a hydrogen economy. It argues that the energy problem cannot be solved in a sustainable way by introducing hydrogen as an energy carrier. Instead, energy from renewable sources and high energy efficiency between source and service will become the key points of a sustainable solution. The establishment of an efficient "electron economy" appears to be more appropriate than the creation of a much less efficient "hydrogen economy."

The Challenge

The following examples illustrate the nature of the challenge involved in creating a hydrogen economy.

It takes about 1 kg of hydrogen to replace 1 U.S. gal of gasoline. About 200 MJ (55 kWh) of dc electricity are needed to liberate 1 kg of hydrogen from 9 kg of water by electrolysis. Steam reforming of methane (natural gas) requires only 4.5 kg of water for each kilogram of hydrogen, but 5.5 kg of CO_2 emerge from the process. One kilogram of hydrogen can also be obtained from 3 kg of coal and 9 kg of water, but 11 kg of CO_2 are released and need to be sequestered. Even with most efficient fuel cell systems, at most 50% of the hydrogen energy can be converted back to electricity.

The full dimensions of the challenge become apparent when these numbers are translated to a specific case. The following case study may serve to illustrate the point. About 50 jumbo jets leave Frankfurt Airport every day, each loaded with 130 tons of kerosene. If replaced on a 1 : 1 energy base by 50 tons of liquid hydrogen, the daily needs would be 2500 tons or 36 000 m^3 of the cryogenic liquid, enough to fill 18 Olympic-size swimming pools. Every day 22 500 tons of water would have to be electrolyzed. The continuous output of eight 1-GW power plants would be required for electrolysis, liquefaction, and transport of hydrogen. If all 550 planes leaving the airport were converted to hydrogen, the entire water consumption of Frankfurt (650 000 inhabitants) and the output of 25 full-size power plants would be needed to meet the hydrogen demand of air planes leaving just one airport in Germany.

For hydrogen derived from fossil hydrocarbons, the availability of water and the safe sequestration of CO_2 may pose serious problems, not because of inadequate technology, but with respect to logistics, infrastructure, costs, safety, and energy consumption. To fuel the 50 jumbo jets with hydrogen, about 7500 tons of coal and 11 250 tons of water are needed daily and 27 500 tons of carbon dioxide must be liquefied for transport, shipped to a suitable disposal site (perhaps in the deep waters of the mid-Atlantic) and safely deposited. The significant energy needs for hydrogen liquefaction and transport are the same for any source of hydrogen. Fueling the 50 jumbo jets at Frankfurt airport is only an insignificant part of a hydrogen economy. Has the magnitude of the task been recognized?

Questions of this nature need to be addressed before resources are invested in a hydrogen infrastructure. The mission should not be the development of technology and the introduction of new energy carriers, but the establishment of a sustainable energy future. There are other options to be considered before we make major commitments to a hydrogen future.

Sustainable Energy Future

In this paper, fossil and nuclear energy are defined as unsustainable because the resources are finite and the waste cannot be absorbed by nature. If one accepts this definition, renewable energy harvested in a sustainable way becomes the key to a sustainable energy future.

With the exception of biomass, all renewable energy is of a physical nature: heat (solar, geothermal), solar radiation (photovoltaic) and mechanical energy (wind, hydro, waves, etc.). Heat obtained from solar collectors, geothermal sources, and waste incineration may also be converted to electricity. Thus, in one vision of a sustainable future, electricity from renewable sources will become the dominant primary energy carrier replacing chemical carriers of today's economy.

Physical energy provided by nature is best distributed as physical energy without intermediate chemical carriers, because, excepting food, people need physical energy for transport, space conditioning, fabrication processes, cooking, lighting, and communication. Hydrogen would make sense only if its production, distribution, and use are superior to the distribution of electricity by wires.

For centuries hydrogen has fascinated people. Hydrogen can be derived from water and other chemical compounds. The conversion of hydrogen to heat or power is often simplified by the popular equation "hydrogen plus air yields electricity and drinking water." Also, hydrogen, the most common chemical element on the planet, is hailed as an everlasting energy source. But nature does not provide hydrogen in its elemental form. High-grade energy (electricity or heat) is needed to liberate hydrogen from its chemical source.

Economy means trade. A hydrogen economy involves all economic stages between hydrogen production and hydrogen use, i.e., between renewable electricity received to electrolyzers and useful electricity drawn from fuel cells. Between the two ends of the economic chain hydrogen has to be packaged by compression or liquefaction to become a commodity. In the transportation, hydrogen has to be produced, packaged, transported, stored, transferred to cars, then stored and transported again before it is finally admitted to fuel cells.

All these processes require energy. Compared to natural gas (methane) or liquid fuels much more energy is required for the marketing of hydrogen. This is directly related to the physical properties of hydrogen (density 0.09 kg/m^3, boiling point 20.3 K). Compared to methane, the volumetric energy density of hydrogen is less than one third. Even in the liquid state, the density of hydrogen (70 kg/m^3) is not much above the density of heavy duty styrofoam. Gasoline and even wood pellets carry 3.5 or 1.2 times more energy per volume than liquefied hydrogen. One cubic meter of the cold liquid holds 70 kg, the same volume of gasoline 128 kg of hydrogen. The best way to store hydrogen is in chemical combination with carbon. . . .

Energy Needs of a Hydrogen Economy

The energy needed to produce, compress, liquefy, transport, transfer, and store hydrogen and the energy lost for its conversion back to electricity with fuel cells can never be recovered. The heat of formation or [higher heat in value (HHV)] has been used throughout to base the analysis on true energy contents in agreement with the law of energy conservation.

In contrast, the lower heating value (LHV), a man-created accounting convention, is appropriate only when energetic processes are compared for identical fuels. In many "well-to-wheel" studies, hydrogen solutions are embellished by 10% as a result of an LHV accounting. When hydrogen is made by whatever process at least the heat of formation HHV of the synthetic energy carrier has to be invested in form of electricity, heat, or HHV energy content of precursor materials. For a correct accounting the output of a fuel cell should also be related to the HHV, not the LHV energy content of the hydrogen gas. Also, LHV accounting may turn conventional energy equipment into perpetual motion machines with efficiencies exceeding 100%. The use of the higher heating value HHV is appropriate for all serious energy analyses.

Although cost of energy is an important issue, this study is only concerned with energy balances. Energy is needed for solving the energy problem and energy waste has to be minimized. However, a quick visit to the market is helpful. . . . Every GJ of hydrogen energy will cost around $5.60 when produced from natural gas, $10.30 from coal, and $20.10 from electrolysis of water. Before taxes, gasoline costs about $3.00 per GJ.

Production of Hydrogen by Electrolysis

Making hydrogen from water by electrolysis is an energy-intensive process. However, in a sustainable energy future, this is the direct route from renewable electricity to a chemical energy carrier. The standard potential for the water formation is 1.48 V, corresponding to the heat of formation or the higher heating value HHV of hydrogen. . . .

The electrolysis is frequently performed under pressure. In that case, part of the electrical energy input is used for an isothermal compression. Pressure is not obtained for free, but by this meaningful procedure compression losses and equipment costs are reduced. Pressure electrolysis offers energetic and commercial advantages over atmospheric electrolyzers.

Electrolysis may be the only practical link between renewable energy and hydrogen. Although solar or nuclear heat can also be used for high-temperature cyclic processes, it is unlikely that a recognizable fraction of the global energy demand can be served with hydrogen from solar concentrators or high-temperature reactors. Local wind farms may deliver energy at lower costs than distant solar or nuclear installations.

Hydrogen from Biomass

Hydrogen from biomass is another option with uncertain future. Biomass has to be converted to biomethane by aerobic fermentation or gasification before hydrogen can be made. However, biomethane of natural gas quality (above 96% CH_4) is already a perfect fuel for transport and stationary applications. Why reform it to hydrogen? In many European countries, biomethane from sewage digesters is already sold at fueling stations to a growing number of satisfied drivers.

In a sustainable future, hydrogen could also be obtained by reforming of alcohols or wood. This is not likely to happen, because the listed biofuels are much better energy carriers than hydrogen. The inherent value of these substances is the natural bond of hydrogen and carbon atoms. By chemical rearrangement (e.g., Fischer Tropsch) it is possible to synthesize liquid hydrocarbons for long distance transport by air, ship, rail, or road. Hydrogen production from biomass shall not be considered in this context.

Using autothermal processes the conversion can be very efficient. The process heat obtained by burning some of the biomass is transferred to the hydrogen stream. Industrial natural gas reformers generate hydrogen with energetic HHV efficiencies of 90%. Today, this is the most economical method to obtain hydrogen. As stated earlier, hydrogen production from fossil hydrocarbons is not here considered sustainable.

Packaging of Hydrogen by Compression

Compressing gas requires energy. . . . Compared to methane, about nine times more energy per kg is required to compress hydrogen, and 15 times more (ratio of molecular masses) than for air. The energy consumption for compression of hydrogen is substantial and has to be considered.

Multistage compressors with intercoolers operate somewhere between the isothermal and adiabatic limits. Compared with methane, hydrogen passes the compression heat faster to the cooler walls thus bringing the process closer to isothermal. Data provided by a leading manufacturer of hydrogen compressors show that the energy required for a five-stage compression of 1000 kg of hydrogen per hour from ambient pressure to 20 MPa is about 7.2% of its HHV. . . .

For multistage compression to a final pressure of 20 MPa, about 8% of the HHV energy content of hydrogen is required. This analysis does not include any losses in the electrical power supply system. At least 1.08 units of energy must be invested in compression to obtain 1 unit of hydrogen HHV at 20 MPa. The number becomes 1.12 for compression to 80 MPa for hydrogen transfer to the proposed 70 MPa standard vehicle tanks of automobiles. If mechanical and electrical losses are also considered, the total electricity needs for compression may reach 20% of the HHV hydrogen energy leaving the process.

Packaging of Hydrogen by Liquefaction

Even more energy is needed to compact hydrogen by liquefaction. Theoretically, only about 14.2 MJ/kgLH_2 have to be removed to cool hydrogen gas from 298 K (25 °C) to 20.3 K and to condense the gas at 20.3 K and atmospheric pressure. However, at such low temperatures, no heat sinks exist for cooling and condensing hydrogen. Generally, a three-stage propane refrigeration system is used for cooling hydrogen gas from ambient temperature to about 170 K, followed by multistage nitrogen expansion to obtain 77 K, and a multistage helium compression–expansion to complete the liquefaction of hydrogen at 20.3 K and atmospheric pressure. The energy consumed by these three stages is much higher than the exergetic limit mentioned above. Therefore, published data of representative hydrogen liquefaction plants are used for reference.

The medium size liquefaction plant of Linde Gas AG at Ingolstadt in Germany produces 182 kg/h of LH_2 at a specific energy consumption of about 54 MJ/kgLH_2. Advanced larger plants in the United States require 36 MJ/kgLH_2 to liquefy hydrogen. In a Japanese feasibility study of a hydrogen liquefaction plant of 300 metric tons LH_2 per day or 12 500 kgLH_2/h, the best case power consumption is given at 105.2 MW. This corresponds to 30.3 MJ/kgLH_2 for a plant about six times larger than any existing facility. The use of helium–neon mixture for the low-temperature cycle has been suggested to reduce the energy consumption to, perhaps, 25.2 MJ/kgLH_2(= 7 kWh/kgLH_2) for a plant producing 7200 kgLH_2 per hour, or 173 metric tons LH_2 per day. However, experimental results are not yet available.

The real-world requirements are much higher. Twenty-five hundred metric tons of liquid hydrogen would be required daily to fuel 50 jumbo jets departing from Frankfurt Airport. For this, 22 500 m^3 of clean water must be split by electrolysis. Hydrogen production and liquefaction consumes the continuous output of eight 1-GW power plants. The numbers may be multiplied by five if Frankfurt airport were totally converted to hydrogen.

Large liquefaction plants are more efficient than small facilities. . . . More electrical energy is consumed for the liquefaction of hydrogen in small plants than in large facilities.

For very small liquefaction plants (> 5 kgLH_2/h), the energy needed to liquefy hydrogen may exceed the HHV energy. Even 10 000 kgLH_2/h plants (perhaps four times larger than any existing liquefaction facility) would consume about 25% of the HHV energy of the liquefied hydrogen. For the available technology, 40% would be a reasonable number. [In] other words, 1.4 units of energy would have to be supplied to the liquefier as hydrogen and electricity to obtain 1 HHV unit of liquid hydrogen. However, no liquefaction plants of comparable performance have yet been built.

Moreover, liquid hydrogen storage systems lose some hydrogen gas by boiloff. This is due to unavoidable heat leakage, and must be permitted for safety reasons. The loss rate is dependent on the size of the store, but would be significant for those used in vehicles, and may amount to 3%–4% a day. Boiloff hydrogen has to be vented from parked vehicles. For example, when a car is left at an airport for two weeks, 50% of the original hydrogen may be lost by evaporation.

Physical Metal Hydrides

Hydrogen may be stored physically, e.g., by adsorption in spongy matrices of special alloys of metal hydrides. The hydrogen forms a very close physical, but not a perfect chemical bond with alloys like $LaNi_5$ or $ZrCr_2$.

The energy balance shall be described in general terms. Again, energy is needed to produce and compress hydrogen. Some of this energy is lost. Also, heat is released and normally lost when metal hydride storage containers are filled with hydrogen. Conversely, heat must be added to liberate the stored hydrogen from the hydrides. The energy needed to store hydrogen in physical metal hydrides and to liberate it later is significantly more than the energy needed to compress the gas to 3 MPa, the typical filling pressure of hydride storage containers.

However, metal hydrides store only around 55–60 kg of hydrogen per m^3 of storage volume. For comparison, liquid hydrogen has a volumetric density of 70 kg/m^3. Moreover, metal hydride cartridges are heavy. A small metal hydride container holding less than 2 g of hydrogen has a weight of 230 g. Hence, around 50 kg of hydrides are required to store 1 kg of hydrogen, the equivalent of about 4 L or 1 U.S. gal of gasoline. Hydride storage of hydrogen is not practical for automotive application, unless the volumetric and gravimetric energy density of the storage medium can be raised. Today, the specific energy density of metal hydride storage devices is comparable to that of advanced Li-Ion batteries.

Chemical Metal Hydrides

Hydrogen may also be stored chemically in alkali metal hydrides. Alkali metal hydrides have high energy densities with gravimetric energy content comparable to firewood. The weight of alkali hydride materials poses no problems. One kg of CaH_2 or LiH reacting with water yields 13.6 or 36.1 MJ of HHV hydrogen energy, respectively. However, the energy needed to produce the alkali metal hydrides would discourage their commercial use on a larger scale.

There are many options in the alkali group like LiH, NaH, KH, and CaH_2. Complex binary hydride compounds like $LiBH_4$, $NaBH_4$, KBH_4, $LiAlH_4$, or $NaAlH_4$ have also been proposed for hydrogen storage. None of these compounds can be found in nature. All have to be synthesized from pure metals and hydrogen. . . .

For hydrogen storage in hydrides, at least 1.6 times more high-grade energy has to be invested to produce 1 HHV energy unit of hydrogen, resulting in a stage efficiency of less than 60%.

Road Delivery of Hydrogen

Although pipeline transport is preferred for gases, hydrogen transport by trucks will play a role in a hydrogen economy. Because of the low density of the gaseous energy carrier, transport of pressurized or liquid hydrogen is extremely inefficient. Forty-ton trucks can carry only 350 kg of hydrogen at 200 bar in the gaseous, or 3500 kg in the liquid state. The bulk weight is steel for pressure tanks and cryogenic vessels. It takes about 22 hydrogen tube trailers to deliver the same amount of energy as a single gasoline tanker.

The energy analysis is based on information obtained from some of the leading providers of industrial gases in Germany and Switzerland. . . . [The] following assumptions are made. Hydrogen gas (at 20 MPa = 200 bar), liquid hydrogen, methanol, ethanol, propane, and octane (representing gasoline) are trucked from the refinery or hydrogen plant to the consumer. Trucks with a gross weight of 40 metric tons are fitted with suitable containers. Fuel consumption is 40 kg of diesel fuel per 100 km and metric ton. The engine efficiency does not depend on the vehicle weight.

The 40-metric-ton tanker trucks are designed to carry a maximum of fuel. For liquids like gasoline, ethanol, and methanol, the payload is about 26 metric tons. One hundred percent of the liquid fuels are delivered to the customer. In contrast, only 80% of the compressed gases are transferred by blow-down. The remaining 20% of the gas load is returned to the gas plant. Such pressure cascades are standard practice today. As a consequence, the payload of pressurized gas carriers is 80% of the load. However, in anticipation of technical developments, this analysis assumes that in future, trucks will be able to carry 4000 kg methane or 500 kg of hydrogen, of which 80% (3200 kg or 400 kg, respectively) are delivered to the consumer.

The transport of liquid hydrogen is limited by volume, not by weight. A large trailer-truck may have a useful box volume of 2.4-m width, 2.5-m height, and 10-m length, i.e., 60 m^3. As the density of 70 kg/m^3, only 4200 kg of liquid hydrogen could possibly be loaded. But space is needed for the cryogenic container, thermal insulation, safety equipment, etc. In fact, a large truck has room for about 2100 kg of the cryogenic liquid. However, trucking liquid hydrogen is more energy efficient than delivering the pressurized gas.

. . . The energy needed to transport any of the liquid hydrocarbon fuels is reasonably small. For a one-way delivery distance of 100 km, the diesel fuel consumption remains below 0.5% of the HHV energy content of the delivered liquid fuels. However, for delivering pressurized hydrogen, the parasitic energy consumption is significant. About 7% of the delivered energy is consumed for delivery, about 13 times more than for gasoline. For liquid hydrogen the ratio is about 3.5.

Pipeline Delivery of Hydrogen

Hydrogen pipelines exist to transport the chemical commodity "hydrogen" from sources to production sites. The energy required to deliver the gas is part of the production process and energy costs are absorbed in the final price of the product. People do not mind paying for hydrogen in aspirin, plastic materials, or steel. However, energy is the currency in pipeline transport of hydrogen. Parasitic energy losses reduce the amount of energy available for useful purposes. Hydrogen transport by pipelines has to compete with electricity transport by wires.

The assessment of the energy required to pump hydrogen through pipelines is derived from natural gas pipeline operating experience. It is assumed that the same amount of energy is delivered through identical pipelines. In reality, existing pipelines must be modified for hydrogen, because of diffusion losses (mainly in sealing areas), brittleness of materials and seals, compressor lubrication, and other technical issues. Also, as the volumetric HHV energy content of hydrogen is about 3.5 times less than that of natural gas, pipes of larger diameters are needed to accommodate similar energy flow rates. Natural gas is diluted by adding hydrogen, not upgraded. . . .

Typically, a compressor is installed every 150 km for natural gas transport through pipelines at 10 m/s. The compressor motors are fueled from the gas taken from the stream, each compressor consuming about 0.3% of the local energy flow. Applying this model to the transport of hydrogen through the same pipeline, each compressor would require 3.85 more energy or 1.16% of the local energy flow. The remaining mass flow is decreasing with pipeline length. This crude model needs to be refined by pipeline experts. It does not consider the higher energy needs for hydrogen compression discussed above.

For a pipeline length of 3000 km (e.g., for gas from Russian fields to Germany), the mass fraction consumed for transporting natural gas is about 20%, while transporting hydrogen gas over the same distance would require about 35% of the original mass flow. This result was obtained for pipes of equal diameter. . . .

For a transport distance of 3000 km, at least 1.5 kg of hydrogen must be fed into the line for the delivery of 1 kg to the customer. Moving hydrogen over long distances by pipeline is not a good option. However, hydrogen pipelines have been suggested for the transport of solar energy from northern Africa or the Middle East to central Europe.

On-Site Generation of Hydrogen

One option for providing hydrogen at filling stations and dispersed depots is on-site generation of the gas by electrolysis. Again, the energy needed to generate and compress hydrogen by this scheme is compared to the HHV energy content of the hydrogen transferred to cars. Natural gas reforming is not a sustainable solution and thus not considered for the reasons stated earlier.

Consider a filling station now pumping 60 000 L of fuel (gasoline or diesel) into 1000 cars, trucks, or buses per day. This number is typical for service areas along European freeways. In most parts of the United States, many smaller filling stations are located roadside at freeway exits. On a 1 : 1 energy base, 60 000 L of fuel corresponds to about 17 000 kg of hydrogen. However, hydrogen vehicles are assumed to have a 1.5 times higher tank-to-wheel efficiency than IC engine cars. The frequently cited number of 2.5 cannot be justified any longer in light of the high efficiency of diesel or hybrid vehicles. In fact, the well-to-wheel studies of 2002 are based on lower heating values, optimistic assumptions of fuel cells, and disregard of the efficiency potentials of diesel engines and hybrid systems. Furthermore, more recent well-to-wheel studies appropriately based on the higher heating values do not identify hydrogen-fuel-cell cars as the best transportation option. In fact, the efficiency of all-electric cars is three times better than for hydrogen-fuel-cell vehicles.

Under the favorable assumption of a 1.5 advantage of hydrogen versus gasoline, 60 000 liters of fuel will be replaced by 12 000 kg of hydrogen per day. The electrolyzer efficiency may be 75%. Also, losses occur in the ac-dc power conversion. Making 12 000 kg of hydrogen per day by electrolysis requires 25 MW of continuous power and 108 000 liters of water must be pumped and demineralized. Compression power is needed for storing the hydrogen to 10 MPa and for transfer at 40 MPa to vehicle tanks at 35 MPa. In all, to generate and store 12 000 kg of hydrogen per day, the filling station must be supplied with continuous electric power of about 28 MW. There are many sites in arid regions where neither the electricity nor the water is available for hydrogen production.

For 12 000 kg of hydrogen per day (this corresponds to 1000 conventional vehicles per day), about 1.65 units of energy must be invested to obtain 1 unit of hydrogen HHV, giving a stage efficiency of 60%.

Assuming continuous operation, a 1-GW electric power plant must be available for every 20–30 hydrogen filling stations on European freeways. Today, about one fifth of the total energy consumption is electricity. The national electric power generating capacity must be significantly increased to power the transition from fossil fuels to hydrogen. It may be difficult to derive the needed electrical energy from "renewable sources" as suggested by hydrogen promoters. One would certainly use off-peak power from wind and solar sources for hydrogen production. However, electrolyzers, pumps, and storage tanks must be sized for peak demand during rush hours and vacation traffic. Not only must the electric peak power demand be considered, but also the storage of substantial amounts of hydrogen to meet the daily and seasonal demands at filling stations. . . .

Energy Efficiency of a Hydrogen Economy

When the original report was published in 2003, the parasitic energy needs of a hydrogen economy had not even been considered by promoters of a hydrogen economy. The intent of the original study was to create an awareness of the fundamental energetic weaknesses of using hydrogen as an energy vector. Since then equations and results for producing, packaging, distributing, storing, and transferring hydrogen have been checked by others and found correct.

For selected hydrogen strategies, the accumulated parasitic energy needs of all important stages can be determined by multiplication or addition of the losses of the stages involved. Four cases may serve to illustrate the point

a. Hydrogen is produced by electrolysis, compressed to 20 MPa and distributed by road to filling stations, stored at 10 MPa, then compressed to 40 MPa for rapid transfer to vehicles at 35 MPa. Energy input to hydrogen energy delivered: 1.59
b. Hydrogen is produced by electrolysis, liquefied, and distributed by road to filling stations, then transferred to vehicles.
Energy input to hydrogen energy delivered: 2.02
c. Hydrogen is produced by electrolysis on-site at filling stations or consumers, stored at 10 MPa, and subsequently compressed to 40 MPa for rapid transfer to vehicles at 35 MPa.
Energy input to hydrogen energy delivered: 1.59
d. Hydrogen is produced by electrolysis and used to make alkali metal hydrides. Hydrogen is then released by reaction of the hydride with water.
Energy input to hydrogen energy delivered: 1.90

The analysis reveals that between 1.6 and 2.0 electrical energy units must be harvested from renewable sources for every energy unit of hydrogen gas sold to the user. The high energy losses may be tolerated for some niche markets, but it is unlikely that hydrogen will ever become an important energy carrier in a sustainable energy economy built on renewable sources and efficiency.

Moreover, the delivered hydrogen must be converted to motion for all transport applications. IC engines convert hydrogen within 45% efficiency directly into mechanical motion, while equally efficient fuel cells systems produce dc electricity for traction motors. Further losses may occur in transmissions, etc. All in all, hardly 50% of the hydrogen energy contained in a vehicle tank is converted to motion of a car. The overall efficiency between electricity from renewable sources and wheel motion is only 20 to 25%. In comparison, over 60% of the original electricity can be used for transportation, if the energy is not converted to hydrogen, but directly used in electric vehicles. The energy advantages of battery-electric cars over hydrogen-fuel-cell-electric vehicles are obvious. However, further work is needed in the area of electricity storage, converters, drive systems, and electricity transfer.

Hydrogen Economy or Electron Economy

The foregoing analysis of the parasitic energy losses within a hydrogen economy shows that a hydrogen economy is an extremely inefficient proposition for the distribution of electricity from renewable sources to useful electricity from fuel cells. Only about 25% of the power generated from wind, water, or sun is converted to practical use. If the original electricity had been directly supplied by wires, as much as 90% could have been put to service. This has two serious consequences to be considered in future energy strategies.

a. About four renewable power plants have to be erected to deliver the output of one plant to stationary or mobile consumers via hydrogen and fuel cells. Three of these plants generate energy to cover the parasitic losses of the hydrogen economy while only one of them is producing useful energy. Can we base our energy future on such wasteful schemes?
b. As energy losses will be charged to the customer, electricity from hydrogen fuel cells will be at least four times more expensive than electricity from the grid. Who wants to use fuel cells? Who wants to drive a hydrogen-fuel-cell car?

Fundamental laws of physics expose the weakness of a hydrogen economy. Hydrogen, the artificial energy carrier, can never compete with its own energy source, electricity, in a sustainable future.

The discussion about a hydrogen economy is adding irritation to the energy debate. We need to focus our attention on sustainable energy solutions. It seems that the establishment of an efficient electron economy should become the common goal. There are many topics to be addressed, like electricity storage and automatic electricity transfer to vehicles, yet electric cars equipped with Li–Ion-batteries already have a driving range of 250 km. In 2010, Mitsubishi will commercialize an electric car with 260 hp on four wheels and a driving range of 500 km (300 mi). It seems that by focusing attention on hydrogen we are missing the chance to meet the challenges of a sustainable energy future.

The title question "Does a hydrogen economy make sense?" must be answered with a definite "Never." However, niche applications for the use of hydrogen energy are abundant and should be addressed.

Ulf Bossel is on the Board of Advisors of the European Fuel Cell Forum in Lucerne, Switzerland.

EXPLORING THE ISSUE

Does a Hydrogen Economy Make Sense?

Critical Thinking and Reflection

1. Discuss why we need one or more replacements for fossil fuel energy (natural gas, oil, and coal).
2. What requirements must a replacement for fossil fuel energy satisfy?
3. Why can't the various energy-conversion efficiency factors discussed by Ulf Bossel be improved?

Is There Common Ground?

Does a hydrogen economy make sense? Both sides agree that we need to develop a replacement for the fossil fuel economy we are accustomed to and that there are serious difficulties in implementing a hydrogen-based replacement (among which is the need to distribute fuel). Both also agree that there is a place for electricity-powered vehicles.

1. What technological changes would make electricity-powered vehicles more satisfactory to all concerned?
2. What changes in the structure of society might make hydrogen a more affordable option?

Additional Resources

M. Balat and E. Kirtay, "Major Technical Barriers to a 'Hydrogen Economy'," *Energy Sources, Part A: Recovery, Utilization & Environmental Effects* (June 2010).

Joan M. Ogden, "Hydrogen: The Fuel of the Future?" *Physics Today* (April 2002).

Piotr Tomczyk, "Fundamental Aspects of the Hydrogen Economy," *World Futures* (July 2009).

Laurie Wiegler, "The Future of Hydrogen Cars," *Technology Review* (September 21, 2011) (www.technologyreview.com/energy/38647/).

Create Central

www.mhhe.com/createcentral

Internet References . . .

International Association for Hydrogen Energy

The International Association for Hydrogen Energy works toward the time when hydrogen energy will be the principal means by which the world achieves its long-sought goal of abundant clean energy for mankind.

www.iahe.org/

Some other groups and sites with a similar mission are:

Renewable Energy World

www.renewableenergyworld.com/rea/tech/hydrogen

Hydrogen Energy Center

www.h2eco.org/

U.S. Department of Energy Hydrogen and Fuel Cells Program

www.hydrogen.energy.gov/

Unit 3

UNIT

Human Health and Welfare

Many people are concerned about new technological and scientific discoveries because they fear their potential impacts on human health and welfare. In the past, fears have been expressed concerning nuclear bombs and power plants, irradiated food, the internal combustion engine, medications such as thalidomide and diethylstilbestrol, vaccines, pesticides and other chemicals, and more. Because human birth rates have declined, at least in developed nations, the hazards of excess population have fallen out of the headlines, but a few people do still struggle to remind us that a smaller population makes many problems less worrisome. On the public-health front, people worry about whether new "synthetic biology" organisms pose a threat and about whether research into infectious animal diseases such as hoof-and-mouth disease should be kept far away from livestock operations. It is worth stressing that risks may be real (as they are with toxic chemicals), but there may be a trade-off for genuine health benefits.

Selected, Edited, and with Issue Framing Material by:
Thomas A. Easton, *Thomas College*

ISSUE

Do We Have a Population Problem?

YES: David Attenborough, from "This Heaving Planet," *New Statesman* (April 25, 2011)

NO: Tom Bethell, from "Population, Economy, and God," *The American Spectator* (May 2009)

Learning Outcomes

After studying this issue, students will be able to explain:

- The nature of the "population problem."
- The concept of "carrying capacity."
- The potential benefits of stabilizing or reducing population.
- The potential drawbacks of stabilizing or reducing population.

ISSUE SUMMARY

YES: Sir David Attenborough argues that the environmental problems faced by the world are exacerbated by human numbers. Without population reduction, the problems will become ever more difficult—and ultimately impossible—to solve.

NO: Tom Bethell argues that population alarmists project their fears onto popular concerns, currently the environment, and every time their scare-mongering turns out to be based on faulty premises. Blaming environmental problems will be no different. Societies are sustained not by population control but by belief in God.

In 1798 the British economist Thomas Malthus published his *Essay on the Principle of Population*. In it, he pointed with alarm at the way the human population grew geometrically (a hockey-stick-shaped curve of increase) and at how agricultural productivity grew only arithmetically (a straight-line increase). It was obvious, he said, that the population must inevitably outstrip its food supply and experience famine. Contrary to the conventional wisdom of the time, population growth was not necessarily a good thing. Indeed, it led inexorably to catastrophe. For many years, Malthus was something of a laughing stock. The doom he forecast kept receding into the future as new lands were opened to agriculture, new agricultural technologies appeared, new ways of preserving food limited the waste of spoilage, and the birth rate dropped in the industrialized nations (the "demographic transition"). The food supply kept ahead of population growth and seemed likely—to most observers—to continue to do so. Malthus's ideas were dismissed as irrelevant fantasies.

Yet overall population kept growing. In Malthus's time, there were about 1 billion human beings on Earth. By 1950—when Warren S. Thompson worried that civilization would be endangered by the rapid growth of Asian and Latin American populations during the next five decades (see "Population," *Scientific American*, February 1950)—there were a little over 2.5 billion. In 1999 the tally passed 6 billion. It passed 7 billion in 2011. By 2025 it will be over 8 billion. Statistics like these, which are collected and published by the World Resources Institute (www.wri.org), are positively frightening. The Worldwatch Institute's yearly *State of the World* reports (W.W. Norton) are no less so. By 2050 the UN expects the world population to be about 9 billion (see *World Population Prospects: The 2010 Revision Population Database*; http://esa.un.org/unpd/wpp/index.htm; United Nations, 2010). By 2100, it will be 10.1 billion; see Jocelyn Keiser, "10 Billion Plus: Why World Population Projections Were Too Low," *ScienceInsider* (May 4, 2011) (http://scim.ag/_worldpop). While global agricultural production has also increased, it has not kept up with rising demand, and—because of the loss of topsoil to erosion, the exhaustion of aquifers for irrigation water, and the high price of energy for making fertilizer (among other things)—the prospect of improvement seems exceedingly slim to many observers.

Two centuries never saw Malthus's forecasts of doom come to pass. Population continued to grow, and environmentalists pointed with alarm at a great many problems that resulted from human use of the world's resources (air and water pollution, erosion, loss of soil fertility and groundwater, loss of species, and a great deal more). "Cornucopian" economists such as the late Julian Simon insisted that the more people there are on Earth, the more people there are to solve problems and that humans can find ways around all possible resource shortages. See Simon's essay, "Life on Earth Is Getting Better, Not Worse," *The Futurist* (August 1983). See also David Malakoff, "Are More People Necessarily a Problem?" *Science* (July 29, 2011) (a special issue on population).

Was Malthus wrong? Both environmental scientists and many economists now say that if population continues to grow, problems are inevitable. But earlier predictions of a world population of 10 or 12 billion by 2050 are no longer looking very likely. The UN's population statistics show a slowing of growth, to be followed by an actual decline in population size.

Fred Pearce, *The Coming Population Crash: and Our Planet's Surprising Future* (Beacon, 2010), is optimistic about the effects on human well-being of the coming decline in population. Do we still need to work on controlling population? Historian Matthew Connolly, *Fatal Misconception: The Struggle to Control World Population* (Belknap Press, 2010), argues that the twentieth-century movement to control population was an oppressive movement that failed to deliver on its promises. Now that population growth is slowing, the age of population control is over. Yet there remains the issue of "carrying capacity," defined very simply as the size of the population that the environment can support, or "carry," indefinitely, through both good years and bad. It is not the size of the population that can prosper in good times alone, for such a large population must suffer catastrophically when droughts, floods, or blights arrive or the climate warms or cools. It is a long-term concept, where "long-term" means not decades or generations, nor even centuries, but millennia or more. See Mark Nathan Cohen, "Carrying Capacity," *Free Inquiry* (August/September 2004), and T. C. R. White, "The Role of Food, Weather, and Climate in Limiting the Abundance of Animals," *Biological Reviews* (August 2008).

What is Earth's carrying capacity for human beings? It is surely impossible to set a precise figure on the number of human beings the world can support for the long run. As Joel E. Cohen discusses in *How Many People Can the Earth Support?* (W. W. Norton, 1996), estimates of Earth's carrying capacity range from under a billion to over a trillion. The precise number depends on our choices of diet, standard of living, level of technology, willingness to share with others at home and abroad, and desire for an intact physical, chemical, and biological environment (including wildlife and natural environments), as well as on whether or not our morality permits restraint in reproduction and our political or religious ideology permits educating and empowering women. The key, Cohen stresses, is human choice, and the choices are ones we must make within the next 50 years. Phoebe Hall, "Carrying Capacity," *E—The Environmental Magazine* (March/April 2003), notes that even countries with large land areas and small populations, such as Australia and Canada, can be overpopulated in terms of resource availability. The critical resource appears to be food supply; see Russell Hopfenberg, "Human Carrying Capacity Is Determined by Food Availability," *Population & Environment* (November 2003).

Andrew R. B. Ferguson, in "Perceiving the Population Bomb," *World Watch* (July/August 2001), sets the maximum sustainable human population at about 2 billion. Sandra Postel, in the Worldwatch Institute's *State of the World 1994* (W.W. Norton, 1994), says, "As a result of our population size, consumption patterns, and technology choices, we have surpassed the planet's carrying capacity. This is plainly evident by the extent to which we are damaging and depleting natural capital" (including land and water). The point is reiterated by Robert Kunzig, "By 2045 Global Population Is Projected to Reach Nine Billion. Can the Planet Take the Strain?" *National Geographic* (January 2011) (*National Geographic* ran numerous articles on population-related issues during 2011). Thomas L. Friedman, "The Earth Is Full," *New York Times* (June 7, 2011), thinks a crisis is imminent but we will learn and move on; see also Paul Gilding, *The Great Disruption: Why the Climate Crisis Will Bring on the End of Shopping and the Birth of a New World* (Bloomsbury Press, 2011).

If population growth is now declining and world population will actually begin to decline during this century, there is clearly hope. But most estimates of carrying capacity put it at well below the current world population size, and it will take a long time for global population to fall far enough to reach such levels. We seem to be moving in the right direction, but it remains an open question whether our numbers will decline far enough soon enough (i.e., before environmental problems become critical). On the other hand, Jeroen Van den Bergh and Piet Rietveld, "Reconsidering the Limits to World Population: Meta-Analysis and Meta-Prediction," *Bioscience* (March 2004), set their best estimate of human global carrying capacity at 7.7 billion, which is distinctly reassuring. However, there is still concern that global population will not stop at that point; see David R. Francis, "'Birth Dearth' Worries Pale in Comparison to Overpopulation," *Christian Science Monitor* (July 14, 2008).

How high a level will population actually reach? Fertility levels are definitely declining in many developed nations; see Alan Booth and Ann C. Crouter (eds.), *The New Population Problem: Why Families in Developed Countries Are Shrinking and What It Means* (Lawrence Erlbaum Associates, 2005). The visibility of this fertility decline is among the reasons mentioned by Martha Campbell, "Why the Silence on Population?" *Population and Environment* (May 2007). Yet Doug Moss, "What Birth Dearth?" *E—The Environmental Magazine* (November–December 2006), reminds us that there is still a large surplus of births—and therefore a growing population—in the less developed world. If we think globally, there is no shortage of people. However, many countries are so concerned about changing age distributions that they are trying to encourage larger—not smaller—families. See Robert Engelman, "Unnatural Increase? A Short History of Population Trends and Influences," *World Watch* (September/October 2008—a special issue on population issues), "Population and Sustainability," *Scientific American Earth 3.0* (Summer 2009), and his book *More: Population, Nature, and What Women Want* (Island Press, 2008). On the other hand, David E. Bloom, "7 Billion and Counting," *Science* (July 29, 2011), notes that "Despite alarmist predictions, historical increases in population have not been economically catastrophic. Moreover, changes in population age structure [providing for more workers] have opened the door to increased prosperity." Jonathan A. Foley, "Can We Feed the World & Sustain the Planet?" *Scientific American* (November 2011), thinks that with revisions to the world's agricultural systems, a growing population's demand for food can be met, at least through 2050.

Some people worry that a decline in population will not be good for human welfare. Michael Meyer, "Birth Dearth," *Newsweek* (September 27, 2004), argues that a shrinking population will mean that the economic growth that has meant constantly increasing standards of living must come to an end, government programs (from war to benefits for the poor and elderly) will no longer be affordable, a shrinking number of young people will have to support a growing elderly population, and despite some environmental benefits, quality of life will suffer. China is already feeling some of these effects; see Wang Feng, "China's Population Destiny: The Looming Crisis," *Current History* (September 2010), and Mara Hvistendahl, "Has China Outgrown the One-Child Policy?" *Science* (September 17, 2010). Julia Whitty, "The Last Taboo," *Mother Jones* (May–June 2010), argues that even though the topic of overpopulation has become unpopular, it is clear that we are already using the Earth's resources faster than they can be replenished and the only answer is to slow and eventually reverse population growth. Scott Victor Valentine, "Disarming the Population Bomb," *International Journal of Sustainable Development and World Ecology* (April 2010), calls for "a renewed international focus on managed population reduction as a key enabler of sustainable development." As things stand, the current size and continued growth of the population threaten the United Nations' Millennium Development Goals (including alleviating global poverty, improving health, and protecting the environment; see www.un.org/millenniumgoals/); see Willard Cates, Jr., et al., "Family Planning and the Millennium Development Goals," *Science* (September 24, 2010).

In the YES selection, Sir David Attenborough argues that the environmental problems faced by the world are exacerbated by human numbers. Without population reduction, the problems will become ever more difficult—and ultimately impossible—to solve. In the NO selection, Tom Bethell argues that population alarmists project their fears onto popular concerns, currently the environment, and every time their scare-mongering turns out to be based on faulty premises. Blaming environmental problems will be no different. Societies are sustained not by population control but by belief in God.

YES

David Attenborough

This Heaving Planet

Fifty years ago, on 29 April 1961, a group of far-sighted people in this country got together to warn the world of an impending disaster. Among them were a distinguished scientist, Sir Julian Huxley; a bird-loving painter, Peter Scott; an advertising executive, Guy Mountford; a powerful and astonishingly effective civil servant, Max Nicholson—and several others.

They were all, in addition to their individual professions, dedicated naturalists, fascinated by the natural world not just in this country but internationally. And they noticed what few others had done—that all over the world, charismatic animals that were once numerous were beginning to disappear.

The Arabian oryx, which once had been widespread all over the Arabian Peninsula, had been reduced to a few hundred. In Spain, there were only about 90 imperial eagles left. The Californian condor was down to about 60. In Hawaii, a goose that once lived in flocks on the lava fields around the great volcanoes had been reduced to 50. And the strange rhinoceros that lived in the dwindling forests of Java—to about 40. These were the most extreme examples. Wherever naturalists looked they found species of animals whose populations were falling rapidly. This planet was in danger of losing a significant number of its inhabitants, both animals and plants.

Something had to be done. And that group determined to do it. They would need scientific advice to discover the causes of these impending disasters and to devise ways of slowing them and, they hoped, of stopping them. They would have to raise awareness and understanding of people everywhere; and, like all such enterprises, they would need money to enable them to take practical action.

They set about raising all three. Since the problem was an international one, they based themselves not in Britain but in the heart of Europe, in Switzerland. They called the organisation that they created the World Wildlife Fund (WWF).

As well as the international committee, separate action groups would be needed in individual countries. A few months after that inaugural meeting in Switzerland, Britain established one—and was the first country to do so.

The methods the WWF used to save these endangered species were several. Some, such as the Hawaiian goose and the oryx, were taken into captivity in zoos, bred up into a significant population and then taken back to their original home and released. Elsewhere—in Africa, for example—great areas of unspoiled country were set aside as national parks, where the animals could be protected from poachers and encroaching human settlement. In the Galápagos Islands and in the home of the mountain gorillas in Rwanda, ways were found of ensuring that local people who also had claims on the land where such animals lived were able to benefit financially by attracting visitors.

Ecotourism was born. The movement as a whole went from strength to strength. Twenty-four countries established their own WWF national appeals. Existing conservation bodies, of which there were a number in many parts of the world but which had been working largely in isolation, acquired new zest and international links. New ones were founded focusing on particular areas or particular species. The world awoke to conservation. Millions—billions—of dollars were raised. And now, 50 years on, conservationists who have worked so hard and with such foresight can justifiably congratulate themselves on having responded magnificently to the challenge.

Yet now, in spite of a great number of individual successes, the problem seems bigger than ever. True, thanks to the vigour and wisdom of conservationists, no major charismatic species has yet disappeared. Many are still trembling on the brink, but they are still hanging on. Today, however, overall there are more problems not fewer, more species at risk of extinction than ever before. Why?

Fifty years ago, when the WWF was founded, there were about three billion people on earth. Now there are almost seven billion—over twice as many—every one of them needing space. Space for their homes, space to grow their food (or to get others to grow it for them), space to build schools, roads and airfields. Where could that come from? A little might be taken from land occupied by other people but most of it could only come from the land which, for millions of years, animals and plants had had to themselves—the natural world.

But the impact of these extra billions of people has spread even beyond the space they physically claimed. The spread of industrialisation has changed the chemical constituents of the atmosphere. The oceans that cover most of the surface of the planet have been polluted and increasingly acidified. The earth is warming. We now realise that the disasters that continue increasingly to afflict the natural world have one element that connects them all—the unprecedented increase in the number of human beings on the planet.

There have been prophets who have warned us of this impending disaster. One of the first was Thomas Malthus. His surname—Malthus—leads some to suppose that he was some continental European philosopher, a German perhaps. But he was not. He was an Englishman, born in Guildford, Surrey, in the middle of the 18th century. His most important book, *An Essay on the Principle of Population,* was published in 1798. In it, he argued that the human population would increase inexorably until it was halted by what he termed "misery and vice." Today, for some reason, that prophecy seems to be largely ignored—or, at any rate, disregarded. It is true that he did not foresee the so-called Green Revolution (from the 1940s to the late 1970s), which greatly increased the amount of food that can be produced in any given area of arable land. And there may be other advances in our food producing skills that we ourselves still cannot foresee. But such advances only delay things. The fundamental truth that Malthus proclaimed remains the truth: there cannot be more people on this earth than can be fed.

Many people would like to deny that this is so. They would like to believe in that oxymoron "sustainable growth."

Kenneth Boulding, President Kennedy's environmental adviser 45 years ago, said something about this: "Anyone who believes in indefinite growth in anything physical, on a physically finite planet, is either mad—or an economist."

The population of the world is now growing by nearly 80 million a year. One and a half million a week. A quarter of a million a day. Ten thousand an hour. In this country [UK] it is projected to grow by 10 million in the next 22 years. That is equivalent to ten more Birminghams.

All these people, in this country and worldwide, rich or poor, need and deserve food, water, energy and space. Will they be able to get it? I don't know. I hope so. But the government's chief scientist and the last president of the Royal Society have both referred to the approaching "perfect storm" of population growth, climate change and peak oil production, leading inexorably to more and more insecurity in the supply of food, water and energy.

Consider food. For animals, hunger is a regular feature of their lives. The stoical desperation of the cheetah cubs whose mother failed in her last few attempts to kill prey for them, and who consequently face starvation, is very touching. But that happens to human beings, too. All of us who have travelled in poor countries have met people for whom hunger is a daily background ache in their lives. There are about a billion such people today—that is four times as many as the entire human population of this planet a mere 2,000 years ago, at the time of Christ.

You may be aware of the government's Foresight project, Global Food and Farming Futures. It shows how hard it is to feed the seven billion of us alive today. It lists the many obstacles that are already making this harder to achieve—soil erosion, salinisation, the depletion of aquifers, over-grazing, the spread of plant diseases as a result of globalisation, the absurd growing of food crops to turn into biofuels to feed motor cars instead of people—and so on. So it underlines how desperately difficult it is going to be to feed a population that is projected to stabilise "in the range of eight to ten billion people by the year 2050." It recommends the widest possible range of measures across all disciplines to tackle this. And it makes a number of eminently sensible recommendations, including a second green revolution.

But, surprisingly, there are some things that the project report does not say. It doesn't state the obvious fact that it would be much easier to feed eight billion people than ten billion. Nor does it suggest that the measures to achieve such a number—such as family planning and the education and empowerment of women—should be a central part of any programme that aims to secure an adequate food supply for humanity. It doesn't refer to the prescient statement 40 years ago by Norman Borlaug, the Nobel laureate and father of the first green revolution.

Borlaug produced new strains of high-yielding, short-strawed and disease-resistant wheat and in doing so saved many thousands of people in India, Pakistan, Africa and Mexico from starvation. But he warned us that all he had done was to give us a "breathing space" in which to stabilise our numbers. The government's report anticipates that food prices may rise with oil prices, and makes it clear that this will affect poorest people worst and discusses various way to help them. But it doesn't mention what every mother subsisting on the equivalent of a dollar a day already knows—that her children would be better fed if there were four of them around the table instead of ten. These are strange omissions.

How can we ignore the chilling statistics on arable land? In 1960 there was more than one acre of good cropland per person in the world—enough to sustain a reasonable European diet. Today, there is only half an acre each. In China, it is only a quarter of an acre, because of their dramatic problems of soil degradation.

Another impressive government report on biodiversity published this year, *Making Space for Nature in a Changing World,* is rather similar. It discusses all the rising pressures on wildlife in the UK—but it doesn't mention our growing population as being one of them—which is particularly odd when you consider that England is already the most densely populated country in Europe.

Most bizarre of all was a recent report by a royal commission on the environmental impact of demographic change in this country which denied that population size was a problem at all—as though 10 million extra people, more or less, would have no real impact. Of course it is not our only or even our main environmental problem but it is absurd to deny that, as a multiplier of all the others, it is a problem.

I suspect that you could read a score of reports by bodies concerned with global problems—and see that population is one of the drivers that underlies all of them—and yet find no reference to this obvious fact in any of them. Climate change tops the environmental agenda at present. We all know that every additional person will need to use some carbon energy, if only firewood for cooking, and will therefore create more carbon dioxide—though a rich person will produce vastly more than a poor one. Similarly, we can all see that every extra person is—or will be—an extra victim of climate change—though the poor will undoubtedly suffer more than the rich. Yet not a word of it appeared in the voluminous documents emerging from the Copenhagen and Cancún climate summits.

Why this strange silence? I meet no one who privately disagrees that population growth is a problem. No one—except flat-earthers—can deny that the planet is finite. We can all see it—in that beautiful picture of our earth taken by the Apollo mission. So why does hardly anyone say so publicly? There seems to be some bizarre taboo around the subject.

This taboo doesn't just inhibit politicians and civil servants who attend the big conferences. It even affects the environmental and developmental non-governmental organisations, the people who claim to care most passionately about a sustainable and prosperous future for our children.

Yet their silence implies that their admirable goals can be achieved regardless of how many people there are in the world or the UK, even though they all know that they can't.

I simply don't understand it. It is all getting too serious for such fastidious niceties. It remains an obvious and brutal fact that on a finite planet human population will quite definitely stop at some point. And that can only happen in one of two ways. It can happen sooner, by fewer human births—in a word, by contraception. That is the humane way, the powerful option that allows all of us to deal with the problem, if we collectively choose to do so. The alternative is an increased death rate—the way that all other creatures must suffer, through famine or disease or predation. That, translated into human terms, means famine or disease or war—over oil or water or food or minerals or grazing rights or just living space. There is, alas, no third alternative of indefinite growth.

The sooner we stabilise our numbers, the sooner we stop running up the "down" escalator. Stop population increase—stop the escalator—and we have some chance of reaching the top; that is to say, a decent life for all.

To do that requires several things. First and foremost, it needs a much wider understanding of the problem, and that will not happen while the taboo on discussing it retains such a powerful grip on the minds of so many worthy and intelligent people. Then it needs a change in our culture so that while everyone retains the right to have as many children as they like, they understand that having large families means compounding the problems their children and everyone else's children will face in the future.

It needs action by governments. In my view, all countries should develop a population policy—as many as 70 countries already have them in one form or another—and give it priority. The essential common factor is to make family planning and other reproductive health services freely available to every one, and empower and encourage them to use it—though without any kind of coercion.

According to the Global Footprint Network, there are already more than a hundred countries whose combination of numbers and affluence have already pushed them past the sustainable level. They include almost all developed countries. The UK is one of the worst. There the aim should be to reduce over time both the consumption of natural resources per person and the number of people—while, needless to say, using the best technology to help maintain living standards. It is tragic that the only current population policies in developed countries are, perversely, attempting to increase their birth rates in order to look after the growing number of old people. The notion of ever more old people needing ever more young people, who will in turn grow old and need even more young people, and so on ad infinitum, is an obvious ecological Ponzi scheme.

I am not an economist, nor a sociologist, nor a politician, and it is from their disciplines that answers must come. But I am a naturalist. Being one means that I know something of the factors that keep populations of different species of animals within bounds and what happens when they aren't.

I am aware that every pair of blue tits nesting in my garden is able to lay over 20 eggs a year but, as a result of predation or lack of food, only one or two will, at best, survive. I have watched lions ravage the hundreds of wildebeest fawns that are born each year on the plains of Africa. I have seen how increasing numbers of elephants can devastate their environment until, one year when the rains fail on the already over-grazed land, they die in hundreds.

But we are human beings. Because of our intelligence, and our ever-increasing skills and sophisticated technologies, we can avoid such brutalities. We have medicines that prevent our children from dying of disease. We have developed ways of growing increasing amounts of food. But we have removed the limiters that keep animal populations in check. So now our destiny is in our hands.

There is one glimmer of hope. Wherever women have the vote, wherever they are literate and have the medical facilities to control the number of children they bear, the birth rate falls. All those civilised conditions exist in the southern Indian state of Kerala. In India as a whole, the total fertility rate is 2.8 births per woman. In Kerala, it is 1.7 births per woman. In Thailand last year, it was 1.8 per woman, similar to that in Kerala. But compare that with the mainly Catholic Philippines, where it is 3.3.

Here and there, at last, there are signs of a recognition of the problem. Save the Children mentioned it in its last report. The Royal Society has assembled a working party of scientists across a wide range of disciplines who are examining the problem.

But what can each of us do? Well, there is just one thing that I would ask. Break the taboo, in private and in public—as best you can, as you judge right. Until it is broken there is no hope of the action we need. Wherever and whenever we speak of the environment, we should add a few words to ensure that the population element is not ignored. If you are a member of a relevant NGO, invite them to acknowledge it.

If you belong to a church—and especially if you are a Catholic, because its doctrine on contraception is a major factor in this problem—suggest they consider the ethical issues involved. I see the Anglican bishops in Australia have dared to do so. If you have contacts in government, ask why the growth of our population, which affects every department, is as yet no one's responsibility. Big empty Australia has appointed a sustainable population minister, so why can't small crowded Britain?

The Hawaiian goose, the oryx, and the imperial eagle that sounded the environmental alarm 50 years ago were, you might say, the equivalent of canaries in coal mines—warnings of impending and even wider catastrophe.

Make a list of all the other environmental problems that now afflict us and our poor battered planet—the increase of greenhouse gases and consequential global warming, the acidification of the oceans and the collapse of fish stocks, the loss of rainforest, the spread of deserts, the shortage of arable land, the increase in violent weather, the growth of mega-cities, famine, migration patterns. The list goes on and on. But they all share one underlying cause. Every one of these global problems, social as well as environmental, becomes more difficult—and ultimately impossible—to solve with ever more people.

Sir David Attenborough is a British naturalist and broadcaster who has produced numerous popular wildlife documentaries.

Tom Bethell

NO

Population, Economy, and God

World population, once "exploding," is still increasing, and "momentum" ensures that it will do so for decades to come. But fertility rates have tumbled. In Europe every country has fallen below replacement level. Some governments, especially France's, are beginning to use financial incentives to restore fertility rates but the effort, if generous enough to work—by paying women to have a third child—could bankrupt the welfare state.

In rich countries, a total fertility rate of 2.1 babies per woman is needed if population is to remain stable. But in the European Union as a whole the rate is down to 1.5. Germany is at 1.4, and Italy, Spain, and Greece are at 1.3. The fertility rate in France is now 2.0, or close to replacement. But the uneasy question is whether this is due to subsidies or to the growing Muslim population.

All over the world, with a few anomalies, there is a strong inverse correlation between GDP per capita and babies per family. It's a paradox, because wealthier people can obviously afford lots of children. But very predictably they have fewer. Hong Kong (1.02), Singapore, and Taiwan are three of the richest countries in the world, and three of the four lowest in total fertility. The countries with the highest fertility rates are Mali (7.4), Niger, and Uganda. Guess how low they are on the wealth chart.

Here's a news item. Carl Djerassi, one of the inventors of the birth control pill, recently deplored the sharp decline of total fertility in Austria (1.4), the country of his birth. A Catholic news story seized on that and reported that one of the pill's inventors had said the pill had caused a "demographic catastrophe." Austria's leading Catholic, Cardinal Schönborn, said the Vatican had predicted 40 years ago that the pill would promote a dramatic fall in birth rates.

Djerassi, 85, an emeritus professor of chemistry at Stanford, did warn of a catastrophe and he said that Austria should admit more immigrants. But he denied that people have smaller families "because of the availability of birth control." They do so "for personal, economic, cultural, and other reasons," of which "changes in the status of women" was the most important. Japan has an even worse demographic problem, he said, "yet the pill was only legalized there in 1999 and is still not used widely." (Japan's fertility rate is 1.22.) (In fact, if the pill and abortion really were illegal more children surely would be born, if only because unintentional pregnancies would come to term.)

Austrian families who had decided against children wanted "to enjoy their schnitzels while leaving the rest of the world to get on with it," Djerassi also said. That may have rankled because the country had just put his face on a postage stamp.

So what is causing these dramatic declines? It's under way in many countries outside Europe too. In Mexico, fertility has moved down close to replacement level—having been as high as six babies per woman in the 1970s.

Obviously economic growth has been the dominant factor but there are other considerations.

Young couples hardly read Paul Ehrlich before deciding whether to have children, but scaremongering authors have played a key role in creating our anti-natalist mood. Books warning of a (then) newfangled emergency, the "population explosion," began appearing soon after World War II. Consider *Road to Survival* (1948), by William Vogt, or *People! Challenge to Survival*, by the same author. An anti-people fanatic before his time, Vogt was hypnotized by the Malthusian doctrine that population growth would overtake the food supply. That would lead to a war of all against all. Paul Ehrlich projected that the 1980s would see massive die-offs from starvation. (Obesity turned out to be the greater health threat.)

In that earlier period, the population controllers didn't feel they had to mince words. Vogt wrote in 1960 that "tens of thousands of children born every year in the United States should, solely for their own sakes, never have seen the light of day. . . . There are hundreds of thousands of others, technically legitimate since their parents have engaged in some sort of marriage ritual, but whose birth is as much of a crime against them as it is against the bastards."

At a time when the world population still had not reached 3 billion—today it is 6.7 billion—Vogt thought "drastic measures are inescapable." He warned of "mounting population pressures in the Soviet Union," where, by the century's end, "there may be 300 million Russians." It was time for them "to begin control of one of the most powerful causes of war—overpopulation."

Note: the population of Russia by 2000 was 145 million; today it is 141 million. (Fertility rate: 1.4.)

Population alarmists have long enjoyed the freedom to project their fears onto whatever cause is uppermost in the progressive mind. Then it was war. Today it is the environment, which, we are told, human beings are ruining. This will be shown to have been as false as the earlier warnings, but not before our environmental scares have done much harm to a fragile economy (at the rate things are going with Obama). All previous scares were based on faulty premises, and the latest one, based on "science," will be no different.

I believe that two interacting factors shape population growth or decline: economic prosperity and belief in God. As to the first, there is no doubt that rising material prosperity discourages additional children. Fewer infants die; large families are no longer needed to support older parents. The welfare state—which only rich countries can afford—has greatly compounded this effect. When people believe that the government will take care of them, pay their pensions and treat their maladies, children do seem less essential.

A rise in prosperity also encourages people to think that they can dispense with God. Religion diminishes when wealth increases—that's my theory. But with a twist that I shall come to. Wealth generates independence, including independence from God, or (if you will) Providence. God is gradually forgotten, then assumed not to exist. This will tend to drive childbearing down even further. Hedonism will become predominant. Remember, Jesus warned that it's the rich, not the poor, who are at spiritual hazard.

The legalization of abortion reflected the decline of religious faith in America, but it must also have led others to conclude that God was no longer to be feared. That's why I don't quite believe Djerassi when he tries to disassociate the pill from fertility. The ready availability of the pill told society at large that sex without consequences was perfectly acceptable. Then, by degrees, that self-indulgent view became an anti-natalist worldview.

It became so ingrained that many people now think it obvious. Sex became a "free" pastime as long as it was restricted to consenting adults. Furthermore, anyone who questioned that premise risked denunciation as a bigot.

The U.S. has been seen as the great stumbling block to any theory linking prosperity, lack of faith, and low fertility. Prosperity here has been high, and overall fertility is at replacement. But I am wary of this version of American exceptionalism. How much lower would U.S. fertility fall without the influx of Latino immigrants and their many offspring? Nicholas Eberstadt, a demographer at AEI, tells me that Mexican immigrants now actually have a higher fertility rate in the U.S. than they do in Mexico. (Maybe because they come to American hospitals for free medical care?)

I wonder also if religious vitality here is what it's cracked up to be. Surely it has weakened considerably. A recent survey by Trinity College in Hartford, funded by the Lilly Endowment, showed that the percentage of Americans identifying themselves as Christian dropped to 76 percent from 86 percent in 1990; those with "no" religion, 8.2 percent of the population in 1990, are now 15 percent.

As a social force, the U.S. Catholic bishops have withered away to a shocking extent. Hollywood once respected and feared their opinion. Today, the most highly placed of these bishops are unwilling to publicly rebuke pro-abortion politicians who call themselves Catholic, even when they give scandal by receiving Communion in public. How the mitered have fallen. They daren't challenge the rich and powerful.

But there is another factor. Calling yourself a Christian when the pollster phones imposes no cost and self-reported piety may well be inflated. We have to distinguish between mere self-labelers and actual churchgoers. And beyond that there are groups with intense religious belief who retain the morale to ignore the surrounding materialism and keep on having children.

The ultra-Orthodox in Israel are the best example. Other Jewish congregations may go to synagogue, but they have children at perhaps one-third the ultra-Orthodox rate. At about seven or eight children per family, theirs is one of the highest fertility rates in the world. And they don't permit birth control—Carl Djerassi, please note. In the U.S. Orthodox Jews again far outbreed their more secular sisters.

The Mormons are also distinctive. Utah, about two-thirds Mormon, has the highest fertility rate (2.63 in 2006) among the 50 states; Vermont has the lowest (1.69). In the recent Trinity Survey, Northern New England is now "the least religious section of the country." Vermont is the least religious state; 34 percent of residents say they have "no religion." So minimal faith and low fertility are demonstrably linked. Mormon fertility is declining, to be sure, and I recognize that I am flirting with a circular argument: deciding which groups are the most fervent by looking at their birth rates.

Then there's the Muslim concern. It's hard to avoid concluding that the lost Christian zeal has been appropriated by Islam. In the U.S., Muslims have doubled since 1990 (from a low base, to 0.6% of the population). The rise of Islam suggests that the meager European fertility rates would be even lower if Muslims had not contributed disproportionately to European childbearing.

It's hard to pin down the numbers, though. Fertility in France has risen, but Nick Eberstadt tells me that the French government won't reveal how many of these babies are born to Muslim parents. "They treat it as a state secret," he said. In other countries such as Switzerland, where lots of guest workers are employed, the fertility rate would be much lower than it already is (1.44) were it not for the numerous offspring of those guest workers.

When a population is not replacing itself, the welfare state creates its own hazard. Lots of new workers are needed to support the retirees. Germany's low fertility will require an annual immigration of 200,000 just to maintain the current population. Where will they come from? Many arrive from Turkey, where the fertility rate has also declined (to about 2.0). But not as far as it has declined among native Germans. So the concern is that in the welfare states of Europe, believing Muslims are slowly replacing the low-morale, low-fertility, materialistic non-believers who once formed a Christian majority.

I could summarize the argument with this overstatement: The intelligentsia stopped believing in God in the 19th century. In the 20th it tried to build a new society, man without God. It failed. Then came a new twist. Man stopped believing in himself. He saw himself as a mere polluter—a blot on the landscape. Theologians tell us that creatures cannot exist without the support of God. A corollary may be that societies cannot long endure without being sustained by a *belief* in God.

Tom Bethell is a senior editor of *The American Spectator.*

EXPLORING THE ISSUE

Do We Have a Population Problem?

Critical Thinking and Reflection

1. Is it possible to have too many people on Earth?
2. What is wrong with the statement that there is no population problem because all of Earth's human population could fit inside the state of Texas?
3. What does population have to do with sustainability?
4. What is more important for long-term survival of the human species—population control or belief in God?

Is There Common Ground?

The essayists for this issue agree that human population continues to grow and that long-term human survival (or sustainability) matters. They disagree on the best way to achieve long-term human survival.

1. Does quality of life seem likely to suffer more with a declining population or a growing population?
2. What are the key features of "quality of life"? (One good place to start your research is www.foe.co.uk/community/tools/isew/)
3. How might we determine what the Earth's carrying capacity for human beings really is?
4. What is the influence (if any) of religious faith on carrying capacity?

Create Central

www.mhhe.com/createcentral

Additional Resources

Matthew Connolly, *Fatal Misconception: The Struggle to Control World Population* (Belknap Press, 2010).

Jonathan A. Foley, "Can We Feed the World & Sustain the Planet?" *Scientific American* (November 2011).

David Malakoff, "Are More People Necessarily a Problem?" *Science* (July 29, 2011).

Fred Pearce, *The Coming Population Crash: And Our Planet's Surprising Future* (Beacon, 2010).

Julia Whitty, "The Last Taboo," *Mother Jones* (May–June 2010).

Internet References . . .

Facing the Future: People and the Planet

Facing the Future strives to educate people about critical global issues, including population growth, poverty, overconsumption, and environmental destruction.

www.facingthefuture.org/

United States & World Population Clocks

www.census.gov/main/www/popclock.html

Population Reference Bureau

The Population Reference Bureau provides timely and objective information on United States and international population trends and their implications.

www.prb.org/

Selected, Edited, and with Issue Framing Material by:
Thomas A. Easton, *Thomas College*

ISSUE

Is There Sufficient Scientific Evidence to Conclude That Cell Phones Cause Cancer?

YES: Olga V. Naidenko, from testimony before Senate Committee on Appropriations, Subcommittee on Labor, Health and Human Services, and Education, and Related Agencies, hearing on "The Health Effects of Cell Phone Use" (September 14, 2009)

NO: Linda S. Erdreich, from testimony before Senate Committee on Appropriations, Subcommittee on Labor, Health and Human Services, and Education, and Related Agencies, hearing on "The Health Effects of Cell Phone Use" (September 14, 2009)

Learning Outcomes

After studying this issue, students will be able to explain:

- What the evidence says about the link between cell phone use and brain cancer.
- Why the scientific method does not require a mechanism that produces an effect to be confident the effect exists.
- What the greatest risks associated with cell phone use are.
- How one may reduce possible cell phone cancer risks without giving up the technology.

ISSUE SUMMARY

YES: Olga V. Naidenko argues that even though past research into the link between cell phones and cancer has produced ambiguous results, more recent research on people who have used cell phones for many years has produced more worrisome results. More research is needed, but concern is already amply justified, especially in connection with children's exposure to cell phone emissions of radio waves.

NO: Linda S. Erdreich argues that independent scientific organizations have reviewed the research to date on the supposed link between cell phones and cancer and concluded that current evidence does not demonstrate that wireless phones cause cancer or have other adverse health effects.

It seems inevitable that new technologies will alarm people. For example, in the late 1800s, when electricity was new, people feared the new wires that were strung overhead. See Joseph P. Sullivan, "Fearing Electricity: Overhead Wire Panic in New York City," *IEEE Technology and Society Magazine* (Fall 1995). More recently, electromagnetic fields (EMFs) have drawn attention. Now cell phones and other forms of wireless communications technology, including wireless networks (Wi-Fi), are the focus of controversy.

EMFs are emitted by any device that uses electricity. They weaken rapidly as one gets farther from the source, but they can be remarkably strong close to the source. Users of electric blankets (before the blankets were redesigned to minimize EMFs) and personal computers are thus subject to high exposures. Since EMF strength also depends on how much electricity is flowing through the source, people who live near power lines, especially high-tension, long-distance transmission lines, are also open to high EMF exposure.

Are EMFs dangerous? There have been numerous reports suggesting a link between EMF exposure and cancer, but inconsistency has been the curse of research in this area. In 1992 the Committee on Interagency Radiation Research and Policy Coordination, an arm of the White House's Office of Science and Technology Policy, released *Health Effects of Low Frequency Electric and Magnetic Fields,* a report that concluded, "There is no convincing [published] evidence . . . to support the contention that exposures to extremely low frequency electric and magnetic fields generated by sources such as household appliances, video terminals, and local powerlines are demonstrable health hazards." Jon Palfreman, in "Apocalypse Not," *Technology Review* (April 1996), summarized the controversy and the evidence against any connection between cancer and EMFs. And in "Residential Exposure to Magnetic Fields and Acute Lymphoblastic Leukemia in Children," *The New England Journal of Medicine* (July 3, 1997), Martha S. Linet, et al. report that they failed to find any support for such a connection.

Since cell phones are electrical devices, they emit EMFs. But they—or their antennae—also emit electromagnetic radiation in the form of radio signals. And after a few cell phone users developed brain cancer and sued the phone makers, people began to worry. See Gordon Bass, "Is Your Cell Phone Killing You?" *PC Computing* (December 1999). George Carlo and Martin Schram, *Cell Phones: Invisible Hazards in the Wireless Age: An Insider's Alarming Discoveries about Cancer and Genetic Damage* (Basic Books, 2002), contend that there is a genuine risk that cell phone EMFs may cause cancer and other health problems. Tamar Nordenberg, "Cell Phones and Brain Cancer: No Clear Connection," *FDA Consumer* (November–December 2000), reported no real signs that cell phones caused cancer but noted that the evidence was sufficient to justify continuing research.

Do cell phones pose a genuine hazard? L. Hardell, et al. reported, in "Cellular and Cordless Telephones and the Risk for Brain Tumours," *European Journal of Cancer Prevention* (August 2002), that long-term users of older, analog phones were more likely to suffer brain tumors. U.S. District Judge Catherine Blake, presiding over the most famous phone cancer lawsuit, was not swayed. She declared that the claimant had provided "no sufficiently reliable and relevant scientific evidence" and said she intended to dismiss the case (Mark Parascandola, "Judge Rejects Cancer Data in Maryland Cell Phone Suit," *Science*, October 11, 2002). Robert Clark, "Clean Bill of Health for Cell Phones," *America's Network* (April 1, 2004), reports that "A survey by the Danish Institute of Cancer Epidemiology . . . says there is no short-term danger of developing brain tumors." Studies mentioned by Olga Naidenko in her essay as supporting worries about the link between cell phones and cancer have not been supported by other studies. There are even apparent reasons to doubt reports of DNA damage from cell phone radiation; see Gretchen Vogel, "Fraud Charges Cast Doubt on Claims of DNA Damage from Cell Phone Fields," *Science* (August 29, 2008). In addition, warns Michael Repacholi, "The Reality of Mobile Phones and Cancer," *New Scientist* (December 12, 2009), there are serious weaknesses in many studies of the association between cell phones and cancer. E. Cardis, et al. (The Interphone Study Group), "Brain Tumour Risk in Relation to Mobile Telephone Use: Results of the Interphone International Case-Control Study," *International Journal of Epidemiology* (vol. 39, no. 3, 2010), conclude, "Overall, no increase in risk of glioma or meningioma was observed with use of mobile phones. There were suggestions of an increased risk of glioma at the highest exposure levels, but biases and error prevent a causal interpretation. The possible effects of long-term heavy use of mobile phones require further investigation." Janet Raloff, "Cell Phone-Cancer Study an Enigma," *Science News* (June 19, 2010), notes that the same study actually suggests that moderate cell phone users experience *less* risk of brain cancer than users of landlines.

Skeptics insist that the threat is real. However, if it is real, it is not yet clear beyond a doubt. Unfortunately, society cannot always wait for certainty. In connection with EMFs, Gordon L. Hester, in "Electric and Magnetic Fields: Managing an Uncertain Risk," *Environment* (January/February 1992), asserts that just the possibility of a health hazard is sufficient to justify more research into the problem. The guiding principle, says Hester, is "'prudent avoidance,' which was originally intended to mean that people should avoid fields 'when this can be done with modest amounts of money and trouble.'" The same guideline surely applies to cell phone radiation. Sari N. Harar, "Do Cell Phones Cause Cancer?" *Prevention* (August 2006), notes that the consensus answer is that the risks are low and adds that risk can easily be reduced even further by using hands-free headsets and keeping calls short. In July 2008, Ronald B. Herberman, director of the University of Pittsburgh Cancer Institute, warned staff and faculty to limit cell phone use because of the possible health risks, basing his warning on early unpublished data.

Is it possible to prove that cell phones do *not* cause cancer? Unfortunately, no, because small, sporadic effects might not be detected even in massive studies. Thus, for some people, the jury will forever be out. Meanwhile, the jury is getting new charges to consider: George Carlo is now contending that wireless computer networks (Wi-Fi) also involve radiation that can cause tumors (see "Wi-Fi Fear," *The Ecologist*, April 2007). As with cell phones, there is a lack of evidence to support the charges. What should society do in the face of weak, uncertain, and even contradictory data? Can we afford to conclude that there is no hazard? Or must we ban or redesign a useful technology with no justification other than our fear that there might be a real hazard? Many scientists and politicians argue that even if there is no genuine medical risk, there is a genuine impact in terms of public anxiety. See Gary Stix, "Closing the Book," *Scientific American* (March 1998). It is therefore appropriate, they say, to fund further research and to take whatever relatively inexpensive steps to minimize exposure are possible. Failure to do so increases public anxiety and distrust of government and science. Some of those "relatively inexpensive steps are pretty simple"; as Olga Naidenko notes, they include using headsets and even texting instead of talking. But as Tamar Nordenberg, "Cell Phones and Brain Cancer: No Clear Connection," *FDA Consumer* (November–December 2000), says, quoting Professor John Moulder, using a cell phone while driving is much more hazardous even than using a conventional high-radiation cell phone. By 2003, cell phones were being broadly indicted as hazards on the highway. The basic problem is that using a cell phone increases the mental workload on the driver, according to Roland Matthews, Stephen Legg, and Samuel Charlton, "The Effect of Cell Phone Type on Drivers' Subjective Workload During Concurrent Driving and Conversing," *Accident Analysis & Prevention* (July, 2003); they too recommend using a hands-free phone. As a result of such studies, many states have already banned the use of handheld phones while driving, with initial good effect; see Anne T. McCartt, Elisa R. Braver, and Lori L. Geary, "Drivers' Use of Handheld Cell Phones Before and After New York State's Cell Phone Law," *Preventive Medicine* (May 2003). Unfortunately, the initial good results have not lasted. See "Motorists' Cell Phone Use Rising: NHTSA," *Safety & Health* (May 2005).

For a time, it seemed that the lack of evidence for a connection between cell phones and cancer had quieted the debate. However, in September 2009, Environmental Working Group (EWG), a nonprofit advocacy group, released a report claiming that new evidence justified concern. In the YES selection, EWG's Olga V. Naidenko argues that even though past research into the link between cell phones and cancer has produced ambiguous results, more recent research on people who have used cell phones for many years has produced more worrisome results. More research is needed, but concern is already amply justified, especially in connection with children's exposure to cell phone emissions of radio waves. In the NO selection, Linda S. Erdreich argues that independent scientific organizations have reviewed the research to date on the supposed link between cell phones and cancer and concluded that current evidence does not demonstrate that wireless phones cause cancer or have other adverse health effects.

YES

Olga V. Naidenko

The Health Effects of Cell Phone Use

Mr. Chairman and distinguished Members of the Subcommittee . . . I thank [you] for holding this important hearing and for the opportunity to testify.

Last week, EWG released the results of a 10-month investigation of more than 200 peer-reviewed studies, government advisories, and industry documents on the safety of cell phone radiation. We found that the studies amassed during the first two decades of cell phone use produced conflicting results and few definitive conclusions on cell phone safety. But the latest research, in which scientists are for the first time able to study people who have used cell phones for many years, suggests the potential for serious safety issues.

Studies published over the past several years find significantly higher risks for brain and salivary gland tumors among people using cell phones for 10 years or longer. The state of the science is provocative and troubling, and more research is essential. We at Environmental Working Group are still using our cell phones, but we also believe that until scientists know much more about cell phone radiation, it's smart for consumers to buy phones with the lowest emissions.

As of December 2008, U.S. wireless subscribers numbered 270.3 million—87 percent of Americans—a 30 percent jump in three years. Some 60 percent of the global population—four billion people—subscribe to wireless service. As the market for new devices has grown, so has the urgency that cell phone safety be well understood, and that cell phone radiation standards be sufficient to protect public health.

In this testimony we highlight five key areas of concern:

- Consumers have a right to know the level of radiation their phones emit;
- Latest science points to potential risks to children's health;
- Federal standards for cell phone radiation need to be modernized;
- What consumers can do to reduce exposures to cell phone radiation;
- EWG's recommendations to the government, industry, and the public.

1. Consumers Have a Right to Know the Level of Radiation Their Phones Emit

EWG advocates that cell phone companies label their products' radiation output so that consumers can make informed choices at the point of sale, and that the government require this disclosure. Currently, most people are given no information at all about radiation emissions when they purchase a phone.

To fill this information void, EWG's research team created a user-friendly, interactive online guide to cell phone emissions, covering over 1,200 phones currently on the market. Consumers can use this free online database to make informed decisions about which cell phones to buy. The EWG guide uses easy-to-read graphics to illustrate each phone's radiofrequency emissions, enabling consumers to make quick comparisons of radiation output of various wireless devices.

In the 64 hours following the publication of our science review and cell phone radiation database, 442,000 people accessed these materials on our website, collectively viewing 1.4 million online pages. During those same 3 days our findings were reported in 100 news articles and in national and local broadcast news, including *The New York Times*, *NBC Nightly News*, *WebMD*, and *USA Today*. This powerful response from the public and from news media outlets reflects consumers' keen interest in the issue of cell phone safety. Clearly, people are eager to know if cell phones are safe and how they can protect themselves and their families from potential adverse effects of excessive exposure to cell phone radiation.

2. The Latest Science Point to Potential Risks to Children's Health

Prior to 2003, studies of cancer risk and cell phone use produced conflicting results. The Food and Drug Administration (FDA) told consumers that scientists had found no harmful health effects from exposure to cell phone emissions. But FDA's assurances were based on studies of people who had used cell phones for just 3 years, on average, not long enough to develop cancer. At that time, studies had not addressed the risks of longer-term cell phone radiation exposures. The research gap is closing. Recent studies find significantly higher risks for brain and salivary gland tumors among people using cell phones for 10 years or longer. The state of the science is provocative and troubling, especially for the health of children. Among recent findings are the following:

- A joint study by researchers in Denmark, Finland, Norway, Sweden and the United Kingdom found that people who had used cell phones for more than 10 years had a significantly increased risk

Naidenko, Olga V. From statement before U.S. Senate, September 14, 2009.

of developing glioma, a usually malignant brain tumor, on the side of the head they had favored for cell phone conversations.
- French and German scientists reported an increased risk of glioma for long-term cell phone users. Analysis of all published cell phone-brain tumor studies found that people who had used a cell phone for 10 or more years, the overall risk for developing a glioma on the cell phone side of the head increased by 90 percent.
- Cell phone use for 10 years and longer has been also associated with significantly increased risk of acoustic neuroma, a type of benign brain tumor, on the primary side of cell phone use. An extensive review of published studies of acoustic neuroma found that long-term cell phone users had a 60 percent greater risk of being diagnosed with the disease.
- A study from Israel reported an association between frequent and prolonged mobile phone use and parotid (salivary) gland tumors. Scientists analyzing data from Sweden and Denmark combined found that people who had used cell phones for at least 10 years ran an increased risk of benign parotid gland tumors.

The National Research Council (NRC) has observed that "with the rapid advances in technologies and communications utilizing [radiation in the range of cell phone frequencies], children are increasingly exposed . . . at earlier ages (starting at age 6 or before)." Research by France Telecom scientists showed that under standard conditions of use, twice as much cell phone radiation would penetrate a child's thinner, softer skull than an adult's. Children will be exposed to cell phone radiation for more years and therefore in greater total amounts than the current generation of adults.

Children are likely to be more susceptible than adults to effects from cell phone radiation, since the brain of a child is still developing and its nervous tissues absorb a greater portion of incoming radiation compared to that of an adult. Much more research is essential. However, in response to the information already available over the potential health risks of cell phone emissions, government agencies in Germany, Switzerland, Israel, United Kingdom, France, and Finland and the European Parliament have recommended actions to help consumers reduce exposures to cell phone radiation, especially for young children. Among warnings issued by government agencies are the following:

- **United Kingdom Department of Health.** "UK Chief Medical Officers strongly advise that where children and young people do use mobile phones, they should be encouraged to: use mobile phones for essential purposes only; keep all calls short—talking for long periods prolongs exposure and should be discouraged."
- **Canada—City of Toronto Department of Public Health.** "Today's children have started to use cell phones at a younger age, therefore their lifetime exposure to cell phone RFs will likely be greater. As a result, the chances that a child could develop harmful health effects from using a cell phone for a long time may be greater . . . Toronto Public Health is recommending that children, especially pre-adolescent children, use landlines whenever possible, keeping the use of cell phones for essential purposes only, limiting the length of cell phone calls and using headsets or hands-free options, whenever possible."
- **Finland—Finnish Radiation and Nuclear Safety Authority.** "It would be good to restrict children's use of mobile phones." "Precaution is recommended for children as all of the effects are not known. . . . Parents are recommended to guide their children to use a handsfree that minimises the exposure of head significantly. When using a handsfree it is recommended to keep the mobile phone at least a few centimetres away from the body."

In contrast, the two U.S. federal agencies that regulate cell phones, the FDA and the Federal Communications Commission (FCC), have all but ignored evidence that long-term cell phone use may be risky.

3. Federal Standards for Cell Phone Radiation Need to Be Modernized

The FCC set cell phone radiation standards 17 years ago, when few people used cell phones. These standards fail to provide an adequate margin of safety for cell phone radiation exposure and do not account for risks to children. The FCC standards closely follow the 1992 recommendations of the Institute of Electrical and Electronics Engineers (IEEE). The FCC adopted IEEE's proposal to allow 20 times more radiation to the head than the average amount allowed for the whole body, even though the brain may well be one of the most sensitive parts of human body with respect to radiofrequency radiation and should have more protection. EWG's conclusion: current U.S. cell phone radiation standards are outdated and may not be sufficiently protective. EWG urges the FDA and the FCC to upgrade its standards to take account of the newest scientific evidence and also increasing cell phone use by children.

4. What Consumers Can Do to Reduce Exposures to Cell Phone Radiation

EWG recommends a number of simple actions consumers can take to reduce exposures to cell phone radiation. We recommend these simple precautionary measures until the science on cell phone risks is settled, and until the federal government modernizes current radiation limits to reflect the latest research.

- **Use a low-radiation phone.** Consumers can find radiation emissions for their current phone on EWG's database (www.ewg.org/cellphone-radiation), in their user's manual, or by contacting the manufacturer. EWG's database lists alternate, low-radiation phones, allowing people to consider purchasing a phone that emits the lowest radiation possible and still meets their needs.
- **Use a headset or speakers.** Headsets emit much less radiation than phones. Experts are split on whether wireless or wired is safer. Some wireless headsets emit continuous, low-level radiation, so EWG advises removing the headset from the ear between calls. Using a phone in speaker mode also reduces radiation to the head.
- **Listen more, talk less.** Cell phones emit radiation to transmit voice or text messages, but not to receive messages. Listening more and talking less reduces exposures.
- **Hold phone away from the body.** Holding the phone away from the torso when talking (while using the headset or speaker) reduces radiation exposures. EWG advises against holding the phone against the ear, in a pocket, or on the belt where soft body tissues absorb radiation.
- **Choose texting over talking.** Phones use less power (less radiation) to send text than voice. And unlike speaking with the phone at the ear, texting keeps radiation away from the head.
- **Stay off the phone if the signal is poor.** Fewer signal bars on the phone means that it emits more radiation to get the signal to the tower. EWG recommends that people make and take calls when the phone has a strong signal.
- **Limit children's phone use.** Young children's brains absorb twice the cell phone radiation as an adult's. EWG joins health agencies in at least six countries in recommending limits for children's phone use, such as for emergency situations only.
- **Skip the "radiation shield."** Radiation shields such as antenna caps or keypad covers reduce the connection quality and force the phone to transmit at a higher power with higher radiation.

5. Recommendations

The government should invest in additional research on the health effects of cell phone radiation, with special emphasis on children and teens.

The government should require industry to make cell phone radiation level information available at the point of sale, so consumers can make informed decisions about the phones they buy.

Given the troubling questions raised by the research thus far, the cell phone industry should not wait for government action, but instead, offer consumers phones that operate with the least possible radiation, and should offer radiation information at the point of sale.

In the meanwhile, cell phone users can protect themselves and their families by buying low-radiation phones. Cell phone users can also reduce radiation exposures by using their phone in speaker mode or with a headset.

In conclusion, EWG strongly believes that the government should support additional research into this important health question, and that the public has the right to know what levels of radiation they may be exposed to, what may be the potential risks, and what precautionary measures they can take to protect themselves and their families from any adverse health effects of cell phone radiation. . . .

Olga V. Naidenko is a senior scientist at Environmental Working Group (EWG), a nonprofit research and advocacy organization based in Washington, DC; Ames, Iowa; and Oakland, California.

Linda S. Erdreich

NO

The Health Effects of Cell Phone Use

. . . Mobile phones operate using radio waves. Radio waves, or radiofrequency (RF) energy, is a range of the electromagnetic spectrum that includes AM and FM broadcast radio, television, and many other devices and technologies including cordless phones, baby monitors, radar, and microwave ovens. Visible light is also part of the electromagnetic spectrum, but is at a higher frequency and shorter wavelength than RF. RF energy is not "radiation" in the same sense as used for high frequency X rays, because the energy of RF is so much lower and is unable to change the DNA of cells. Although RF energy is sometimes referred to as "EMF" the contemporary usage of EMF refers primarily to the electric and magnetic fields associated with electricity from power lines and all electric devices. Electricity operates in the extremely low frequency (ELF) range, 60 cycles per second (60 Hz), in the United States. To avoid confusion, I will use RF in my discussion of mobile phones.

Standard Scientific Methods Are Used to Access Possible Risks to Human Health

The standard scientific approach used to determine whether an exposure source, such as to RF energy, poses a health risk, is to look at all of the available research, including both studies that have reported effects, and those that did not. The goal is an objective, comprehensive review, in which the strengths and weaknesses of each study are evaluated, and more weight is given to studies of better quality. This approach is designed to ensure that reviewers do not single out studies, consciously or inadvertently, to support a preconceived opinion. Then, all of the studies are evaluated together to arrive at a conclusion. This is the method that I have used for evaluating the RF research and for other assessments throughout my career.

The relevant research to be considered includes a broad spectrum of scientific research that uses different approaches to study potential effects of RF energy on humans. These different approaches have different strengths and limitations and provide complementary information: laboratory studies in cells and in animals, experimental studies of human volunteers, and epidemiologic studies of human populations. For this reason, scientific organizations convene panels of independent experts from the various areas of expertise (e.g., health physics, engineering, toxicology, clinical medicine, and epidemiology) relevant to the topic. Many scientific organizations consider pertinent studies to be those reports of scientific research or reviews that have been published or accepted for publication in the peer-reviewed scientific literature.

Independent Scientific Organizations Worldwide Have Reviewed the Research

Independent scientific organizations worldwide have reviewed the research and proposed exposure limits. Many studies have been conducted over the past 50 years to examine whether exposure to RF energy has adverse effects on health, and to determine allowable levels of exposure. Several scientific organizations have reviewed the laboratory and epidemiologic research to assess the potential for health effects from RF exposure, and to set exposure limits to ensure occupational and public safety. These expert groups have included scientists with diverse skills to reflect the different research expertise required to answer questions about RF energy and health. Numerous government agencies and professional organizations have reviewed the science related to potential health effects from using wireless phones. While the specific conclusions vary, all of the reports that assess the evidence using multidisciplinary panels and a comprehensive approach reach similar conclusions; the current scientific evidence does not demonstrate that wireless phones cause cancer or other adverse health effects.

The Federal Communications Commission (FCC) and the Food and Drug Administration (FDA), the agencies with regulatory authority over radiofrequency emissions in the U.S., have both concluded that the current scientific evidence does not indicate that there are health hazards from using a wireless phone. The FCC's website states that "[t]here is no scientific evidence that proves that wireless phone usage can lead to cancer or a variety of other problems, including headaches, dizziness or memory loss."(www.fcc.gov/cgb/cellular.html#evidence) The FDA's website similarly states that "[t]he weight of scientific evidence has not linked cell phones with any health problems."(http://www.fda.gov/Radiation-EmittingProducts/RadiationEmittingProductsandProcedures/HomeBusinessandEntertainment/CellPhones/ucm116282.htm)

Erdreich, Linda S. From statement before U.S. Senate, September 14, 2009.

In September 2008, the National Cancer Institute (NCI), the U.S. government's principal agency for cancer research, published a Fact Sheet on Cellular Telephone Use and Cancer Risk that concluded that there is no consistent link between cellular telephone use and cancer.[1] The NCI also stated that "incidence data from the Surveillance, Epidemiology, and End Results (SEER) program of the National Cancer Institute have shown no increase between 1987 and 2005 in the age-adjusted incidence of brain or other nervous system cancers despite the dramatic increase in use of cellular telephones."[2] http://www.cancer.gov/cancertopics/factsheet/Risk/cellphones.

The conclusions of these U.S. agencies are similar to the conclusions reached in reports prepared by various commissions and agencies around the world, including for example:

- **The Australian Radiation Protection and Nuclear Safety Agency**

"There is essentially no evidence that microwave exposure from mobile telephones causes cancer, and no clear evidence that such exposure accelerates the growth of an already-existing cancer." http://www.arpansa.gov.au/mobilephones/index.cfm

- **Health Canada**

"There is no convincing scientific evidence that RF exposures have any link to cancer initiation or promotion. The body of peer-reviewed literature in this area overwhelmingly demonstrates a lack of linkage, and where the few reports of linkage effects were found, some may be attributed to factors other than RF energy."

- **The Health Council of the Netherlands**

"The Committee maintained its conclusion that no causal link has thus far been demonstrated between health problems and exposure to electromagnetic fields generated by mobile phones or base stations for mobile telephony." http://www.gezondheidsraad.nl/sites/default/files/200902.pdf.

- **The Scientific Committee on Emerging and Newly Identified Health Risks of the European Commission**

"Overall, research indicates that mobile phone use does not increase the risk of cancer, especially when used for less than ten years." http://ec.europa.eu/health/opinions2/en/electromagnetic-fields/index.htm#3

- **The World Health Organization**

"Considering the very low exposure levels and research results collected to date, there is no convincing scientific evidence that the weak RF signals from base stations and wireless networks cause adverse health effects." http://www.who.int/mediacentre/factsheets/fs304/en/index.html

The United Kingdom's Health Protection Agency and New Zealand Ministry of Health's National Radiation Laboratory also have reached similar conclusions after reviewing the available science.

In September 2009, the International Commission on Non-Ionizing Radiation Protection's (ICNRP) Standing Committee on Epidemiology published a scientific review of all of the available epidemiologic evidence on wireless phones and brain tumors. That review concludes:

> "In the last few years, the epidemiologic evidence on mobile phone use and risk of brain and other tumors of the head has grown considerably. In our opinion, overall the studies published to date do not demonstrate a raised risk within approximately 10 years of use for any tumor of the brain or any other head tumor."

Conclusion

Based on my review of the epidemiologic studies and consideration of experimental data in animals, I agree with the conclusions of the scientific organizations: The current scientific evidence does not demonstrate that wireless phones cause cancer or other adverse health effects.

Notes

1. *See* http://www.cancer.gov/cancertopics/factsheet/Risk/cellphones.
2. *Id.*

Linda S. Erdreich is a senior managing scientist in Exponent's Health Sciences Center for Epidemiology, Biostatistics, and Computational Biology, and have 30 years of experience in environmental epidemiology and health risk assessment.

EXPLORING THE ISSUE

Is There Sufficient Scientific Evidence to Conclude That Cell Phones Cause Cancer?

Critical Thinking and Reflection

1. How could one tell whether there is really a causative link between cell phones and brain cancer? How could one rule out coincidence?
2. Some people think there is also a problem with Wi-Fi radiation. Should we also worry about Bluetooth headsets?
3. How certain do we have to be before we can justify spending large sums of money on possible problems?
4. Should we accept as real a proposed association between an environmental agent and a disease if there is no biologically plausible mechanism for the effect?

Is There Common Ground?

The "common ground" with this issue lies in the repeated use of the phrase "no convincing evidence," with stress on the word "convincing." Many studies have found weak hints of an association between cell phone use and brain cancer, but when the results of the studies are analyzed statistically, those hints are not strong enough to rule out coincidence.

1. Go back to the introduction to this book and re-read the material on the use of controls in research. What is the purpose of using controls?
2. How does the use of controls help to rule out coincidence?
3. Can one ever totally rule out the role of coincidence? Look up "confidence intervals" in a statistics text.

Create Central

www.mhhe.com/createcentral

Additional Resources

George Carlo and Martin Schram, *Cell Phones: Invisible Hazards in the Wireless Age: An Insider's Alarming Discoveries about Cancer and Genetic Damage* (Basic Books, 2002).

Patrizia Frei, et al., "Use of Mobile Phones and Risk of Brain Tumours: Update of Danish Cohort Study," *British Medical Journal* (October 20, 2011).

Sari N. Harar, "Do Cell Phones Cause Cancer?" *Prevention* (August 2006).

Internet Reference . . .

Cell Phone Facts

The Food and Drug Administration (FDA) summarizes current knowledge of health risks from cell phone use at its Cell Phone Facts page.

www.fda.gov/radiation-emittingproducts/radiationemittingproductsandprocedures/homebusinessandentertainment/cellphones/default.htm

Selected, Edited, and with Issue Framing Material by:
Thomas A. Easton, *Thomas College*

ISSUE

Should Society Impose a Moratorium on the Use and Release of "Synthetic Biology" Organisms?

YES: Jim Thomas, Eric Hoffman, and Jaydee Hanson, from "Offering Testimony from Civil Society on the Environmental and Societal Implications of Synthetic Biology" (May 27, 2010)

NO: Gregory E. Kaebnick, from "Written Testimony of Gregory E. Kaebnick to the House Committee on Energy and Commerce" (May 27, 2010)

Learning Outcomes

After studying this issue, students will be able to:

- Explain what "dual-use" technologies are and why they warrant special regulation.
- Discuss the impact of the ability to make "synthetic cells" on traditional views of life.
- Discuss the difficulty of preventing all the potential risks of a new technology.
- Make a reasonable forecast of future developments of synthetic biology technology.

ISSUE SUMMARY

YES: Jim Thomas, Eric Hoffman, and Jaydee Hanson, representing the Civil Society on the Environmental and Societal Implications of Synthetic Biology, argue that the risks posed by synthetic biology to human health, the environment, and natural ecosystems are so great that Congress should declare an immediate moratorium on releases to the environment and commercial uses of synthetic organisms and require comprehensive environmental and social impact reviews of all federally funded synthetic biology research.

NO: Gregory E. Kaebnick of the Hastings Center argues that although synthetic biology is surrounded by genuine ethical and moral concerns—including risks to health and environment—which warrant discussion, the potential benefits are too great to call for a general moratorium.

In the past century, biologists have learned an enormous amount about how the cell—the basic functional unit of all living things—works. By the early 1970s, they were beginning to move genes from one organism to another and dream of designing plants and animals (including human beings) with novel combinations of features. By 2002, with Defense Department funding, Jeronimo Cello, Aniko Paul, and Eckard Wimmer were able to construct a live poliovirus from raw laboratory chemicals. This feat was a long way from constructing a bacterium or animal from raw chemicals, but it was enough to set alarm bells of many kinds ringing. Some people thought this work challenged the divine monopoly on creation. Others feared that if one could construct one virus from scratch, one could construct others, such as the smallpox virus, or even tailor entirely new viruses with which natural immune systems and medical facilities could not cope. Some even thought that the paper was irresponsible and should not have been published because it pointed the way toward new kinds of terrorism. See Michael J. Selgelid and Lorna Weir, "Reflections on the Synthetic Production of Poliovirus," *Bulletin of the Atomic Scientists* (May/June 2010).

In 2010, the next step was taken. Craig Venter's research group announced that they had successfully synthesized a bacterial chromosome (the set of genes that specifies the function and form of the bacterium) and implanted it in a bacterium of a different species whose chromosome had been removed. The result was the conversion of the recipient bacterium into the synthesized chromosome's species. See Daniel G. Gibson, et al., "Creation of a Bacterial Cell Controlled by a Chemically Synthesized Genome," *Science* (July 2, 2010). The report received a great deal of media attention, much of it saying that Venter's group had created a living cell, even though only the chromosome had been synthesized. The chromosome's biochemically complex container—a cell minus its chromosome—had *not* been synthesized.

The goal of this work is not the creation of life, but rather the ability to exert unprecedented control over what cells do. In testimony before the House Committee on Energy and Commerce Hearing on Developments in Synthetic Genomics and Implications for Health and Energy (May 27, 2010), Venter said "The ability to routinely write the 'software of life' will usher in a new era in science, and with it, new products and applications such as advanced biofuels, clean water technology, food products, and new vaccines and medicines. The field is already having an impact in some of these areas and will continue to do so as long as this powerful new area of science is used wisely." See also Pamela Weintraub, "J. Craig Venter on Biology's Next Leap: Digitally Designed Life-Forms that Could Produce Novel Drugs, Renewable Fuels, and Plentiful Food for Tomorrow's World," *Discover* (January/February 2010); and Michael A. Peters and Priya Venkatesan, "Bioeconomy and Third Industrial Revolution in the Age of Synthetic Life," *Contemporary Readings in Law and Social Justice* (vol. 2, no. 2, 2010). However, the ETC Group, which anticipated a synthetic organism in 2007, condemns the lack of rules governing synthetic biology, calls it "a quintessential Pandora's box moment," and calls for a global moratorium on further work; see "Synthia Is Alive . . . and Breeding: Panacea or Pandora's Box?" ETC Group News Release (May 20, 2010) (www.etcgroup.org/en/node/5142). A number of artists have also joined the debate; see Sara Reardon, "Visions of Synthetic Biology," *Science* (September 2, 2011). Some biologists have already established do-it-yourself "community labs," looking ahead to the day when synthetic biology is something anyone can do; see Sam Kean, "A Lab of Their Own," *Science* (September 2, 2011). And the FBI's Weapons of Mass Destruction Directorate's Biological Countermeasures Unit encourages "a kind of neighborhood watch" among the do-it-yourselfers; see Delthia Ricks, "Bio Hackers," *Discover* (October 2011).

Researchers had been working on synthetic biology for a number of years, and well before Craig Venter's group announced their accomplishment, prospects and consequences were already being discussed. Michael Specter, "A Life of Its Own," *New Yorker* (September 28, 2009), describes progress to date and notes "the ultimate goal is to create a synthetic organism made solely from chemical parts and blueprints of DNA." If this sounds rather like manipulating living things the way children manipulate Legos, Drew Endy of MIT and colleagues created in 2005 the BioBricks Foundation to make that metaphor explicit. See also Rob Carlson, *Biology Is Technology: The Promise, Peril, and Business of Engineering Life* (Harvard University Press, 2010). David Deamer, "First Life and Next Life," *Technology Review* (May/June 2009), notes that the next step is to create entire cells, not just a single bacterial chromosome. Charles Petit, "Life from Scratch," *Science News* (July 3, 2010), describes the even more ambitious work of Harvard's Jack Szostak, who is trying to understand how life began by constructing a pre-cell just sophisticated enough to take in components, grow, divide, and start evolving. Szostak expects to succeed within a few years. Such efforts, say Steven A. Benner, Zunyi Yang, and Fei Chen, "Synthetic Biology, Tinkering Biology, and Artificial Biology: What Are We Learning?" *Comptes Rendus Chimie* (April 2011), will drive a better understanding of biology in ways that mere analysis cannot. Some researchers are more focused on modifying existing cells with genetic engineering; see Alexandra Witze, "Factory of Life," *Science News* (January 12, 2013).

We are a long way from designing or modifying cells at will, but that is not to say that we will not get there; see Allen A. Cheng and Timothy K. Lu, "Synthetic Biology: An Emerging Engineering Discipline," *Annual Review of Biomedical Engineering* (August 2012). Immediately after the Venter group's announcement of their accomplishment, Vatican representatives declared that synthetic biology was "a potential time bomb, a dangerous double-edged sword for which it is impossible to imagine the consequences" and "Pretending to be God and parroting his power of creation is an enormous risk that can plunge men into barbarity"; see "Vatican Greets First Synthetic Cell with Caution," *America* (June 7–14, 2010). Chuck Colson, "Synthetic Life: The Danger of God-Like Pretensions," *Christian Post* (June 16, 2010), says "God-like control [of risks] isn't only hubris, it's pure fantasy. The only real way to avoid the unthinkable is not to try and play God in the first place. But that would require the kind of humility that Venter and company reject out-of-hand." Nancy Gibbs, "Creation Myths," *Time* (June 28, 2010), says "The path of progress cuts through the four-way intersection of the moral, medical, religious and political—and whichever way you turn, you are likely to run over someone's deeply held beliefs. Venter's bombshell revived the oldest of ethical debates, over whether scientists were playing God or proving he does not exist because someone reenacted Genesis in suburban Maryland." The "playing God" objection seems likely to grow louder as synthetic biology matures, but it is also likely to fade just as it has done after previous advances such as in vitro fertilization and surrogate mothering. Henk van den Belt, "Playing God in Frankenstein's Footsteps: Synthetic Biology and the Meaning of Life," *NanoEthics* (December 2009), notes that "While syntheses of artificial life forms cause some vague uneasiness that life may lose its special meaning, most concerns turn out to be narrowly anthropocentric. As long as synthetic biology creates only new microbial life and does not directly affect human life, it will in all likelihood be considered acceptable." On the other hand, we may owe our creations the same moral regard we owe to natural species; see Robin Attfield, "Biocentrism, Religion and Synthetic Biology," *Worldviews: Global Religions, Culture & Ecology* (vol. 17, no. 1, 2013).

What will be more significant will be discussions such as Gautam Mukunda, Kenneth A. Oye, and Scott C.

Mohr, "What Rough Beast? Synthetic Biology, Uncertainty, and the Future of Biosecurity," *Politics and the Life Sciences* (September 2009). Mukunda, et al., see synthetic biology as seeking "to create modular biological parts that can be assembled into useful devices, allowing the modification of biological systems with greater reliability, at lower cost, with greater speed, and by a larger pool of people than has been the case with traditional genetic engineering." It is thus a "dual-use" technology, meaning that it has both benign and malign applications. This has clear implications for national security, both offensive and defensive, but they find those implications least alarming in the short term. In the long term, the defensive implications are most important. Because the offensive implications are there, regulation and surveillance of research and development will be necessary in order to forestall terrorists and criminals. Jonathan B. Tucker, "Could Terrorists Exploit Synthetic Biology?" *New Atlantis: A Journal of Technology & Society* (Spring 2011), sees potential problems. Mildred K. Cho and David A. Relman, "Synthetic 'Life,' Ethics, National Security, and Public Discourse," *Science* (July 2, 2010), caution that some concerns about biosecurity and ethics are real but some are imagined; being realistic and avoiding exaggeration are essential if the science is not to become a victim of public mistrust. Meera Lee Sethi and Adam Briggle, "Making Stories Visible: The Task for Bioethics Commissions," *Issues in Science and Technology* (Winter 2011), caution that the stories we tell ourselves about technology (such as "synthetic biology is like computers") may hide issues that warrant deep and careful thought. Paul B. Thompson, "Synthetic Biology Needs a Synthetic Bioethics," *Ethics, Policy, & Environment* (2012), argues that proper consideration of the ethics of synthetic biology will require integrating biomedical and environmental ethics. Walter E. Block, on the other hand, objects that "Synthetic Biology Does Not Need a Synthetic Bioethics: Give Me That Old Time (Libertarian) Ethics," *Ethics, Policy & Environment* (2012). The Biotechnology Industry Organization's Brent Erickson, Rina Singh, and Paul Winters, "Synthetic Biology: Regulating Industry Uses of New Biotechnologies," *Science* (September 2, 2011), think it crucial that regulation not impede innovation and development of new products. See also Tania Bubela, Gregory Haden, and Edna Einsiedel, "Synthetic Biology Confronts Publics and Policy Makers: Challenges for Communication, Regulation, and Commercialization," *Trends in Biotechnology* (May 2012).

In the YES selection, Jim Thomas, Eric Hoffman, and Jaydee Hanson, representing the Civil Society on the Environmental and Societal Implications of Synthetic Biology, argue that the risks posed by synthetic biology to human health, the environment, and natural ecosystems are so great that Congress should declare an immediate moratorium on releases to the environment and commercial uses of synthetic organisms and require comprehensive environmental and social impact reviews of all federally funded synthetic biology research. In the NO selection, Gregory E. Kaebnick of the Hastings Center argues that although synthetic biology is surrounded by genuine ethical and moral concerns—including risks to health and environment—which warrant discussion, the potential benefits are too great to call for a general moratorium.

YES

Jim Thomas, Eric Hoffman, and Jaydee Hanson

Offering Testimony from Civil Society on the Environmental and Societal Implications of Synthetic Biology

. . . Last week, the J. Craig Venter Institute announced the creation of the first living organism with a synthetic genome claiming that this technology would be used in applications as diverse as next generation biofuels, vaccine production and the clean up of oil spills. We agree that this is a significant technical feat however; we believe it should be received as a wake-up call to governments around the world that this technology must now be accountably regulated. While attention this week has been on the activities of a team from Synthetic Genomics Inc, the broader field of synthetic biology has in fact quickly and quietly grown into a multi-billion dollar industry with over seventy DNA foundries and dozens of "pure play" synthetic biology companies entering the marketplace supported by large investments from Fortune 500 energy, forestry, chemical and agribusiness companies. That industry already has at least one product in the marketplace (Du Pont's 'Sorona' bioplastic), and another recently cleared for market entry in 2011 (Amyris Biotechnology's 'No Compromise' biofuel) as well as several dozen near to market applications. We believe the committee should consider the implications of this new industry as a whole in its deliberations not just the technical breakthrough reported last week. Without proper safeguards in place, we risk introducing synthetically constructed living organisms into the environment, intentionally or inadvertently through accident and worker error, that have the potential to destroy ecosystems and threaten human health. We will see the widespread commercial application of techniques with grave dual-use implications. We further risk licensing their use in industrial applications that will unsustainably increase the pressure of human activities on both land and marine ecologies through the increased take of biomass, food resources, water and fertilizer or displacement of wild lands to grow feedstocks for bio-based fuel and chemical production.

We call on Congress to:

1. Implement a moratorium on the release of synthetic organisms into the environment and also their use in commercial settings. This moratorium should remain in place until there is an adequate scientific basis on which to justify such activities, and until due consideration of the associated risks for the environment, biodiversity, and human health, and all associated socio-economic repercussions, are fully and transparently considered.
2. As an immediate step, all federally funded synthetic biology research should be subject to a comprehensive environmental and societal impact review carried out with input from civil society, also considering indirect impacts on biodiversity of moving synthetic organisms into commercial use for fuel, chemicals and medicines. This should include the projects that received $305 million from the Department of Energy in 2009 alone.
3. All synthetic biology projects should also be reviewed by the Recombinant DNA Advisory Committee.

On Synthetic Biology for Biofuels—Time for a Reality Check

Much of the purported promise of the emerging Synthetic Biology industry resides in the notion of transforming biomass into next generation biofuels or bio-based chemicals where synthetic organisms work as bio-factories transforming sugars to high value products. On examination much of this promise is unrealistic and unsustainable and if allowed to proceed could hamper ongoing efforts to conserve biological diversity, ensure food security and prevent dangerous climate change. The sobering reality is that a switch to a bio-based industrial economy could exert much more pressure on land, water, soil, fertilizer, forest resources and conservation areas. It may also do little to address greenhouse gas emissions, potentially worsening climate change.

By way of an example, the team associated with Synthetic Genomics Inc who have recently announced the creation of a synthetic cell have specifically claimed that they would use the same technology to develop an algal species that efficiently converts atmospheric carbon dioxide into hydrocarbon fuel, supposedly addressing both the climate crisis and peak oil concerns in one fell swoop. Yet, contrary to the impression put forth by these researchers in the press, algae, synthetic or otherwise, requires much more than just carbon dioxide to grow—it also requires water,

Thomas et al., Jim. U.S. House of Representatives Committee on Energy and Commerce, May 27, 2010.

nutrients for fertilizer and also sunlight (which therefore means one needs land or open ocean—this can't be done in a vat without also consuming vast quantities of sugar).

In order for Synthetic Genomics or their partners to scale up algal biofuel production to make a dent in the fuel supply, the process would likely exert a massive drain on both water and on fertilizers. Both fresh water and fertilizer (especially phosphate-based fertilizers) are in short supply, both are already prioritized for agricultural food production and both require a large amount of energy either to produce (in the case of fertilizers) or to pump to arid sunlight-rich regions (in the case of water). In a recent life-cycle assessment of algal biofuels published in the journal *Environmental Science and Technology* researchers concluded that algae production consumes more water and energy than other biofuel sources like corn, canola, and switch grass, and also has higher greenhouse gas emissions. "Given what we know about algae production pilot projects over the past 10 to 15 years, we've found that algae's environmental footprint is larger than other terrestrial crops," said Andres Clarens, an assistant professor in U.Virginia's Civil and Environmental Department and lead author on the paper. Moreover scaling-up this technology in the least energy-intensive manner will likely need large open ponds sited in deserts, displacing desert ecosystems. Indeed the federally appointed Invasive Species Advisory Committee has recently warned that non-native algal species employed for such biofuel production could prove ecologically harmful and is currently preparing a fuller report on the matter.

Meanwhile it is not clear that the yield from algal biofuels would go far to meeting our energy needs. MIT inventor Saul Griffiths has recently calculated that even if an algae strain can be made 4 times as efficient as an energy source than it is today it would still be necessary to fill one Olympic-size swimming pool of algae every second for the next twenty five years to offset only half a terawatt of our current energy consumption (which is expected to rise to 16 TW in that time period). That amounts to massive land use change. Emissions from land use change are recognized as one of the biggest contributors to anthropogenic climate change.

Moving Forward—Time for New Regulation

The rapid adoption of synthetic biology is moving the biotechnology industry into the driving seat of industrial production across many previously disparate sectors with downstream consequences for monopoly policy. Meanwhile its application in commercial settings uses a set of new and extreme techniques whose proper oversight and limits has not yet been debated. It also enables many more diverse living organisms to be produced using genetic science at a speed and volume that will challenge and ultimately overwhelm the capacity of existing biosafety regulations. For example, Craig Venter has claimed in press and in his patent applications that when combined with robotic techniques the technology for producing a synthetic cell can be perfected to make millions of new species per day. Neither the US government nor any other country has the capacity to assess such an outpouring of new synthetic species in a timely or detailed manner. The Energy and Commerce Committee urgently needs to suggest provisions for regulating these new organisms and chemicals derived from them under the Toxic Substances Control Act, Climate Change legislation and other legislation under its purview before allowing their release into the environment. It also needs to identify how it intends to ensure that the use of such organisms whether in biorefineries, open ponds or marine settings does not impinge on agriculture, forestry, desert and marine protection, the preservation of conservation lands, rural jobs or livelihoods.

To conclude, Congress must receive this announcement of a significant new lifeform as a warning bell, signifying that the time has come for governments to fully regulate all synthetic biology experiments and products. It is imperative that in the pursuit of scientific experimentation and wealth creation, we do not sacrifice human health, the environment, and natural ecosystems. These technologies could have powerful and unpredictable consequences. These are life forms never seen on the planet before now. Before they are unleashed into the environment and commercial use, we need to understand the consequences, evaluate alternatives properly, and be able to prevent the problems that may arise from them.

Jim Thomas is a program manager at ETC Group (Action Group on Erosion, Technology and Concentration) (www.etcgroup.org/en/issues/synthetic_biology).

Eric Hoffman is a genetic technology policy campaigner with Friends of the Earth (www.foe.org).

Jaydee Hanson is a policy director at the International Center for Technology Assessment (www.icta.org).

Gregory E. Kaebnick **NO**

Written Testimony of Gregory E. Kaebnick to the House Committee on Energy and Commerce

. . . The ethical issues raised by synthetic biology are familiar themes in an ongoing conversation this nation has been having about biotechnologies for several decades. . . .

The concerns fall into two general categories. One has to do with whether the creation of synthetic organisms is a good or a bad thing in and of itself, aside from the consequences. These are thought of as intrinsic concerns. Many people had similar intrinsic concerns about reproductive cloning, for example; they just felt it was wrong to do, regardless of benefits. Another has to do with potential consequences—that is, with risks and benefits. The distinction between these categories can be difficult to maintain in practice, but it provides a useful organizational structure.

1. Intrinsic Concerns

I will start with the more philosophical, maybe more baffling, kind of concern—the intrinsic concerns. They are an appropriate place to start because the work just published by researchers at Synthetic Genomics, Inc., has been billed as advancing our understanding of these issues in addition to making a scientific advance.

This announcement is not the first time we have had a debate about whether biotechnology challenges deeply held views about the status of life and the power that biotechnology and medicine give us over it. There was a similar debate about gene transfer research in the 1970s and 1980s, about cloning and stem cell research in the 1990s, and—particularly in the last decade but also earlier—about various tools for enhancing human beings. They have been addressed by the President's Commission for the Study of Ethical Problems in Medicine and Biomedical and Behavioral Research in 1983, by President Clinton's National Bioethics Advisory Council, and by President Bush's President's Council on Bioethics. These concerns are related to even older concerns in medicine about decisions to withhold or withdraw medical treatment at the end of life.

The fact that we have had this debate before speaks to its importance. I believe the intrinsic concerns deserve respect, and with some kinds of biotechnology I think they are very important, but for synthetic biology, I do not think they provide a basis for decisions about governance.

A. Religious or Metaphysical Concerns

The classic concern about synthetic biology is that it puts human beings in a role properly held by God—that scientists who do it are "playing God," as people say. Some may also believe that life is sacred, and that scientists are violating its sacredness. Prince Charles had this in mind in a famous polemic some years ago when he lamented that biotechnology was leading to "the industrialisation of Life."

To object to synthetic biology along these lines is to see a serious moral mistake in it. This kind of objection may be grounded in deeply held beliefs about God's goals in creating the world and the proper role of human beings within God's plan. But these views would belong to particular faiths—not everybody would share them. Moreover, there is a range of opinions even within religious traditions about what human beings may and may not do. Some people celebrate human creativity and science. They may see science as a gift from God that God intends human beings to develop and use.

The announcement that Synthetic Genomics, Inc., has created a synthetic cell appears to some to disprove the view that life is sacred, but I do not agree. Arguably, what has been created is a synthetic genome, not a completely synthetic cell. Even if scientists manage to create a fully synthetic cell, however, people who believe that life is sacred, that it is something more than interacting chemicals, could continue to defend that belief. A similar question arises about the existence of souls in cloned people: If people have souls, then surely they would have souls even if they were created in the laboratory by means of cloning techniques. By the same reasoning, if microbial life is more than a combination of chemicals, then even microbial life created in the laboratory would be more than just chemicals. In general, beliefs about the sacredness of life are not undermined by science. Moreover, even the creation of a truly synthetic cell would still start with existing materials. It would not be the kind of creating with which God is credited, which is creating something from nothing—creation ex nihilo.

Kaebnick, Gregory E. From statement before U.S. House of Representatives Committee on Energy and Commerce, May 27, 2010.

B. Concerns that Synthetic Biology Will Undermine Morally Significant Concepts

A related but different kind of concern is that synthetic biology will simply undermine our shared understanding of important moral concepts. For example, perhaps it will lead us to think that life does not have the specialness we have often found in it, or that we humans are more powerful than we have thought in the past. This kind of concern can be expressed without talking about God's plan.

Synthetic biology need not change our understanding of the value of life, however. The fact that living things are created naturally, rather than by people, would be only one reason for seeing them as valuable, and we could continue to see them as valuable when they are created by people. Further, in its current form, synthetic biology is almost exclusively about engineering single-celled organisms, which may be less troubling to people than engineering more complex organisms. If the work is contained within the laboratory and the factory, then it might not end up broadly changing humans' views of the value of life.

Also, of course, the fact that the work challenges our ideas may not really be a moral problem. It would not be the first time that science has challenged our views of life or our place in the cosmos, and we have weathered these challenges in the past.

C. Concerns about the Human Relationship to Nature

Another way of saying that there's something intrinsically troubling about synthetic biology, again without necessarily talking about the possibility that people are treading on God's turf, is to see it as a kind of environmentalist concern. Many environmentalists want to do more than make the environment good for humans; they also want to save nature from humans—they want to save endangered species, wildernesses, "wild rivers," old-growth forests, and mountains, canyons, and caves, for example. We should approach the natural world, many feel, with a kind of reverence or gratitude, and some worry that synthetic biology—perhaps along with many other kinds of biotechnology—does not square with this value.

Of course, human beings have been altering nature throughout human history. They have been altering ecosystems, affecting the survival of species, affecting the evolution of species, and even creating new species. Most agricultural crop species, for example, are dramatically different from their ancestral forebears. The issue, then, is where to draw the line. Even people who want to preserve nature accept that there is a balance to be struck between saving trees and harvesting them for wood. There might also be a balance when it comes to biotechnology. The misgiving is that synthetic biology goes too far—it takes human control over nature to the ultimate level, where we are not merely altering existing life forms but creating new forms.

Another environmentalist perspective, however, is that synthetic biology could be developed so that it is beneficial to the environment. Synthetic Genomics, Inc. recently contracted with Exxon Mobil to engineer algae that produce gasoline in ways that not only eliminate some of the usual environmental costs of producing and transporting fuel but simultaneously absorb large amounts of carbon dioxide, thereby offsetting some of the environmental costs of burning fuel (no matter how it is produced). If that could be achieved, many who feel deeply that we should tread more lightly on the natural world might well find synthetic biology attractive. In order to achieve this benefit, however, we must be confident that synthetic organisms will not escape into the environment and cause harms there.

Concerns Involving Consequences

The second category of moral concerns is about consequences—that is, risks and benefits. The promise of synthetic biology includes, for example, better ways of producing medicine, environmentally friendlier ways of producing fuel and other substances, and remediation of past environmental damage. These are not morally trivial considerations. There are also, however, morally serious risks. These, too, fall into three categories.

Concerns about Social Justice

Synthetic biology is sometimes heralded as the start of a new industrial age. Not only will it lead to new products, but it will lead to new modes of production and distribution; instead of pumping oil out of the ground and shipping it around the world, we might be able to produce it from algae in places closer to where it will be used. Inevitably, then, it would have all sorts of large-scale economic and social consequences, some of which could be harmful and unjust. Some commentators hold, for example, that if synthetic biology generates effective ways of producing biofuels from feedstocks such as sugar cane, then farmland in poor countries would be converted from food production to sugar cane production. Another set of concerns arises over the intellectual property rights in synthetic biology. If synthetic biology is the beginning of a new industrial age, and a handful of companies received patents giving them broad control over it, the results could be unjust.

Surely we ought to avoid these consequences. It is my belief that we can do so without avoiding the technology. Also, traditional industrial methods themselves seem to be leading to disastrous long-term social consequences; if so, synthetic biology might provide a way toward better social outcomes.

Concerns about Biosafety

Another concern is about biosafety—about mechanisms for containing and controlling synthetic organisms, both during research and development and in industrial applications. The concern is that organisms will escape, turn out to have properties, at least in their new environment, different from what was intended and predicted, or maybe mutate to acquire them, and then pose a threat to public health, agriculture, or the environment. Alternatively, some of their genes might be transferred to other, wild microbes, producing wild microbes with new properties.

Controlling this risk means controlling the organisms—trying to prevent industrial or laboratory accidents, and then trying to make sure that, when organisms do escape, they are not dangerous. Many synthetic biologists argue that an organism that devotes most of its energy to producing jet fuel or medicine, that is greatly simplified (so that it lacks the genetic complexity and therefore the adaptability of a wild form), and that is designed to work in a controlled, contained environment, will simply be too weak to survive in the wild. For added assurance, perhaps engineering them with failsafe mechanisms will *ensure* that they are incapable of surviving in the wild.

Concerns about Deliberate Misuse

I once heard a well-respected microbiologist say that he was very enthusiastic about synthetic biology, and that the only thing that worries him is the possibility of catastrophe. The kind of thing that worries him is certainly possible. The 1918 flu virus has been recreated in the laboratory. In 2002, a scientist in New York stitched together stretches of nucleotides to produce a string of DNA that was equivalent to RNA polio virus and eventually produced the RNA virus using the DNA string. More recently, the SARS virus was also created in the laboratory. Eventually, it will almost certainly be possible to recreate bacterial pathogens like smallpox. We might also be able to enhance these pathogens. Some work in Australia on mousepox suggests ways of making smallpox more potent, for example. In theory, entirely new pathogens could be created. Pathogens that target crops or livestock are also possible.

Controlling this risk means controlling the people and companies who have access to DNA synthesis or the tools they could use to synthesize DNA themselves. There are some reasons to think that the worst will never actually happen. To be wielded effectively, destructive synthetic organisms would also have to be weaponized; for example, methods must be found to disperse pathogens in forms that will lead to epidemic infection in the target population while sparing one's own population. Arguably, terrorists have better forms of attacking their enemies than with bioweapons, which are still comparatively hard to make and are very hard to control. However, our policy should amount to more than hoping for the best.

Governance

In assessing these risks and establishing oversight over synthetic biology, we do not start from square one. There is an existing framework of laws and regulations, put into action by various agencies and oversight bodies, that will apply to R&D and to different applications. The NIH is extending its guidelines for research on genetic engineering to ensure that they are applicable to research on synthetic biology. These Guidelines are enforced by the NIH's Recombinant DNA Advisory Committee and a network of Institutional Biosafety Committees at research institutions receiving federal funding. Many applications would fall under the purview of various federal laws and the agencies that enforce them. For example, a plan to release synthetic organisms into the sea to produce nutrients that would help rebuild ocean food chains would have to pass muster with the EPA. The USDA and FDA also have regulatory authority over applications. The FBI and the NIH's National Science Advisory Board for Biosecurity are formulating policy to regulate the sale of synthetic DNA sequences that might pose a threat to biosecurity.

At the same time, the current regulatory framework may need to be augmented. First, there are questions about whether the existing laws leave gaps. Research conducted by entirely privately funded laboratory might not [be] covered by the NIH's Guidelines, for example. Field testing of a synthetic organism—that is, release into the environment as part of basic research—might not be covered by the existing regulations of the EPA or the USDA. Questions about the adequacy of existing regulations are even more pointed when it comes to concerns about biosecurity, particularly if or when powerful benchtop synthesizers are available in every lab.

The other big question is whether the regulatory bodies' ability to do risk assessment of synthetic biology is adequate. Synthetic biology differs from older forms of genetic engineering in that a synthetic organism could combine DNA sequences found originally in many different organisms, or might even contain entirely novel genetic code. The eventual behavior of these organisms in new environments, should they accidentally end up in one, may therefore be hard to predict.

The synthetic biologists' goal of simplicity is crucial. One of the themes of traditional biology is that living things are usually more complex than they first appear. We should not assume at the outset that synthetic organisms will shed the unpredictability inherent to life. Life tends to find a way. As a starting assumption, we should expect that artificial life will try to find a way as well.

Another difficulty in assessing concerns about both biosafety and deliberate misuse is that, if the field evolves so that important and even innovative work could be done in small, private labs, even in homes, then it could be very difficult to monitor and regulate. The threats of biosafety and deliberate misuse would have to be taken yet more seriously.

Concluding Comments

I take seriously concerns that synthetic biology is bad in and of itself, and I believe that they warrant a thorough public airing, but I do not believe that they provide a good basis for restraining the technology, at least if we can be confident that the organisms will not lead to environmental damage. Better yet would be to get out in front of the technology and ensure that it benefits the environment. Possibly, some potential applications of synthetic biology are more troubling than others and should be treated differently.

Ultimately, I think the field should be assessed on its possible outcomes. At the moment, we do not understand the possible outcomes well enough. We need, I believe:

- more study of the emergence, plausibility, and impact of potential risks;
- a strategy for studying the risks that is multidisciplinary, rather than one conducted entirely within the field;
- a strategy that is grounded in good science rather than sheer speculation, yet flexible enough to look for the unexpected; and
- an analysis of whether our current regulatory framework is adequate to deal with these risks and how the framework should be augmented.

Different kinds of applications pose different risks and may call for different responses. Microbes intended for release into the environment, for example, would pose a different set of concerns than microbes designed to be kept in specialized, contained settings. Overall, however, while the risks of synthetic biology are too significant to leave the field alone, its potential benefits are too great to call for a general moratorium.

Gregory E. Kaebnick is a research scholar at The Hastings Center and editor of the *Hastings Center Report.*

EXPLORING THE ISSUE

Should Society Impose a Moratorium on the Use and Release of "Synthetic Biology" Organisms?

Critical Thinking and Reflection

1. What are "dual-use" technologies?
2. Does creating a synthetic cell disprove the idea that life is sacred?
3. How long do you think it will be before synthetic biology can be done at home? Is the prospect frightening?
4. Can all risks be prevented?

Is There Common Ground?

As with many technologies, some people see mostly risks and would, if they could, stop the development of the technology. Others see mostly benefits and think that those benefits are worth putting up with the risks. A more nuanced approach is to determine which risks and benefits seem most likely and then to carefully weigh them against each other. This approach is known as risk–benefit or cost–benefit analysis, and it is used in medicine, engineering, business, and other areas.

1. What seem to be the most likely or worrisome risks associated with synthetic biology technology?
2. What seem to be the most likely benefits associated with synthetic biology technology?
3. Do you think the benefits are worth the risks?

Additional Resources

Michael A. Peters and Priya Venkatesan, "Bioeconomy and Third Industrial Revolution in the Age of Synthetic Life," *Contemporary Readings in Law and Social Justice* (vol. 2, no. 2, 2010).

Michael J. Selgelid and Lorna Weir, "Reflections on the Synthetic Production of Poliovirus," *Bulletin of the Atomic Scientists* (May/June 2010).

Jonathan B. Tucker, "Could Terrorists Exploit Synthetic Biology?" *New Atlantis: A Journal of Technology & Society* (Spring 2011).

Pamela Weintraub, "J. Craig Venter on Biology's Next Leap: Digitally Designed Life-Forms that Could Produce Novel Drugs, Renewable Fuels, and Plentiful Food for Tomorrow's World," *Discover* (January/February 2010).

Create Central

www.mhhe.com/createcentral

Internet Reference . . .

The J. Craig Venter Institute

The J. Craig Venter Institute, formed in October 2006, is a world leader in genomics research, including the effort to create synthetic cells.

www.jcvi.org

Selected, Edited, and with Issue Framing Material by:
Thomas A. Easton, *Thomas College*

ISSUE

Can Infectious Animal Diseases Be Studied Safely in Kansas?

YES: Bruce Knight, from "Statement on the National Bio- and Agro-Defense Facility," before the Subcommittee on Oversight and Investigation, House Energy and Commerce Committee (May 22, 2008)

NO: Ray L. Wulf, from "Written Testimony," submitted for the Record to the Subcommittee on Oversight and Investigation, House Energy and Commerce Committee (May 22, 2008)

Learning Outcomes

After studying this issue, students will be able to:

- Explain the need for reliable isolation or containment measures when doing research on infectious animal and human diseases.
- Compare the advantages of geographic and technological isolation or containment measures.
- Discuss the economic impact of an outbreak of foot-and-mouth disease.

ISSUE SUMMARY

YES: Bruce Knight argues that although the U.S. Department of Agriculture's research facility at Plum Island, New York, has served well since it was built over half a century ago, modern technology is capable of ensuring safety at a mainland facility, which would also be cheaper to operate, more easily accessible, and more responsive to potential disease threats.

NO: Ray L. Wulf argues that an island location is much more effective at containing infectious diseases such as foot-and-mouth disease. A mainland research facility would permit unhampered spread of such diseases throughout the continental United States, with devastating consequences for the agricultural economy. Modern technology is not adequate to ensure safety, and federal, state, and local authorities are not prepared to deal with an outbreak.

Plum Island, located off the coast of Long Island in New York State, became a center of research into deadly animal diseases in 1954. At that time, responding to outbreaks of foot-and-mouth disease (FMD) in Mexico and Canada, the U.S. Army gave the island to the U.S. Department of Agriculture (USDA) to establish a research center for studying FMD. The island location was chosen because it was isolated from the mainland and the prevailing winds blow out to sea. FMD can be spread by the wind, and it is highly contagious. The island location was regarded as the safest possible place to work with diseases such as FMD.

Today, the Plum Island Animal Disease Center is responsible for protecting the U.S. livestock industry against catastrophic economic losses caused by foreign animal disease agents accidentally or deliberately introduced into the United States. It does this by performing research into disease detection and diagnosis, vaccines, drugs, and risk assessment. It also trains animal health professionals. It is proud of its safety record; its Web site claims that "Not once in our nearly 50 years of operation has an animal pathogen escaped from the island."

The island was transferred from the USDA to the Department of Homeland Security (DHS) in 2003. The DHS soon began to rethink the facility as the National Bio- and Agro-Defense Facility, upgraded to provide more space for the study of diseases that can infect both animals and humans. Such research would require Biosafety Level 4 laboratories, the highest security level. Plum Island at the time had only Biosafety Level 3 laboratories, and area residents had resisted proposals to upgrade the laboratories to Level 4. DHS also thought it would be advantageous to move the research facility to the mainland and soon narrowed the list of candidate sites to six (including Plum Island). The final choice was Manhattan, Kansas, near to a major university and research community but also very close to large populations of livestock. Critics have objected that the choice of Kansas was unduly influenced by aggressive lobbying by the state's senators and governor; see Yudhijit Bhattacharjee, "How Kansas Nabbed the New Bio- and Agro-Defense Lab," *Science* (December 12, 2008). As of late 2010, the Kansas choice stands, and Plum Island is to be sold.

At the hearing of the Subcommittee on Oversight and Investigation, House Energy and Commerce Committee, for which the testimony presented in the NO selection was prepared, the U.S. Government Accounting Office (GAO) testified that the DHS had not suitably evaluated the risks of moving the Plum Island Animal Disease Center to the mainland. On December 12, 2008, DHS released a final Environmental Impact Statement (EIS), and on January 16, 2009, it announced its choice of Manhattan, Kansas, as the new location, basing the choice on the information and analysis in the final EIS (http://www.dhs.gov) and other factors.

The GAO then undertook to analyze the EIS, noting that DHS was restricted by law from moving the Plum Island facility to the mainland until it had completed a risk assessment on whether FMD research can be done there as safely as on the island. The GAO specifically assessed the evidence DHS said supported its decision. Unfortunately, said the GAO, "DHS's analyses did not effectively characterize and differentiate the risks associated with the release of FMD virus at the six sites. . . . The economic analyses did not incorporate market response to an FMD outbreak—which would be related to the number of livestock in the site's vicinity. They also did not consider the effect of establishing a containment zone to control the effects of a national export ban on the domestic livestock industry—which could have been used to differentiate across National Bio and Agro-Defense Facility sites. The analyses were constrained by limited scope and detail. They did not incorporate worst-case outbreak scenarios. . . . Given the significant limitations in DHS's analyses that we found, the conclusion that FMD work can be done as safely on the mainland as on Plum Island is not supported." See the GAO report at http://www.gao.gov/products/GAO-09-747. In November 2010, the National Research Council issued a safety report, which concluded that there is a 70 percent chance of pathogen release from the proposed Manhattan, Kansas BioLab-4 over a 50-year period; see "National Research Council Questions Safety of Proposed Biocontainment Lab in Kansas," http://www.thefreelibrary.com/National+research+council+questions+safety+of+proposed+biocontainment...-a0243277969. New York officials are objecting to the move on the grounds of expense and jobs, among other things.

According to Carol D. Leonnig, "Infectious Diseases Study Site Questioned: Tornado Alley May Not Be Safe, GAO Says," *Washington Post* (July 27, 2009), DHS officials are claiming that the GAO exceeded its authority in reviewing the DHS risk assessment. They are also pushing to delay further hearings of the Subcommittee on Oversight and Investigation, House Energy and Commerce Committee. No such hearings had been held by the end of 2010.

It is worth noting that risk assessment is a complex activity. One recent textbook, Paolo F. Ricci's *Environmental and Health Risk Assessment and Management: Principles and Practices* (Springer Netherlands, 2009), stresses the need for "sound causal arguments," which is where the GAO says the DHS falls short. However, the president of Kansas State University in Manhattan, Kansas, remains delighted that his campus was chosen by DHS to house Plum Island's replacement, according to a press release, "President Kirk Schulz Keeping K-State at the Forefront of National Animal Health."

In the YES selection taken from testimony before the Subcommittee on Oversight and Investigation, House Energy and Commerce Committee, Bruce Knight, then the USDA's Under Secretary for Marketing and Regulatory Programs, argues that although the USDA's research facility at Plum Island, New York, has served well since it was built over half a century ago, modern technology is capable of ensuring safety at a mainland facility, which would also be cheaper to operate, more easily accessible, and more responsive to potential disease threats. In the NO selection, farmer and rancher Ray L. Wulf argues that an island location is much more effective at containing infectious diseases such as FMD. A mainland research facility would permit unhampered spread of such diseases throughout the continental United States, with devastating consequences for the agricultural economy. Modern technology is not adequate to ensure safety, and federal, state, and local authorities are not prepared to deal with an outbreak.

YES

Bruce Knight

Statement on the National Bio- and Agro-Defense Facility

. . . Agriculture is a vital component of our nation's economy. Of particular importance to homeland security is the significant increase in agricultural trade. This year, we expect agriculture exports to reach approximately $101 billion, making it the highest export sales year ever in our history—and significant to our balance of trade. Agriculture imports are rising as well—increasing from nearly $58 billion in 2005 to an estimated $76.5 billion this year.

We face many challenges in protecting this important infrastructure. As goods move back and forth across the border, we must remain vigilant to safeguard U.S. agriculture from unwelcome pest and disease threats. Our sector is particularly concerned about security because food production is not constrained by political boundaries, and as we all know, diseases and pathogens do not respect state or national borders. The interconnected nature of the global food system is our strength and allows us to feed the world, but it is also a disadvantage in the event of attack or natural disease outbreak. Additionally, one of the agricultural sector's greatest contributions to the quality of life is the fact that products flow quickly through interstate commerce—one of our greatest assets is also one of our greatest concerns because intentionally or unintentionally contaminated products could quickly spread a pest, disease, or other agent.

USDA works diligently to protect U.S. agriculture from the potential introduction of human and animal disease agents, whether unintentionally or through agroterrorism. Many of these pathogens such as the Nipah and Hendra viruses are zoonotic, that is, they cause both human and animal disease, and can pass from animals to humans. If a significant zoonotic or animal disease were to penetrate our borders, it could devastate the agricultural industry, cause numerous casualties, and harm the economy.

We've seen just how disastrous the effects of a foreign animal disease outbreak can be in the 2001 foot-and-mouth disease (FMD) outbreak in the United Kingdom. In that case, over 6 million pigs, sheep, and cattle were destroyed, with the epidemic costing the U.K. economy an estimated $13 billion. This example highlights the need for the best tools and diagnostics to safeguard the U.S. livestock industry from significant foreign animal disease threats such as FMD. At the same time, the 2007 suspected release of live FMD virus from the Pirbright campus in England amplifies the balance needed in undertaking such work. This is why USDA and the Department of Homeland Security (DHS) will use the most modern biosafety practices and procedures, and stringent and rigorous safety measures within NBAF.

Because of the continued emergence of new animal diseases, the leaping of dangerous animal diseases across species, and the possibility of a bioterrorist release, it is even more essential that USDA have a sufficient understanding of these diseases and be well prepared to protect the U.S. livestock industry from their damage. To achieve this, USDA works through its Agricultural Research Service (ARS) and Animal and Plant Health Inspection Service (APHIS) to meet its responsibilities in animal health. ARS is the primary intramural science research agency of USDA, operating a network of over 100 research laboratories across the nation that work on all aspects of agricultural science. APHIS is responsible for safeguarding U.S. agricultural health from foreign pests and diseases of plants and animals.

In order to be able to rapidly identify, respond to, and control outbreaks of foreign animal and zoonotic disease, USDA needs secure, state-of-the-art biocontainment laboratories with adequate space for advanced research, diagnostics, and training. Recognizing this need, the President directed USDA and DHS, via Homeland Security Presidential Directive 9: "Defense of the United States Agriculture and Food," to develop a plan to provide for such facilities. As I will explain further, USDA is working closely with our partners in DHS to fulfill this important need.

Plum Island Animal Disease Center

In 1954, USDA began work at the Plum Island Animal Disease Center (PIADC) in research and diagnostics on foreign animal diseases that, either by accidental or deliberate introduction to the United States, pose significant health and/or economic risks to the U.S. livestock industry. The Plum Island Animal Disease Center has served U.S. agriculture well. It's no accident that this country has the healthiest and most abundant livestock populations in the world. Producers and all of us at USDA work hard every day to keep this up.

An integral part of maintaining animal health is preventing the entry of exotic pest and disease threats. The Plum Island Animal Disease Center, through its diagnostic, research, and reagent production and distribution activities, has stood as American agriculture's bulwark

Knight, Bruce. From statement before U.S. House of Representatives, May 22, 2008.

against potentially devastating foreign animal diseases. Each working day since the facility opened over 50 years ago, the dedicated and highly skilled Plum Island Animal Disease Center staff has equipped veterinarians, scientists, professors, and other animal health professionals here and around the world with the tools they need to fight exotic disease incursions that threaten livestock. In addition to FMD and classical swine fever, other livestock diseases that our scientists have studied at the Plum Island Animal Disease Center include African swine fever, rinderpest, Rift Valley fever, West Nile fever, vesicular stomatitis, and Capri pox (sheep pox and lumpy skin disease).

As you know, in June 2003, operational responsibility for the Plum Island Animal Disease Center transferred from USDA to DHS under the Homeland Security Act of 2002. Since the transfer, we've developed a strong, collaborative partnership with DHS and put in place an interagency agreement to clarify roles and responsibilities. A Board of Directors and Senior Leadership Group were created to facilitate decision-making regarding facility operations and policies, while also allowing the three agencies to focus on accomplishing their specific missions and goals. I believe our relationship with DHS is a very positive one that allows both Departments to achieve our similar goals while making the most of each other's specialized expertise.

After the Plum Island Animal Disease Center transfer, USDA remained responsible for conducting basic and applied research and diagnostic activities at the Plum Island Animal Disease Center to protect U.S. agriculture from foreign animal disease agents. DHS, in turn, assumed responsibility for coordinating the overall national effort to protect key U.S. resources and infrastructure, including agriculture. Science programs at the Plum Island Animal Disease Center now include the APHIS Foreign Animal Disease Diagnostic Laboratory (FADDL), ARS' Foreign Animal Disease Research Unit, and DHS' Targeted Advanced Development Unit. . . .

APHIS scientists perform diagnostic testing of samples collected from U.S. livestock that are showing clinical signs consistent with an exotic disease, as well as testing animal products and live animals being imported into the United States to ensure that unwanted diseases are not accidentally introduced through importation. APHIS scientists at the Plum Island Animal Disease Center have the capability to diagnose more than 30 exotic animal diseases, and perform thousands of diagnostic tests each year. They also prepare diagnostic reagents and distribute them to laboratories throughout the world, and test the safety and efficacy of vaccines for selected foreign animal diseases. Other APHIS activities include improving techniques for the diagnosis or control of foreign animal diseases and validating tests for foreign animal diseases that are deployed to the National Animal Health Laboratory Network (NAHLN). Through the use of these tests in surveillance, the NAHLN provides for early detection and the surge capability needed in the case of an outbreak.

In addition, FADDL staff, in conjunction with APHIS' Professional Development Staff, train veterinarians, scientists, professors, and veterinary students on recognition of clinical signs and pathological changes caused by foreign animal diseases. This training provides the backbone of APHIS' animal disease surveillance and safeguarding programs. These foreign animal disease diagnosticians trained by FADDL are located throughout the country, and can be on-site to conduct an investigation and collect samples within 16 hours of receiving a report of a suspect foreign animal disease. Based on their assessment of the situation and prioritization of the threat, APHIS can then take appropriate steps if necessary to protect the U.S. livestock industry.

Through its involvement in the Plum Island Animal Disease Center, ARS develops new strategies to prevent and control foreign or emerging animal disease epidemics through a better understanding of the nature of infectious organisms, pathogenesis in susceptible animals, host immune responses, and the development of novel vaccines and diagnostic tests. The ARS Foreign Animal Disease Research Unit focuses on developing vaccines that can be produced safely in the United States and used safely on U.S. farms, diagnostic techniques to differentiate between a vaccinated and an infected animal, and methods for identifying carrier animals. Currently, ARS' work at the Plum Island Animal Disease Center includes active research programs working with FMD, Classical Swine Fever, and vesicular stomatitis viruses.

ARS scientists have recently carried out extensive work on FMD, including early development of a FMD vaccine that is safe to produce on the mainland; discovery of an antiviral treatment that prevents FMD replication and spread within 24 hours; and determination of many key aspects of FMD virus structure, function, and replication at the molecular level, leading to highly specific diagnostic tests.

Meeting the Needs of American Agriculture

The Plum Island Animal Disease Center has played a critical role in developing the tools and expertise needed to protect the country from the deliberate or unintentional introduction of significant foreign animal diseases. However, much has changed since the Plum Island Animal Disease Center was first built, and we are even more cognizant of the threat from foreign animal diseases due to the increasingly interconnected world we live in. This need is echoed by our American livestock industries that could be devastated by the introduction of a significant foreign animal disease. Groups such as the United States Animal Health Association and National Institute for Animal Agriculture have appealed for accelerated research to protect their industries. Also, the National Cattlemen's Beef Association, Animal Agriculture Coalition, and National Milk Producers Federation have written to Congress, to show their support for NBAF.

To continue providing U.S. agriculture with the latest research and technological services, as well as world-class approaches to agricultural health safeguarding and foreign-animal disease diagnostics, USDA needs additional space and upgraded biosecurity measures to work on those animal-borne diseases that pose the greatest risk to U.S. livestock industries, and those that can also be transmitted to humans. The Plum Island Animal Disease Center is aging and nearing the end of its lifecycle, and the state of current facilities has created a backlog of needed space for important experiments, diagnostic development, and training efforts.

In particular, USDA is in need of enhanced research and diagnostic capabilities for animal diseases, particularly zoonotic diseases of large animals that require agriculture BSL-3 and BSL-4 capabilities. However, since we cannot currently carry out BSL-4 activities at the Plum Island Animal Disease Center, the nation is left lacking a large animal facility to address high-consequence animal diseases that can be transmitted to humans, such as Nipah and Hendra, as well as Rift Valley Fever (which requires vaccinated personnel; however vaccine is in short supply).

Specifically, USDA would utilize the BSL-4 space to develop diagnostic assays for Rift Valley Fever and Nipah and Hendra viruses, using specimens collected from animals in the BSL-4 lab. In addition, in the event of an emerging pathogen, it would often be necessary to inoculate animals in a BSL-4 suite in order to determine the clinical course of the disease, determine appropriate diagnostic specimens, isolate the agent, and develop diagnostic tools.

In order to protect U.S. agriculture and human health, it is critical that USDA have the capability of diagnosing and working with the disease agents I have mentioned, as well as any new highly infectious pathogen that may emerge. In response, our agencies have begun planning for the next generation facility which we call the NBAF, to replace the current structures at the Plum Island Animal Disease Center. NBAF will integrate research, development, and testing in foreign animal diseases and zoonotic diseases, which will support the complimentary missions of USDA and DHS. NBAF will address USDA needs that are currently not being met by the facilities at the Plum Island Animal Disease Center, including inadequate lab space for processing diagnostic samples, limitations in diagnostic capability for BSL-4 agents, and lack of space to expand to include the development, feasibility testing, and validation of new and emerging technologies for detection of exotic and emerging diseases. In addition, it will provide room to grow as we further enhance our abilities to respond to increasing threats to the U.S. livestock industry.

The NBAF will also have a synergistic effect, to the benefit of each of our agencies, by utilizing the expertise of the academic and scientific community in the area. In addition, we expect that by sharing a well-equipped core facility, we will see a more cost effective utilization of funding. This will also continue to provide a number of opportunities for enhanced interaction among the three agencies. For example, research done by ARS and DHS may identify possible new diagnostic tools that APHIS can use; APHIS' repository of foreign animal disease agents obtained from outbreaks around the world will provide a resource for ARS and DHS research and bioforensics; and APHIS' diagnostic investigations and surveillance will help identify emerging or re-emerging diseases in the field, in turn helping set research priorities for ARS and DHS.

Site Selection

At the time Plum Island was built, biosecurity was much different than it is today. Agriculture biosecurity was defined by biological isolation, so that if there was a problem at the laboratory, there was physical separation from susceptible livestock populations and any breaches were localized. Today, with much more advanced technologies, the ability to manage effective biosecurity and biosafety practices is not dictated by location or physical barriers.

We recognize that there is concern about building the NBAF on the mainland. Since the determination was made over 60 years ago to build the Plum Island Animal Disease Center on an island, assessments have shown that technological advances would allow for safe research and diagnostics of foreign animal diseases to take place on the U.S. mainland. A 2002 study completed by the Science Applications International Corporation (SAIC) and commissioned by USDA found that the FMD virus and other exotic foreign animal diseases of concern to the Department could be fully and safely contained within a BSL-3 laboratory, as was being done in other countries at the time including Canada, Germany, and Brazil. A second SAIC study also concluded that there was a valid USDA need for a BSL-4 facility, and that a BSL-4 facility for large animal work could be safely located on the mainland.

In planning for the NBAF, we recognize the absolutely essential need for state-of-the-art biosafety practices and procedures, including stringent and rigorous safety measures within the laboratories themselves, to prevent disease organisms from escaping into the environment. Situations such as the recent suspected release of live FMD virus from the Pirbright campus in England only serve to highlight this importance. We can use that example as a learning opportunity and make sure that the design and maintenance of the NBAF facility enables us to carry out the essential activities needed to protect the nation from foreign animal diseases while ensuring the highest level of biosafety.

This is why the NBAF will utilize the redundancies built into modern research laboratory designs and the latest biosecurity and containment systems, coupled with continued training and monitoring of employees, to effectively minimize any risks. Personnel controls for the NBAF will include background checks, biometric testing for lab entry, and no solitary access to BSL-4 microorganisms. The NBAF will also feature biological safety cabinets in the wet labs designed to meet the needs of BSL-3 labs, while in BSL-4 labs, these biological safety cabinets will include additional security measures or be used in combination with full-body, air-supplied personal protective suits.

In terms of facility design, the BSL-4 lab at the NBAF will employ a box-in-box principle with a pressure-controlled buffer. All water and air leaving the lab will be purified—that is, no research microorganism will enter the sewage system or outside air. All critical functions will have redundant systems. The design of the BSL-4 laboratories and animal space will comply with the appropriate recommendations and requirements of the Centers for Disease Control and Prevention, National Institutes of Health, Department of Defense, and National Research Council.

I would also like to note some potential advantages to locating the NBAF on the mainland. For example, the lower cost of living, as compared to that in the communities surrounding the Plum Island Animal Disease Center, would likely make recruiting personnel easier for our agencies. This would also eliminate the costs of moving people on and off an island every day, as we currently do. A mainland facility would be more accessible if air traffic is shut down due to weather conditions or an emergency situation, and would not be subject to the occasional wind closures that we experience at the Plum Island Animal Disease Center due to rough waters. And, as I mentioned earlier, locating the facility near an established research community would facilitate innovative collaboration.

A key advantage to locating NBAF on the mainland would be the ability to quickly respond to a potential foreign animal disease threat. Placing the NBAF on the mainland could eliminate the need for additional transport of samples to the island via boat or aircraft, as is currently done at Plum Island. Having a more accessible location, where diagnostic capabilities could be utilized within the first 24 hours of an emergency, is essential. For example, in June 2007, APHIS conducted an investigation into swine showing signs consistent with a significant foreign animal disease. In such a situation, every hour counts when it comes to being able to quickly rule out major diseases. Incidents such as this can have a significant impact on the economy, stop movement and trade in multiple species of livestock, and spread fear throughout the industry.

Although DHS is ultimately responsible for the selection of a NBAF site, USDA has been closely involved throughout this process. APHIS and ARS have provided detailed program requirements to DHS, and have representatives on the site selection committee and site inspection team. We support the criteria used to select the sites: proximity to research capabilities linked to the NBAF mission requirements, site proximity to a skilled workforce, as well as acquisition/construction/operations, and community acceptance, and look forward to the next steps in the process.

DHS is currently preparing an environmental impact statement (EIS) looking at the six sites, which include Plum Island and five mainland locations. The EIS, on which USDA and DHS are working, will consider the risk and potential consequences of an accidental release of a foreign animal disease, and will be integral to moving forward with a sound NBAF site selection.

It is important that we move forward in a timely manner with planning and construction of NBAF so that we can develop the diagnostics and tools needed to protect U.S. agriculture from the threats of dangerous foreign animal diseases. Just as the science behind bioterrorism has advanced in recent years, and new and changing diseases continue to emerge, so too must we arm ourselves with more sophisticated ways of preventing harm to the U.S. livestock industry. If we don't, then bioterrorists will continue to find innovative ways to attack our livestock, new diseases will continue to emerge, and U.S. agriculture will be left vulnerable to these dangers. This is why USDA is committed to working with DHS to move forward with plans for NBAF, after a thorough analysis of the options and development of plans to ensure the utmost biosafety and biosecurity.

Authority to Conduct FMD Research on the Mainland

Lastly, I would like to briefly mention recent legislative activity related to live FMD virus. Current statute (21 U.S.C. 113a.) restricts research involving live FMD virus and other animal diseases that present a significant risk to domestic U.S. livestock to laboratories on coastal islands separated from the mainland United States by deep water. Research involving live FMD virus is carried out at the Plum Island Animal Disease Center under this statute, which dates back to the 1950s. The statute was amended by the 1990 Farm Bill to authorize the Secretary of Agriculture, when necessary, to allow the movement of live FMD virus, under permit, to research facilities on the U.S. mainland.

USDA recognizes DHS' interest in the Secretary being directed, via statute, to issue a permit for live FMD virus at the NBAF. This direction will provide clarity in this important area as DHS moves forward in selecting a site for the NBAF and then in contracting for the construction of the facility. For these reasons, the Administration included in our Farm Bill Proposal an authorization for USDA to conduct research and diagnostics for highly infectious disease agents, such as FMD and rinderpest, on the U.S. mainland. Consistent with the Administration's proposal, section 7524 of the Food, Conservation, and Energy Act of 2008 directs the Secretary to issue a permit for live FMD virus at NBAF, while preserving the Secretary's discretion and ensuring that all biosafety and select agent requirements are being met at the facility.

Conclusion

. . . We believe the planned NBAF is necessary to replace the aging Plum Island Animal Disease Center and provide additional capacity for much needed animal disease research, diagnostics, training, and countermeasures development. The NBAF will play a crucial role in protecting against the future introduction of foreign animal and zoonotic diseases, and ensuring the continued health and vitality of our agricultural industries. We are committed to continuing our work in partnership with DHS in planning the NBAF and making the facility a reality.

Bruce Knight spent several years as the under secretary for Marketing and Regulatory Programs at the U.S. Department of Agriculture. He is now a consultant focusing on conservation and environmental issues related to agriculture.

Ray L. Wulf **NO**

Written Testimony

. . . On behalf of American Farmers & Ranchers [I] thank you for the opportunity to testify on the Department of Homeland Security's recent proposal to close the Plum Island Animal Disease Center and move its biological research laboratory, including, but not limited to, research on foot-and-mouth disease, to a new location on the mainland United States. This is an issue that is of particular interest and concern to our organization and companies.

At the committee's request I will address the following questions:

- Does your organization support moving foot-and-mouth disease from Plum Island to a research facility on the mainland United States?
- What would be the estimated cost to your membership of an outbreak of foot-and-mouth disease in the United States?
- Does your organization believe modern technology is adequate to prevent the accidental release of foot-and-mouth disease—or other contagious diseases affecting livestock—from a research facility located on the mainland United States?
- If an outbreak of foot-and-mouth disease were to occur on the mainland United States, does your organization believe that Federal, State, and local authorities are prepared to identify, isolate, and halt the spread of such an outbreak before it caused significant damage?

Does your organization support moving foot-and-mouth disease from Plum Island to a research facility on the mainland United States?

NO, AFR is *opposed* to the movement of the Plum Island Animal Disease Center to a research facility on the mainland U.S. The Plum Island Animal Disease Center is the only place in the country where certain highly infectious foreign animal diseases are studied, such as foot-and-mouth disease. Foot-and-mouth disease is a highly contagious virus that affects cloven-hoofed animals such as cattle, sheep, pigs, goats and deer.

Foot-and-mouth disease can be carried by the wind, on clothing, footwear, skin, through nasal passages, and on equipment. The current location or one with similar natural barriers should continue to be the site for research and diagnostic activities that protect our nation's food supply. There are simply too many possibilities for error, either by negligence, or accident, that could pose extreme economic impacts on U.S. agriculture producers and consumers.

Specifically foot-and-mouth disease creates a serious threat to the U.S. livestock industry, the overall agriculture economy, as well as the U.S. economy. A GAO report released December of 2005 stated that nationally recognized animal disease experts were interviewed and agreed that foot-and-mouth disease constitutes the greatest threat to American livestock. Furthermore GAO provided a letter on December 17, 2007 stating that some of the pathogens maintained at Plum Island, such as foot-and-mouth disease, are highly contagious to livestock and could cause catastrophic economic losses in the agricultural sector if it was released outside of the facility.

Infrastructure

The results of a possible outbreak on the mainland are magnified and accelerated by the efficiencies of the U.S. infrastructure and the transportation industry. The U.S. infrastructure for moving livestock is second to none, allowing livestock to move rapidly across the U.S. [In] five days cattle were trucked from the Oklahoma City National Livestock Market to 39 states. In addition, other animals that carry foot-and-mouth disease, such as swine, sheep, and goats are also rapidly distributed. Within a matter of days livestock can be transported hundreds to thousands of miles away and intermingled with other livestock. Amplifying the situation is the fact that foot-and-mouth disease is expelled over four to five days after an animal has been infected and may occur several days before the onset of clinical signs. In a matter of a couple of weeks the entire country could be infected.

What would be the estimated cost to your membership of an outbreak of foot-and-mouth disease in the United States?

The economic impacts to AFR members would no doubt be severe and devastating and reach far beyond the livestock industry. Quarantines affecting large areas would be established stopping all incoming and outgoing commerce in the quarantined area. Depending on the time of year, a quarantine could halt grain harvest, a major economic impact to many areas. Trucks and equipment would not be allowed in or out for harvesting, milk trucks would not be allowed in or out and, in addition, travel to and from

Wulf, Ray L. From statement before U.S. House of Representatives, May 22, 2008.

school, for business or leisure would be halted. The impact would not only be felt by the producer, but also the local community, region, nation and could cause irreparable damage to the financial community. In addition the U.S. could expect severe economic consequences in the global market.

Many studies have attempted to assess the economic implications of an outbreak of foot-and-mouth disease in the U.S. Results can vary, but at the same time all point out the significant economic losses as a result of a foot-and-mouth outbreak. Direct economic losses would result from lost production, the cost of destroying disease-ridden livestock, indemnification and the cost of disease containment measures, such as drugs, diagnostics, vaccines, and veterinary services. Indirect costs and multiplier effects from dislocations in agriculture sectors would include the feed and inputs industry, transportation, retail and the loss of export markets.

A foot-and-mouth outbreak would not only be a problem for agriculture. In Britain the outbreak of foot-and-mouth disease resulted in postponing a general election for a month, the cancellation of many sporting events and leisure activities, the cancellation of large events likely to be attended by those from infected areas.

Research at Oklahoma State University

Dr. Clem Ward of Oklahoma State University outlines how estimating the effects is difficult to gauge:

- First, the effects would depend upon how isolated or widespread the incidence was and how quickly it was contained.
- Second, the effects would depend upon the type of livestock operations that were infected and how frequently or recently animals have moved from the sites.
- Third, impacts would depend on how the media handles the news reporting of the outbreak.
- And fourth, markets would likely react immediately to the news, and how long it would take them to rebound to a more normal level would depend on the first three factors mentioned.

Dr. Ward also looked at two studies that estimate the economic impacts of a foot-and-mouth outbreak based on a given set of wide ranging scenarios.

1. A 1979 study with impacts adjusted to 2000; estimated economic impacts from $2.4 billion to $27.6 billion.
2. A 1999 study estimated the impacts for California alone at $8.5 billion to $13.5 billion.

Kansas Research

An article in *ScienceDaily* (Nov. 29, 2007), "Foot-and-mouth Disease Could Cost Kansas Nearly A Billion Dollars," referenced research by Dustin L. Pendell, John Leatherman, Ted C. Schroeder, and Gregory S. Alward—THE ECONOMIC IMPACTS OF A FOOT-AND-MOUTH DISEASE OUTBREAK: A REGIONAL ANALYSIS. The team of researchers analyzed a 14-county region in southwest Kansas that has a high concentration of large cattle feeding operations, as well as other livestock enterprises and beef processing plants. They considered three scenarios:

- one where the disease was introduced at a single cow-calf operation;
- one where a medium-sized feedlot, 10,000 to 20,000 head of cattle, was initially infected;
- one where five large feedlots, each with more than 40,000 head of cattle, were simultaneously exposed.

Schroeder said the first two scenarios were used to predict what could happen if the disease were introduced accidentally, while the larger scenario shows what could happen were there an intentional release.

Generally, researchers found that the greater the number of animals infected in an operation, the longer an outbreak would last and the more it would likely spread—all directly correlating to the level of economic ruin.

- Under the small cow-calf scenario, researchers predicted that 126,000 head of livestock would have to be destroyed and that a foot-and-mouth disease outbreak would last 29 days.
- In the medium-sized operation, those numbers went up to 407,000 animals and 39 days.
- In the scenario where five large feedlots were exposed at the same time, researchers predicted that 1.7 million head of livestock would have to be destroyed and that an outbreak would last nearly three months.

From smallest to largest operation, that translated into regional economic losses of $23 million, $140 million and $685 million, respectively. For the state of Kansas as a whole, those numbers climb to $36 million, $199 million and $945 million.

"Kansas produces about 1.5 million calves, markets 5.5 million head of fed cattle, and slaughters 7.5 million head of cattle annually. The large commercial cattle feedlot and beef packing industries together bring more than 100,000 head of cattle per week on average into the state for feeding or processing," Schroeder said. "Such large volumes of livestock movement provide avenues for contagious animal disease to spread."

Leatherman estimated the statewide impacts of foot-and-mouth for this study and said the effects of an outbreak would go way beyond producers. "This study tells us what the overall stake of the region and state has in preventing such an occurrence," he said. "It isn't just farmers, ranchers, feed lots and packers who would suffer—it's all of us, in some measure."

Other Research

Another report titled "Potential Revenue Impact of an Outbreak of Foot-and-Mouth Disease in the United Sates" by Paarlbwerg, Lee, and Seitzinger was published in the *Journal of American Veterinary Medical Association* in April of 2002. The report stated an outbreak similar to that which occurred in the U.K. during 2001, would cause an estimated U.S. farm income losses of $14 billion. Losses in gross revenue for each sector were estimated to be the following: live swine, −34%; pork, −24%; live cattle −17%; beef, −20%; milk, −16%; live lambs and sheep, −14%; lamb and sheep meat, −10%; forage, −15%; and soybean meal, −7%.

Other Agriculture Markets Impacted

Livestock markets are not the only markets impacted by an outbreak. Feed grains and protein meal feeds would also be impacted. A CRS Report titled "Agroterrorism: Options in Congress," December 19, 2001 states—According to industry officials, every other bushel of U.S. grain goes to animal feed. In addition, information from the U.S. Meat Export Federation states that:

- One milk cow will eat 3 tons of hay and 1,460 lbs of distiller's grain over the course of a year
- It takes 150 lbs of soybean meal to feed a pig to its finished weight
- Every pound of U.S. pork exported utilizes 1.5 pounds of U.S. soybeans
- More than 54 million bushels of soybeans were exported through U.S. red meat in 2006
- More than 300 million bushels of corn were exported through U.S. red meat in 2006
- While direct corn exports have increased by 25% since 1990, indirect exports of corn through the value added process of exporting red meat has increased by 196%

Trade Impact

Ninety-four to ninety-six percent of the world's consumers live outside the U.S. making trade a critical part of U.S. Agriculture. Examples from the pork industry are as follows:

- Source: USDA
  - U.S. has 27% share of the world pork exports
- Source: U.S. Meat Export Federation
  - 2007 Pork Exports add $22.00 per hog
  - The net benefit of U.S. pork exports to the pork industry in 2007 equates to $22 added dollars per market hog
  - Japan, Mexico, Canada and Korea account for 75% of all U.S. pork exports—10% of total production
  - One in every four pounds of pork traded in the world originates from the U.S.
  - The U.S. exports the equivalent of 49,500 market hogs daily

Foot-and-mouth disease is a *"Trade Disease."* To avoid foot-and-mouth disease it is common practice among foot-and-mouth disease-free countries to allow imports only from other foot-and-mouth disease-free countries. This action by countries that are foot-and-mouth disease free is consistent with the provisions of the World Trade Organization's "Agreement on Application of Sanitary and Phytosanitary Measures," which allows countries to adopt and enforce measures necessary to protect human, animal, or plant health. The World Organization of Animal Health (OIE), an independent international organization founded in 1924, monitors and disseminates information about animal diseases throughout the world, and provides a list of countries declared free of foot-and-mouth disease.

Global competition is fierce and in the event a foot-and-mouth outbreak occurred in the U.S., life as we know would no longer exist. Operating as a foot-and-mouth positive country would exclude the U.S. from premium meat markets.

While a foot-and-mouth disease vaccine is available it is used only in emergencies, to create a "disease-free" buffer zone around an infected area. Because vaccinated animals will test positive, they cannot be shipped internationally and protocols require the animals to be destroyed as soon as the disease is eradicated.

Consumer Issues

Foot-and-mouth is not readily transmissible to humans. Only a few cases of human infections, none requiring hospitalization, occurring as a result of direct contact with infected animals have been documented. Even though foot-and-mouth disease does not pose a health risk to humans, consumer fear would occur. Because the average consumer has a lack of knowledge about the disease, more than likely there would be a drop in meat consumption.

. . .

Does your organization believe modern technology is adequate to prevent the accidental release of foot-and-mouth disease—or other contagious diseases affecting livestock—from a research facility located on the mainland United States?

NO, AFR does not believe that there are adequate technologies and safety precautions that can assure U.S. producers and consumers that there would not be an accidental or intentional release of foot-and mouth disease or for that fact any other contagious disease affecting livestock from a research facility located on the mainland U.S. Regardless of how much technology has improved, it does not safeguard from human error, harmful intentions or lack of preparedness.

Plum Island's research and diagnostic activities work to accomplish an important mission to protect U.S. animal industries and exports from deliberate or accidental introductions of foreign animal diseases. Although steps have been taken to implement better security measures at

Plum Island, an outbreak is not out of the question. The U.S. should take note of the most recent U.K. outbreak in August of 2007. Investigations determined that the U.K. outbreak was caused by a strain of virus used for vaccine research at laboratories associated with the institute for Animal Health at Pirbright.

If an outbreak of foot-and-mouth disease were to occur on the mainland United States, does your organization believe that Federal, State, and local authorities are prepared to identify, isolate, and halt the spread of such an outbreak before it caused significant damage?

NO, Although Federal, State and local authorities continue to try to prepare themselves for a foreign animal disease outbreak, AFR believes there are entirely too many unknown variables that would hinder a successful containment of the disease. A U.S. Government simulated outbreak in 2002 called "Crimson Sky" ended with fictional riots in the streets after the simulation's National Guardsmen were ordered to kill tens of millions of farm animals, so many that troops ran out of bullets. In the exercise, the government said it would have been forced to dig a ditch in Kansas 25 miles long to bury carcasses. In the simulation, protests broke out in some cities amid food shortages.

In addition, AFR has concerns about the transportation of infectious disease samples that may need to come into or out of the facility and travel through populated areas. Furthermore AFR has concerns about the number of employees that would be traveling in and out of the facility. The Department of Homeland Security states that a new proposed National Bio and Agro-Defense Facility would generally include between 250 and 350 employees.

Traceability Is Critical

AFR believes that a critical part of being able to control the spread of foot-and-mouth or any animal disease is a national animal identification system. The capacity to trace livestock and product movements is critical for the early control of an outbreak. USDA has been pursuing implementation of an effective animal identification system since the BSE discovery in a U.S. cow in 2003. The U.S. has yet to establish a workable I.D. program. Until traceability is mandatory and in place moving the Plum Island Animal Disease Center to the mainland should *not* be considered and even then it should be reviewed carefully and any consideration should be focused on a remote area with little or no livestock or wild game habitation.

Conclusion

In conclusion, AFR strongly supports full funding for the research performed at Plum Island, including research on foot-and-mouth disease. In addition AFR fully supports funding to update research facilities to the highest standards.

However, AFR believes the U.S. should not risk bringing highly contagious animal disease research to the mainland with so many variables that could wreak havoc on the U.S. livestock industry, communities, the U.S. and global economy.

AFR believes further activities are needed to prepare for an animal disease outbreak. Activities should include:

- An analysis of communication between all stakeholders
- A full economic study that includes control and compensation including businesses reliant on livestock and global trade impacts
- How to adequately establish a quarantine area around an outbreak
- How movement restrictions will be handled
- Procedures in regard to slaughtering all infected herds and other herds that have been in contact with them
- Disposing of animals—Environmental impacts—burial contamination of ground water by leakages from a disposal pit
- Disinfecting properties
- Compensating stock owners for the livestock slaughtered
- Carrying out clinical inspection a surveillance to ensure the disease has not spread

---

Ray L. Wulf is an Oklahoma farmer and rancher. Until 2009, he was the president and CEO of American Farmers and Ranchers Mutual Insurance Company in Oklahoma City.

EXPLORING THE ISSUE

Can Infectious Animal Diseases Be Studied Safely in Kansas?

Critical Thinking and Reflection

1. Why was Plum Island initially favored for working with highly infectious animal diseases?
2. Why does the Department of Homeland Security think Plum Island is no longer an appropriate location?
3. Why is foot-and-mouth disease considered a "trade disease?"
4. How would an outbreak of foot-and-mouth disease affect the U.S. economy?

Is There Common Ground?

All involved in this debate agree that infectious diseases—whether of animals or of humans—should not be permitted to escape from research facilities. One significant difference is in the degree of trust people are willing to put in technological means of preventing such escape.

1. Google on "biodefense labs" and summarize the news stories and reports you find.
2. Do people seem willing to trust isolation or containment measures to work? Why not?
3. What could be done to make isolation or containment measures more reliable, or at least more worthy of public trust?

Create Central

www.mhhe.com/createcentral

Additional Resources

David Malakoff, "Kansas Veterinary Biosecurity Lab Trampled in Spending Plan," *Science* (February 24, 2012).

National Research Council, *Evaluation of the Updated Site-Specific Risk Assessment for the National Bio- and Agro-Defense Facility in Manhattan, Kansas* (National Academies Press, 2012) (www.nap.edu/catalog.php?record_id=13418).

Internet Reference . . .

Plum Island Animal Disease Center

Since 1954, the Plum Island Animal Disease Center has been protecting America's livestock from foreign animal diseases (diseases not present in the United States) such as foot-and-mouth disease.

www.ars.usda.gov/main/site_main.htm?modecode=19-40-00-00

Selected, Edited, and with Issue Framing Material by:
Thomas A. Easton, *Thomas College*

ISSUE

Are Genetically Modified Foods Safe to Eat?

YES: Henry I. Miller and Gregory Conko, from "Scary Food," *Policy Review* (June/July 2006)

NO: Vandana Shiva, from *Introduction to the GMO Emperor Has No Clothes: A Global Citizens Report on the State of GMOs—False Promises, Failed Technologies* (Navdanya International, 2011) (www.navdanya.org/publications)

Learning Outcomes

After studying this issue, students will be able to:

- Describe the potential benefits of applying genetic engineering to food crops.
- Describe the potential adverse effects of genetically modified foods.
- Explain why and on what basis new technologies should be regulated.

ISSUE SUMMARY

YES: Henry I. Miller and Gregory Conko of the Hoover Institution argue that genetically modified (GM) crops are safer for the consumer and better for the environment than non-GM crops.

NO: Vandana Shiva argues that we need to create a GMO-free world to protect biodiversity, human health, and the freedom to choose GMO-free seed and food.

In the early 1970s, scientists first discovered that it was technically possible to move genes—biological material that determines a living organism's physical makeup—from one organism to another and thus (in principle) to give bacteria, plants, and animals new features and to correct genetic defects of the sort that cause many diseases, such as cystic fibrosis. Most researchers in molecular genetics were excited by the potentialities that suddenly seemed within their grasp. However, a few researchers—as well as many people outside the field—were disturbed by the idea; they thought that genetic mix-and-match games might spawn new diseases, weeds, and pests. Some people even argued that genetic engineering should be banned at the outset, before unforeseeable horrors were unleashed.

Researchers in support of genetic experimentation responded by declaring a moratorium on their own work until suitable safeguards could be devised. Once those safeguards were in place in the form of government regulations, work resumed. James D. Watson and John Tooze document the early years of this research in *The DNA Story: A Documentary History of Gene Cloning* (W. H. Freeman, 1981). For a shorter, more recent review of the story, see Bernard D. Davis, "Genetic Engineering: The Making of Monsters?" *The Public Interest* (Winter 1993).

By 1989 the technology had developed tremendously: Researchers could obtain patents for mice with artificially added genes ("transgenic" mice); firefly genes had been added to tobacco plants to make them glow (faintly) in the dark; and growth hormone produced by genetically engineered bacteria was being used to grow low-fat pork and increase milk production by cows. Critics argued that genetic engineering was unnatural and violated the rights of both plants and animals to their "species integrity"; that expensive, high-tech, tinkered animals gave the competitive advantage to big agricultural corporations and drove small farmers out of business; and that putting human genes into animals, plants, or bacteria was downright offensive. See Betsy Hanson and Dorothy Nelkin, "Public Responses to Genetic Engineering," *Society* (November/December 1989). Most of the initial attention aimed at genetic engineering focused first on its use to modify bacteria and other organisms to generate drugs needed to fight human disease and second on its potential to modify human genes and attack hereditary diseases at their roots. See Eric B. Kmiec, "Gene Therapy," *American Scientist* (May–June 1999).

Pharmaceutical and agricultural applications of genetic engineering have been very successful, the latter largely because, as Robert Shapiro, CEO of Monsanto Corporation, said in 1998, it "represents a potentially sustainable solution to the issue of feeding people." In "Biotech's

Plans to Sustain Agriculture," *Scientific American* (October 2009) interviewed several industry representatives, who see biotechnology—including genetic engineering—as essential to meeting future demand in a sustainable way.

Between 1996 and 2012, the area planted with genetically engineered crops jumped from 1.7 million hectares to 170 million hectares, according to the International Service for the Acquisition of Agri-Biotech Applications, "ISAAA Brief 44-2012: Executive Summary: Global Status of Commercialized Biotech/GM Crops: 2012" (www.isaaa.org/resources/publications/briefs/44/executivesummary/default.asp). Many people are not reassured by such data. They see potential problems in nutrition, toxicity, allergies, and ecology. Brian Halweil, "The Emperor's New Crops," *World Watch* (July/August 1999), notes that although genetically engineered crops may have potential benefits, they may also have disastrous effects on natural ecosystems and—because high-tech agriculture is controlled by major corporations such as Monsanto—on less-developed societies. He argues that "ecological" agriculture (using, e.g., organic fertilizers and natural enemies instead of pesticides) offers much more hope for the future. Similar arguments are made by those who demonstrate against genetically modified (GM) foods—sometimes by destroying research labs and test plots of trees, strawberries, and corn—and lobby for stringent labeling requirements or for outright bans on planting and importing these crops. See Claire Hope Cummings, "Risking Corn, Risking Culture," *World Watch* (November/December 2002). Protestors argue against GM technology in terms of the precautionary principle; see "GMOs and Precaution in EU countries," *Outlook on Science Policy* (September 2005). Georgina Gustin, "Seeds of Change?" *Columbia Journalism Review* (January/February 2010), reviews press coverage of GM crops and notes that despite the numerous objections by environmental groups there are no data that indicate problems. She adds that there is a need for more research on safety.

Many researchers see great hope in GM foods. In July 2000, the Royal Society of London, the U.S. National Academy of Sciences, the Indian Academy of Sciences, the Mexican Academy of Sciences, and the Third World Academy of Sciences issued a joint report titled "Transgenic Plants and World Agriculture" (www.nap.edu/catalog.php?record_id=9889). This report stresses that during the twenty-first century, both the population and the need for food are going to increase dramatically, especially in developing nations. According to the report, "Foods can be produced through the use of GM technology that are more nutritious, stable in storage, and in principle, health promoting . . . . New public sector efforts are required for creating transgenic crops that benefit poor farmers in developing nations and improve their access to food . . . . Concerted, organized efforts must be undertaken to investigate the potential environmental effects, both positive and negative, of GM technologies [compared to those] from conventional agricultural technologies . . . . Public Health regulatory systems need to be put in place in every country to identify and monitor any potential adverse human health effects." The United States' National Research Council reports that the economic and environmental benefits of GM crops are clear; see Erik Stokstad, "Biotech Crops Good for Farmers and Environment, Academy Finds," *Science* (April 16, 2010), and Committee on the Impact of Biotechnology on Farm-Level Economics and Sustainability, *The Impact of Genetically Engineered Crops on Farm Sustainability in the United States* (National Academies Press, 2010) (www.nap.edu/catalog.php?record_id=12804).

The worries surrounding GM foods and the scientific evidence to support them are summarized by Kathryn Brown, in "Seeds of Concern," and Karen Hopkin, in "The Risks on the Table," both in *Scientific American* (April 2001). Jeffrey M. Smith, *Seeds of Deception: Exposing Industry and Government Lies about the Safety of the Genetically Engineered Foods You're Eating* (Chelsea Green, 2003), argues that the dangers of GM foods have been deliberately concealed. Henry I. Miller and Gregory Conko, in *The Frankenfood Myth: How Protest and Politics Threaten the Biotech Revolution* (Praeger, 2004), address at length the fallacy that GM foods are especially risky. Rod Addy and Elaine Watson, "Forget 'Frankenfood,' GM Crops Can Feed the World, Says FDF," *Food Manufacture* (December 2007), note that "EU trade commissioner Peter Mandelson said that the inability of European politicians to engage in a rational debate about GM was a source of constant frustration. They were also creating barriers to trade by banning GM crops that had repeatedly been pronounced safe by the European Food Safety Authority (EFSA)." Early in 2010, the EFSA reinforced this point; see "EFSA Rejects Study Claiming Toxicity of GMOs," *European Environment & Packaging Law Weekly* (February 24, 2010). According to Gemma Masip, et al., "Paradoxical EU Agricultural Policies on Genetically Engineered Crops," *Trends in Plant Science* (in press, available online April 25, 2013), EU attitudes toward GM crops obstruct policy goals; GM crops are essential to EU agricultural competitiveness. Nevertheless, many people argue that GM foods should be labeled so that people can choose to avoid them. See Robin Mather, "The Threats from Genetically Modified Foods," *Mother Earth News* (April–May 2012), and Amy Harmon and Andrew Pollack, "Battle Brewing over Labeling of Genetically Modified Food," *New York Times* (May 24, 2012). Jane Black, "As Nature Made Them," *Prevention* (April 2012), adds a call for more independent (not sponsored by seed companies) research into GMO safety.

Is the issue safety? Human welfare? Or economics? In the YES selection, Henry I. Miller and Gregory Conko of the Hoover Institution argue that GM crops are safer for the consumer and better for the environment than non-GM crops. People have failed to embrace them because news coverage has been dominated by the outlandish claims and speculations of antitechnology activists. In the NO selection, activist Vandana Shiva argues that we need to create a GMO-free world to protect biodiversity, human health, and the freedom to choose GMO-free seed and food.

YES

Henry I. Miller and Gregory Conko

Scary Food

Like a scene from some Hollywood thriller, a team of U.S. Marshals stormed a warehouse in Irvington, New Jersey, last summer to intercept a shipment of evildoers from Pakistan. The reason you probably haven't heard about the raid is that the objective was not to seize Al Qaeda operatives or white slavers, but $80,000 worth of basmati rice contaminated with weevils, beetles, and insect larvae, making it unfit for human consumption. In regulation-speak, the food was "adulterated," because "it consists in whole or in part of any filthy, putrid, or decomposed substance, or if it is otherwise unfit for food."

Americans take food safety very seriously. Still, many consumers tend to ignore Mother Nature's contaminants while they worry unduly about high technology, such as the advanced technologies that farmers, plant breeders, and food processors use to make our food supply the most affordable, nutritious, varied, and safe in history.

For example, recombinant DNA technology—also known as food biotechnology, gene-splicing, or genetic modification (GM)—is often singled out by critics as posing a risk that new allergens, toxins, or other nasty substances will be introduced into the food supply. And, because of the mainstream media's "if it bleeds, it leads" approach, news coverage of food biotech is dominated by the outlandish claims and speculations of anti-technology activists. This has caused some food companies—including fastfood giant McDonald's and baby-food manufacturers Gerber and Heinz—to forgo superior (and even cost-saving) gene-spliced ingredients in favor of ones the public will find less threatening.

Scientists agree, however, that gene-spliced crops and foods are not only better for the natural environment than conventionally produced food crops, but also safer for consumers. Several varieties now on the market have been modified to resist insect predation and plant diseases, which makes the harvested crop much cleaner and safer. Ironically (and also surprisingly in these litigious times), in their eagerness to avoid biotechnology, some major food companies may knowingly be making their products less safe and wholesome for consumers. This places them in richly deserved legal jeopardy.

Don't Trust Mother Nature

Every year, scores of packaged food products are recalled from the American market due to the presence of all-natural contaminants like insect parts, toxic molds, bacteria, and viruses. Because farming takes place out-of-doors and in dirt, such contamination is a fact of life. Fortunately, modern technology has enabled farmers and food processors to minimize the threat from these contaminants.

The historical record of mass food poisoning in Europe offers a cautionary tale. From the ninth to the nineteenth centuries, Europe suffered a succession of epidemics caused by the contamination of rye with ergot, a poisonous fungus. Ergot contains the potent toxin ergotamine, the consumption of which induces hallucinations, bizarre behavior, and violent muscle twitching. These symptoms gave rise at various times to the belief that victims were possessed by evil spirits. Witch-hunting and persecution were commonplace—and the New World was not immune. One leading explanation for the notorious 1691–92 Salem witch trials also relates to ergot contamination. Three young girls suffered violent convulsions, incomprehensible speech, trance-like states, odd skin sensations, and delirious visions in which they supposedly saw the mark of the devil on certain women in the village. The girls lived in a swampy meadow area around Salem; rye was a major staple of their diet; and records indicate that the rye harvest at the time was complicated by rainy and humid conditions, exactly the situation in which ergot would thrive.

Worried villagers feared the girls were under a spell cast by demons, and the girls eventually named three women as witches. The subsequent panic led to the execution of as many as 20 innocent people. Until a University of California graduate student discovered this link, a reasonable explanation had defied historians. But the girls' symptoms are typical of ergot poisoning, and when the supply of infected grain ran out, the delusions and persecution likewise disappeared.

In the twenty-first century, modern technology, aggressive regulations, and a vigorous legal liability system in industrialized countries such as the United States are able to mitigate much of this sort of contamination. Occasionally, though, Americans will succumb to tainted food picked from the woods or a backyard garden. However, elsewhere in the world, particularly in less-developed countries, people are poisoned every day by fungal toxins that contaminate grain. The result is birth defects, cancer, organ failure, and premature death.

About a decade ago, Hispanic women in the Rio Grande Valley of Texas were found to be giving birth to an unusually large number of babies with crippling and lethal neural tube defects (NTDS) such as spina bifida, hydrocephalus, and anencephaly—at a rate approximately six times higher than the national average for non-Hispanic women. The cause remained a mystery until recent research revealed a link between NTDS and consumption of large amounts of unprocessed corn like that found in tortillas and other staples of the Latino diet.

The connection is obscure but fascinating. The culprit is fumonisin, a deadly mycotoxin, or fungal toxin, produced by the mold *Fusarium* and sometimes found in unprocessed corn. When insects attack corn, they open wounds in the plant that provide a perfect breeding ground for *Fusarium*. Once molds get a foothold, poor storage conditions also promote their postharvest growth on grain.

Fumonisin and some other mycotoxins are highly toxic, causing fatal diseases in livestock that eat infected corn and esophageal cancer in humans. Fumonisin also interferes with the cellular uptake of folic acid, a vitamin that is known to reduce the risk of NTDS in developing fetuses. Because fumonisin prevents the folic acid from being absorbed by cells, the toxin can, in effect, induce functional folic acid deficiency—and thereby cause NTDS—even when the diet contains what otherwise would be sufficient amounts of folic acid.

The epidemiological evidence was compelling. At the time that the babies of Hispanic women in the Rio Grande Valley experienced the high rate of neural tube defects, the fumonisin level in corn in that locale was two to three times higher than normal, and the affected women reported much higher dietary consumption of homemade tortillas than in women who were unaffected.

Acutely aware of the danger of mycotoxins, regulatory agencies such as the U.S. Food and Drug Administration and Britain's Food Safety Agency have established recommended maximum fumonisin levels in food and feed products made from corn. Although highly processed cornstarch and corn oil are unlikely to be contaminated with fumonisin, unprocessed corn or lightly processed corn (e.g., cornmeal) can have fumonisin levels that exceed recommended levels.

In 2003, the Food Safety Agency tested six organic cornmeal products and twenty conventional cornmeal products for fumonisin contamination. All six organic cornmeals had elevated levels—from nine to 40 times greater than the recommended levels for human health—and they were voluntarily withdrawn from grocery stores.

A Technical Fix

The conventional way to combat mycotoxins is simply to test unprocessed and processed grains and throw out those found to be contaminated—an approach that is both wasteful and dubious. But modern technology—specifically in the form of gene-splicing—is already attacking the fungal problem at its source. An excellent example is "Bt corn," crafted by splicing into commercial corn varieties a gene from the bacterium *Bacillus thuringiensis*. The "Bt" gene expresses a protein that is toxic to corn-boring insects but is perfectly harmless to birds, fish, and mammals, including humans.

As the Bt corn fends off insect pests, it also reduces the levels of the mold *Fusarium*, thereby reducing the levels of fumonisin. Thus, switching to the gene-spliced, insect-resistant corn for food processing lowers the levels of fumonisin—as well as the concentration of insect parts—likely to be found in the final product. Researchers at Iowa State University and the U.S. Department of Agriculture found that Bt corn reduces the level of fumonisin by as much as 80 percent compared to conventional corn.

Thus, on the basis of both theory and empirical knowledge, there should be potent incentives—legal, commercial, and ethical—to use such gene-spliced grains more widely. One would expect public and private sector advocates of public health to demand that such improved varieties be cultivated and used for food—not unlike requirements for drinking water to be chlorinated and fluoridated. Food producers who wish to offer the safest and best products to their customers—to say nothing of being offered the opportunity to advertise "New and Improved!"—should be competing to get gene-spliced products into the marketplace.

Alas, none of this has come to pass. Activists have mounted intractable opposition to food biotechnology in spite of demonstrated, significant benefits, including reduced use of chemical pesticides, less runoff of chemicals into waterways, greater use of farming practices that prevent soil erosion, higher profits for farmers, and less fungal contamination. Inexplicably, government oversight has also been an obstacle, by subjecting the testing and commercialization of gene-spliced crops to unscientific and draconian regulations that have vastly increased testing and development costs and limited the use and diffusion of food biotechnology.

The result is jeopardy for everyone involved in food production and consumption: Consumers are subjected to avoidable and often undetected health risks, and food producers have placed themselves in legal jeopardy. The first point is obvious, the latter less so, but as described first by Drew Kershen, professor of law at the University of Oklahoma, it makes a fascinating story: Agricultural processors and food companies may face at least two kinds of civil liability for their refusal to purchase and use fungus-resistant, gene-spliced plant varieties, as well as other superior products.

Food for Thought

In 1999 the Gerber foods company succumbed to activist pressure, announcing that its baby food products would no longer contain any gene-spliced ingredients. Indeed, Gerber went farther and promised it would attempt to shift to organic ingredients that are grown without synthetic pesticides or fertilizers. Because corn starch and corn sweeteners are often used in a range of foods, this could mean changing Gerber's entire product line.

But in its attempt to head off a potential public relations problem concerning the use of gene-spliced ingredients, Gerber has actually increased the health risk for its baby consumers—and, thereby, its legal liability. As noted above, not only is gene-spliced corn likely to have lower levels of fumonisin than conventional corn; organic corn is likely to have the highest levels, because it suffers greater insect predation due to less effective pest controls.

If a mother some day discovers that her "Gerber baby" has developed liver or esophageal cancer, she might have a legal case against Gerber. On the child's behalf, a plaintiff's lawyer can allege liability based on mycotoxin contamination in the baby food as the causal agent of the cancer. The contamination would be considered a *manufacturing defect* under product liability law because the baby food did not meet its intended product specifications or level of safety. According to Kershen, Gerber could be found liable "even though all possible care was exercised in the preparation and marketing of the product," simply because the contamination occurred.

The plaintiff's lawyer could also allege a *design defect* in the baby food, because Gerber knew of the existence of a less risky design—namely, the use of gene-spliced varieties that are less prone to *Fusarium* and fumonisin contamination—but deliberately chose not to use it. Instead, Gerber chose to use non-gene-spliced, organic food ingredients, knowing that the foreseeable risks of harm posed by them could have been reduced or avoided by adopting a reasonable alternative design—that is, by using gene-spliced Bt corn, which is known to have a lower risk of mycotoxin contamination.

Gerber might answer this design defect claim by contending that it was only responding to consumer demand, but that alone would not be persuasive. Product liability law subjects defenses in design defect cases to a risk-utility balancing in which consumer expectations are only one of several factors used to determine whether the product design (e.g., the use of only non-gene-spliced ingredients) is reasonably safe. A jury might conclude that whatever consumer demand there may be for non-biotech ingredients does not outweigh Gerber's failure to use a technology that is known to lower the health risks to consumers.

Even if Gerber was able to defend itself from the design defect claim, the company might still be liable because it failed to provide adequate instructions or warnings about the potential risks of non-gene-spliced ingredients. For example, Gerber could label its non-gene-spliced baby food with a statement such as: "This product does not contain gene-spliced ingredients. Consequently, this product has a very slight additional risk of mycotoxin contamination. Mycotoxins can cause serious diseases such as liver and esophageal cancer and birth defects."

Whatever the risk of toxic or carcinogenic fumonisin levels in non-biotech corn may be (probably low in industrialized countries, where food producers generally are cautious about such contamination), a more likely scenario is potential liability for an allergic reaction.

Six percent to 8 percent of children and 1 to 2 percent of adults are allergic to one or another food ingredient, and an estimated 150 Americans die each year from exposure to food allergens. Allergies to peanuts, soybeans, and wheat proteins, for example, are quite common and can be severe. Although only about 1 percent of the population is allergic to peanuts, some individuals are so highly sensitive that exposure causes anaphylactic shock, killing dozens of people every year in North America.

Protecting those with true food allergies is a daunting task. Farmers, food shippers and processors, wholesalers and retailers, and even restaurants must maintain meticulous records and labels and ensure against cross-contamination. Still, in a country where about a billion meals are eaten every day, missteps are inevitable. Dozens of processed food items must be recalled every year due to accidental contamination or inaccurate labeling.

Fortunately, biotechnology researchers are well along in the development of peanuts, soybeans, wheat, and other crops in which the genes coding for allergenic proteins have been silenced or removed. According to University of California, Berkeley, biochemist Bob Buchanan, hypoallergenic varieties of wheat could be ready for commercialization within the decade, and nuts soon thereafter. Once these products are commercially available, agricultural processors and food companies that refuse to use these safer food sources will open themselves to products-liability, design-defect lawsuits.

Property Damage and Personal Injury

Potato farming is a growth industry, primarily due to the vast consumption of french fries at fast-food restaurants. However, growing potatoes is not easy, because they are preyed upon by a wide range of voracious and difficult-to-control pests, such as the Colorado potato beetle, virus-spreading aphids, nematodes, potato blight, and others.

To combat these pests and diseases, potato growers use an assortment of fungicides (to control blight), insecticides (to kill aphids and the Colorado potato beetle), and fumigants (to control soil nematodes). Although some of these chemicals are quite hazardous to farm workers, forgoing them could jeopardize the sustainability and profitability of the entire potato industry. Standard application of synthetic pesticides enhances yields more than 50 percent over organic potato production, which prohibits most synthetic inputs.

Consider a specific example. Many growers use methamidophos, a toxic organophosphate nerve poison, for aphid control. Although methamidophos is an EPA-approved pesticide, the agency is currently reevaluating the use of organophosphates and could ultimately prohibit or greatly restrict the use of this entire class of pesticides. As an alternative to these chemicals, the Monsanto Company developed a potato that contains a gene from the bacterium *Bacillus thuringiensis* (Bt) to control the

Colorado potato beetle and another gene to control the potato leaf roll virus spread by the aphids. Monsanto's NewLeaf potato is resistant to these two scourges of potato plants, which allowed growers who adopted it to reduce their use of chemical controls and increase yields.

Farmers who planted NewLeaf became convinced that it was the most environmentally sound and economically efficient way to grow potatoes. But after five years of excellent results it encountered an unexpected snag. Under pressure from anti-biotechnology organizations, McDonald's, Burger King, and other restaurant chains informed their potato suppliers that they would no longer accept gene-spliced potato varieties for their french fries. As a result, potato processors such as J.R. Simplot inserted a nonbiotech-potato clause into their farmer-processor contracts and informed farmers that they would no longer buy gene-spliced potatoes. In spite of its substantial environmental, occupational safety, and economic benefits, NewLeaf became a sort of contractual poison pill and is no longer grown commercially. Talk about market distortions.

Now, let us assume that a farmer who is required by contractual arrangement to plant nonbiotech potatoes sprays his potato crop with methamidophos (the organophosphate nerve poison) and that the pesticide drifts into a nearby stream and onto nearby farm laborers. Thousands of fish die in the stream, and the laborers report to hospital emergency rooms complaining of neurological symptoms.

This hypothetical scenario is, in fact, not at all farfetched. Fish-kills attributed to pesticide runoff from potato fields are commonplace. In the potato-growing region of Prince Edward Island, Canada, for example, a dozen such incidents occurred in one 13-month period alone, between July 1999 and August 2000. According to the UN's Food and Agriculture Organization, "normal" use of the pesticides parathion and methamidophos is responsible for some 7,500 pesticide poisoning cases in China each year.

In our hypothetical scenario, the state environmental agency might bring an administrative action for civil damages to recover the cost of the fish-kill, and a plaintiff's lawyer could file a class-action suit on behalf of the farm laborers for personal injury damages.

Who's legally responsible? Several possible circumstances could enable the farmer's defense lawyer to shift culpability for the alleged damages to the contracting food processor and to the fast-food restaurants that are the ultimate purchasers of the potatoes. These circumstances include the farmer's having planted Bt potatoes in the recent past; his contractual obligation to the potato processor and its fast-food retail buyers to provide only nonbiotech varieties; and his demonstrated preference for planting gene-spliced, Bt potatoes, were it not for the contractual proscription. If these conditions could be proved, the lawyer defending the farmer could name the contracting processor and the fast-food restaurants as cross-defendants, claiming either contribution in tort law or indemnification in contract law for any damages legally imposed upon the farmer client.

The farmer's defense could be that those companies bear the ultimate responsibility for the damages because they compelled the farmer to engage in higher-risk production practices than he would otherwise have chosen. The companies chose to impose cultivation of a non-gene-spliced variety upon the farmer although they knew that in order to avoid severe losses in yield, he would need to use organophosphate pesticides. Thus, the defense could argue that the farmer should have a legal right to pass any damages (arising from contractually imposed production practices) back to the processor and the fast-food chains.

Why Biotech?

Companies that insist upon farmers' using production techniques that involve foreseeable harms to the environment and humans may be—we would argue, *should* be—legally accountable for that decision. If agricultural processors and food companies manage to avoid legal liability for their insistence on nonbiotech crops, they will be "guilty" at least of externalizing their environmental costs onto the farmers, the environment, and society at large.

Food biotechnology provides an effective—and cost-effective—way to prevent many of these injurious scenarios, but instead of being widely encouraged, it is being resisted by self-styled environmental activists and even government officials.

It should not fall to the courts to resolve and reconcile what are essentially scientific and moral issues. However, other components of society—industry, government, and "consumer advocacy" groups—have failed abjectly to fully exploit a superior, life-enhancing, and life-saving technology. Even the biotechnology trade associations have been unhelpful. All are guilty, in varying measures, of sacrificing the public interest to self-interest and of helping to perpetuate a gross public misconception—that food biotechnology is unproven, untested, and unregulated.

If consumers genuinely want a safer, more nutritious, and more varied food supply at a reasonable cost, they need to know where the real threats lie. They must also become better informed, demand public policy that makes sense, and deny fringe anti-technology activists permission to speak for consumers.

Henry I. Miller is a research fellow at Stanford University's Hoover Institution. His research focuses on public policy toward science and technology, especially biotechnology. He is the coauthor, with Gregory Conko, of *The Frankenfood Myth: How Protest and Politics Threaten the Biotech Revolution* (Praeger, 2004).

Gregory Conko is a senior fellow at the Competitive Enterprise Institute. He is the coauthor, with Henry I. Miller, of *The Frankenfood Myth: How Protest and Politics Threaten the Biotech Revolution* (Praeger, 2004).

Vandana Shiva

NO

Introduction to the GMO Emperor Has No Clothes: A Global Citizens Report on the State of GMOs—False Promises, Failed Technologies

We have been repeatedly told that genetically engineered (GE) crops will save the world by increasing yields and producing more food. They will save the world by controlling pests and weeds. They will save the world by reducing chemical use in agriculture. They will save the world with GE drought tolerant seeds and other seed traits that will provide resilience in times of climate change.

However, the GE emperor (Monsanto) has no clothes. All of these claims have been established as false over years of experience all across the world. The Global Citizens Report "The Emperor Has No Clothes" brings together evidence from the ground of Monsanto's and the industry's false promises and failed technology.

Failure to Yield

Contrary to the claim of feeding the world, genetic engineering has not increased the yield of a single crop. Navdanya's research in India has shown that contrary to Monsanto's claim of Bt cotton yield of 1500 kg per acre, the reality is that the yield is an average of 400–500 kg per acre. Although Monsanto's Indian advertising campaign reports a 50 percent increase in yields for its Bollgard cotton, a survey conducted by the Research Foundation for Science, Technology and Ecology found that the yields in all trial plots were lower than what the company promised.

Bollgard's failure to deliver higher yields has been reported all over the world. The Mississippi Seed Arbitration Council ruled that in 1997, Monsanto's Roundup Ready cotton failed to perform as advertised, recommending payments of nearly $2 million to three cotton farmers who suffered severe crop losses.

Failure to Yield, a report by the Union of Concerned Scientists in the U.S., has established that genetic engineering has not contributed to yield increases in any crop. According to this report, increases in crop yields in the U.S. are due to yield characteristics of conventional crops, not genetic engineering.

Australian research shows that conventional crops outperform GE crops.

Yield Comparison of GE Canola Trials in Australia

	2001	
Conventional	1144	
Round UP	1055	(Two application of Round Up)
Ready GE	977	(One application of Round Up)
New South Wales	**2001**	
In Vigor (GE)	109	
Hyola (Conventional)	120	

Despite Monsanto adding the Roundup Ready gene to "elite varieties," the best Australian trials of Roundup Ready Canola yielded only 1.055 t/ha, at least 16 percent below the national average of 1.23 t/ha (www.non-gm-farmers.com/documents/ GM Canola report-full.pdf).

As Marc Lappe and Britt Bailey report in their book *Against the Grain* 1998, herbicide-resistant soybeans yielded 36 to 38 bushels per acre, while hand tilled soybeans yielded 38.2 bushels per acre. According to the authors, this raises the possibility that the gene inserted into these engineered plants may selectively disadvantage their growth when herbicides are not applied. "If true, data such as these cast doubt on Monsanto's principal point that their genetic engineering is both botanically and environmentally neutral," the authors write.

While increased food productivity is the argument used to promote genetic engineering, when the issue of potential economic impacts on farmers is brought up, the biotechnology industry itself argues that genetic engineering does not lead to increased productivity. Robert Shapiro, CEO of Monsanto, referring to Posilac (Monsanto's bovine growth hormone) in *Business Ethics*, said on the one hand that "There is need for agricultural productivity, including dairy productivity, to double if we want to feed all the people who will be joining us, so I think this is unequivocally a good product." On the other hand, when asked about the product's economic impact on farmers, he said that it would "play a relatively small role in the process of increasing dairy productivity."

In twenty years of commercialization of GE crops, only two traits have been developed on a significant scale: herbicide tolerance and insect resistance.

Failed Technology: GE Crops Do Not Control Pests and Weeds, They Create Super Pests and Super Weeds

Herbicide tolerant (Roundup Ready) crops were supposed to control weeds and Bt crops were intended to control pests. Instead of controlling weeds and pests, GE crops have led to the emergence of super weeds and super pests. In the U.S., Round Up Ready crops have produced weeds resistant to Round Up. Approximately 15 million acres are now overtaken by Roundup resistant "superweeds," and, in an attempt to stop the spread of these weeds, Monsanto has started offering farmers a "rebate" of up to $6 per acre for purchasing and using other, more lethal herbicides. These rebates offset approximately 25 to 35 percent of cost of purchasing the other herbicides.

In India, Bt cotton sold under the trade name "Bollgard" was supposed to control the Bollworm pest. Today, the Bollworm has become resistant to Bt cotton and now Monsanto is selling Bollgard II with two additional toxic genes in it. New pests have emerged and farmers are using more pesticides.

Bt Crops: A Recipe for Super Pests

Bt is a naturally occurring organism, *Bacillus thuringiensis*, which produces a toxin. Corporations are now adding genes for Bt toxins to a wide array of crops to enable the plants to produce their own insecticide.

Monsanto sells its Bt potato as "Nature Mark" in Canada and describes it as a plant using "sunshine, air and soil nutrients to make a biodegradable protein that affects just one specific insect pest, and only those individual insects that actually take a bite of the plants."

The camouflaged description of a transgenic crop hides many of the ecological impacts of genetically engineered crops. The illusion of sustainability is manufactured through the following distortions.

1. The Bt Plant does not merely use "sunshine, air, and soil nutrients." Bt crops are transgenic and have a gene from a bacterium called bacillus thuringiensis (bt) which produces the Bttoxin. In addition it has antibiotic resistance marker genes and genes from viruses as promoters.
2. The so called "biodegradable protein" is actually a toxin which the gene continuously produces in the plant. This protein has been found in the blood of pregnant women and their fetuses.
3. Insect pests like the cotton bollworm which destroy cotton can actually evolve resistance because of continuous release of the toxin and hence become "super pests."
4. The Bt crop does not affect "just one specific pest." Beneficial insects like bees and ladybirds can be seriously affected. A Cornell study showed that the Bt toxin affected the Monarch butterfly. Navdanya's studies have shown that soil microorganisms are negatively affected.

The primary justification for the genetic engineering of Bt into crops is that this will reduce the use of insecticides. Bt cotton is among the "miracles" being pushed by corporations like Monsanto as a solution to the pesticide crisis. One of the Monsanto brochures had a picture of a few worms and stated, "You will see these in your cotton and that's O.K. Don't spray." However, in Texas, Monsanto faced a lawsuit filed by 25 farmers over Bt cotton planted on 18,000 acres which suffered cotton bollworm damage and on which farmers had to use pesticides in spite of corporate propaganda that genetic engineering meant an end to the pesticide era. In 1996, two million acres in the US were planted with Monsanto's transgenic Bollgard cotton.

However, cotton bollworms were found to have infested thousands of acres planted with the new breed of cotton in Texas. Not only did the genetically engineered cotton not survive cotton bollworm attack, there are also fears that the strategy will create super bugs by inducing Bt resistance in pests. The question is not whether superpests will be created, but when they will become dominant. The fact that the Environmental Protection Agency (EPA) of the US requires refugia of non-engineered crops to be planted near the engineered crops reflects the reality of the creation of resistant strains of insects.

The widespread use of Bt containing crops could accelerate the development of insect pest resistance to Bt which is used for organic pest control. Already eight species of insects have developed resistance to Bt toxins, either in the field or laboratory, including the diamond back moth, Indian meal moth, tobacco budworm, Colorado potato beetle, and two species of mosquitoes.

The genetically engineered Bt crops continuously express the Bt toxin throughout its growing season. Long term exposure to Bt toxins promotes development of resistance in insect populations, this kind of exposure could lead to selection for resistance in all stages of the insect pest on all parts of the plant for the entire season.

Due to this risk of pest resistance, the EPA offers only conditional and temporary registration of varieties producing Bt. The EPA requires four percent "refugia" with Bt cotton, meaning four percent of planted cotton is conventional and does not express the Bt toxin. It therefore acts as a refuge for insects to survive and breed, and hence keeps the overall level of resistance in the population low. Even at a 4 percent refugia level, insect resistance will evolve in as little as three to four years.

Herbicide Resistant Crops: A Recipe for Superweeds

Herbicide resistant crops such as Roundup Ready cotton can create the risk of herbicide resistant "superweeds" by transferring the herbicide resistance to weeds. Monsanto has confirmed that a notorious Australian weed, rye grass, has developed tolerance to its herbicide Roundup, thus rendering genetic engineering of herbicide resistant crops a useless strategy.

In 1994, research scientists in Denmark reported strong evidence that an oilseed rape plant genetically engineered to be herbicide tolerant transmitted its transgene to a weedy natural relative, *Brassica campestris ssp. Campestris*. This transfer can become established in the plant in just two generations.

In Denmark, *B. campestris* is a common weed in cultivated oilseed rape fields, where selective elimination by herbicides is now impossible. The wild relative of this weed is spread over large parts of the world. One way to assess the risk of releasing transgenic oilseed rape is to measure the rate of natural hybridization with *B. campestris*, because certain transgenes could make its wild relative a more aggressive weed, and even harder to control.

Although crosses with *B. campestris* have been used in the breeding of oilseed rape, natural interspecific crosses with oilseed rape was generally thought to be rare. Artificial crosses by hand pollination carried out in a risk assessment project in the U.K. were reported unsuccessful. However, a few studies have reported spontaneous hybridization between oilseed rape and the parental species *B. campestris* in field experiments. As early as 1962, hybridization rates of zero percent to 88 percent were measured for oilseed rape and wild *B. campestris*. The results of the Danish team showed that high levels of hybridization can occur in the field. Their field tests revealed that between nine percent and 93 percent of hybrid seeds were produced under different conditions.

The scientists also warn that as the gene for herbicide resistance is likely to be transferred to the weed, this herbicide strategy will be useless after a few years. Like many other weeds, *B. campestris* is characterized by seed dormancy and longevity of the seeds. Therefore, *B. campestris* with transgenes from oilseed rape may be preserved for many years in spite of efforts to exterminate it. They conclude that weedy *B. campestris* with this herbicide tolerant transgene may present economic risks to farmers and the biotechnology industry. Finally, natural ecosystems may also be affected.

Other concerned scientists add that the potential spread of the transgene will indeed be wide because oilseed rape is insect-pollinated and bees are known to fly far distances. The existence of the wild relative of *B. campestris* in large parts of the world poses serious hazards once the transgenic oilseed rape is marketed commercially. In response to the Danish findings, the governments of Denmark and Norway have acted against the commercial planting of the engineered plant, but the U.K. Government has approved its marketing.

Wild beets have become a major problem in European sugar beet production since the 1970s. These weedy populations arise from seeds originating from the accidental pollinations of cultivated beets by adventitious beets in the seed production area. The existence of gene exchange via seed and pollen between weed beets and cultivated beets shows genetically engineered sugar beets to be herbicide resistant, with the possibility of becoming "superweeds." In this case, the efficacy of herbicide resistant crops is totally undermined.

Current surveys indicate that almost 20 percent of U.S. producers have found glyphosate resistant (Roundup Resistant) weeds on their farms.

Referring to Round Up Resistant weeds, Andrew Wargo III, the President of the Arkansas Association of Conservation Districts said, "It is the single largest threat to production agriculture that we have ever seen."

There are now ten resistant species in at least 22 states infesting millions of acres, predominantly soybeans, cotton, and corn. Roundup Resistant weeds include pig weed, rag weed, and horse weed.

Today, Roundup Ready crops account for 90 percent of soybeans and 70 percent of corn and cotton grown in the U.S.

Mike Owen, a Weed Scientist at Iowa State University has cautioned: "What we're talking about here is Darwinian evolution in fast-forward."

As a result of this weed resistance, farmers are being forced to use more herbicides to combat weeds. As Bill Freese of the Center for Food Safety in Washington, D.C., says "The biotech industry is taking us into a more pesticide dependent agriculture, and we need to be going in the opposite direction."

The problem of "superweeds" is so severe that U.S. Congress organized a hearing on it titled "Are Superweeds on Outgrowth of USDA Biotech Policy".

As Roy Troush, an Indiana farmer, stated in his testimony: "In 2005 we first began to encounter problems with glyphosate-resistance in both our soybean and corn crops. Despite well documented proof that glyphosate tolerant weeds were becoming a significant problem, the Monsanto scientist insisted that resistance existed and instructed me to increase my application rates. The increase in application proved ineffectual. In 2008, we were forced to include the use of 2,4-D and an AIS residual in our program. Like most farmers, we are very sensitive to environmental issues, and we were very reluctant to return to using tillage and more toxic herbicides for weed control. However, no other solutions were then or now readily available to eradicate the weed problems caused by development of glyphosate resistance."

When introduced to regions such as China, Taiwan, Japan, Korea and former USSR where wild relatives of soy are found, Monsanto's Roundup Ready Soya bean could transfer the herbicide resistant genes to wild relatives leading to new weed problems.

The native biodiversity richness of the Third World thus increases the environmental risks of introduced genetically modified species.

The genetic engineering miracle is quite clearly faltering in farmers' fields. Yet the information on the hazards and risks does not accompany the sales promotion of genetically engineered crops in India. Nor does the false promise of the biotech miracle inform farmers that the genetic engineering era of farming also requires "high-tech slavery" for farmers.

False Promises

1. Reduced Use of Chemicals

Despite claims that genetically modified organisms (GMOs) will lower the levels of chemicals (pesticides and herbicides) used, this has not been the case. This is of great concern both because of the negative impacts of these chemicals on ecosystems and humans, and because there is the danger that increased chemical use will cause pests and weeds to develop resistance, requiring even more chemicals in order to manage them. . . .

2. Climate Resilience

Monsanto has been claiming that through genetic engineering it can breed crops for drought tolerance and other climate-resilient traits. This is a false promise. As the U.S. Department of Agriculture (USDA) has said in its draft environmental assessment of the new drought-resistant GE corn, "Equally comparable varieties produced through conventional breeding techniques are readily available in irrigated corn production reviews."

Helen Wallace of GeneWatch UK cautions: "The GE industry must now stop its cynical attempts to manipulate the public into believing that GE crops are needed to feed the world."

Other biotech industries also falsely claim that they are inventing climate resilient traits. As Ram Kaundiya, CEO of Advanta, India and Chairman of Biotech Led Enterprises—Agriculture Group—writes, "Very exciting input traits are in the pipeline. For example, a water use efficiency trait will reduce the water requirements of the crops considerably and can help vast numbers of farmers who cultivate rainfed crops in the country in more than 100 million ha. Similarly, the nitrogen use efficiency trait which will reduce the use of nitrogenous fertilizer on the crops by an estimated 30 percent. Another trait that is waiting in the wings is a salt tolerance trait which can help farmers grow crops in saline soils of more than 20 million ha in India." There are 1600 patents on climate resilient crops.

But all these traits have already been evolved the traditional way by Indian farmers. Navdanya's seed collections have drought tolerant varieties like Nalibakuri, Kalakaya, Atia, Inkiri etc., flood tolerant varieties like Nalidhulia, Ravana, Seulapuni, Dhosarakhuda etc., and salt tolerant varieties like Bhundi, Kalambank, Lunabakada, Sankarchin etc.

Pulses and beans are nitrogen fixing crops. None of these traits are "invented" by genetic engineering. They are pirated from nature and farmers.

3. Health Safety

While the GE Emperor has no clothes—i.e., GE crops cannot feed the world, it has the potential for harming the world and enslaving the world. Among the false claims made by Monsanto and the Biotechnology industry is that GE foods are safe. However, there are enough independent studies to show that GE foods can cause health damage.

For example, Dr. Arpad Pusztai's research has shown that rats fed with GE potatoes had enlarged pancreases, their brains had shrunk, and their immunity had been damaged. Dr. Eric Seralini's research demonstrated that organ damage can occur.

The Committee of Independent Research and Information on Genetic Engineering (CRIIGEN) and universities at Caen and Rouen were able to get raw data of Monsanto's 2002 feeding trials on rats at the European Council order and made it public in 2005. The researchers found that rats fed with three approved corn varieties of GE corn—Mon 863, insecticide products, Mon 810, and Roundup Ready herbicide—suffered organ damage. The data "clearly underlines adverse impacts on kidneys and liver, the dietary, detoxifying organs as well as different levels of damages to the heart, adrenal glands, spleen and haematopoietic systems," according to Dr. Gilles Eric Seralini, a molecular biologist at the University of Caen.

The Biotechnology Industry attacked Dr. Pusztai and Dr. Seralini and every scientist who has done independent research on GMOs. GMOs cannot co-exist with the independence and freedom of science.

A Canadian study showed that traces of the Bt toxin from Monsanto Bt corn were found in the blood of 93 percent of women and 80 percent of their umbilical cord and fetal blood.

Monsanto's false argument for safety was that the Bt toxin in Bt crops poses no danger to human health because the protein breaks down in the human gut. However, the study shows that the Bt toxin survives in the blood of pregnant women and is also detected in fetal blood.

Evidence of liver and kidney toxicity appeared when rats were fed an approved GE maize variety (Mon 863) Similar effects were observed when Monsanto fed its GT-73 Roundup Ready canola variety to rats. The rats showed a 12 percent to 16 percent increase in liver weight. . . .

4. The Myth of Substantial Equivalence

The safety debate has been repeatedly suppressed by bad science. One of the unscientific strategies used to extinguish the safety discussion is to tautologically define a novel organism or novel food created through genetic engineering as "substantially equivalent" to conventional organisms and foods. However, 9 genetically engineered crop or food is different because it has genes from unrelated organisms—it cannot, therefore, be treated as equivalent to a non-genetically engineered crop or food. In fact, the biotechnology industry itself gives up the claim of "substantial equivalence" when it claims patents on GMOs on grounds of novelty.

While governments and government agencies promoting genetic engineering refer to "sound science" as the basis for their decisions, they are manipulating scientific data and research to promote the interests of the biotechnology industry while putting citizen health and the environment at risk. The report by EPA scientists entitled "Genetic Gene: The premature commercial release of genetically engineered bacteria" and the report by Andrew Christiansen "Recombinant Bovine Growth Hormone: Alarming Tests, Unfounded Approval: The Story Behind the Rush to Bring rBGH to the market" show in detail how regulatory agencies have been manipulated on issues of safety.

Scientific agencies have been split and polarized into two communities—a corporate science community and a public science community. The corporate science community participates in distorting and manipulating science. Among the distortions of corporate science is the assumption of "substantial equivalence" which is falsified both by the research done by the public science community as well as by the intellectual property rights claims of the biotechnology industry itself.

When industry wants to avoid risk assessment and issues of liability, the argument used is that the genetically engineered organism is "substantially equivalent" to the non-engineered parent. However, when industry wants property rights, the same GMO becomes "novel" or substantially inequivalent to the parent organism.

When a safety and intellectual property rights discourse of the genetic engineering industry is put side by side what emerges is an unscientific, incoherent undemocratic structure for total control through which absolute rights are claimed and all responsibility is denied and disclaimed. . . .

Another strategy used to suppress good science by bad science is in the design of trials, and the extrapolation of data from artificially constructed contexts to real ecosystems.

The final strategy used is of direct arm twisting, used by the U.S. administration repeatedly to kill the Biosafety protocol in the Convention of Biological Diversity (CBD), even though the US is not a party to the Convention. In spite of it, the countries of the world adopted the Cartagena Protocol on Biosafety in 2000. It was also the strategy used against labeling of genetically engineered foods. However, the world agreed to GMO labelling in the Codex Alimentarius.

While constantly referring to science the US government is in fact promoting bad science, and with it, promoting ecological and human health risks. Instead of generating scientific understanding of the impacts of transferring genes, it is promoting deliberate ignorance.

'Don't Look, Don't See' "The Strategy of Deliberate Ignorance"

The false assumption of "substantial equivalence" of GMOs and non-engineered organisms establishes a strategy of deliberate ignorance. Ignorance of the risks is then treated as proof of safety. "Don't look—don't see" leads to total lack of information about the ecological impacts of genetic engineering.

It is often claimed that there have been no adverse consequences from more than 500 field releases in the U.S. However, the term "releases" is completely misleading. Those tests were largely not scientific tests of realistic ecological concerns, yet "this sort of non-data on non-releases has been cited in policy circles as though 500 true releases have now informed scientists that there are no legitimate scientific concerns."

Recently, for the first time, the data from the U.S. Department of Agriculture field trials were evaluated to see whether they support the safety claims. The Union of Concerned Scientists (UCS) that conducted the evaluation found that the data collected by the USDA on small-scale tests have little value for commercial risk assessment. Many reports fail to even mention—much less measure—environmental risks. Of those reports that allude to environmental risk, most have only visually scanned field plots looking for stray plants or isolated test crops from relatives. The UCS concluded that the observations that "nothing happened" in those hundreds of tests do not say much. In many cases, adverse impacts are subtle and would never be registered by scanning a field. In other cases, failure to observe evidence of the risk is due to the contained conditions of the tests. Many test crops are routinely isolated from wild relatives, a situation that guarantees no outcrossing. The UCS cautioned that ". . . care should be taken in citing the field test record as strong evidence for the safety of genetically engineered crops" (Jane Rissler & Margaret Mellon, *The Ecological Risks of Engineered Crops*, The MIT Press, 1996).

The myth of safety of genetic engineering is manufactured through deliberate ignorance. Deliberate ignorance of the impacts is not proof of safety; it is a guarantee for disaster.

The scientific corruption by the biotech industry and the sacrifice of knowledge sovereignty began in 1992 with the concoction of the false principle of substantial equivalence. The false assumption of "susbtantial equivalence" was introduced by President George H.W. Bush in US policy immediately after the Earth Summit in Rio de Janeiro to blunt the call for biosafety regulation. It was later formalized and introduced in 1993 by OECD (UN Organization for Economic Cooperation and Development), and subsequently endorsed by FAO (UN Food and Agriculture Organization) and WHO (World Health Organization). The OECD document states:

> "For foods and food components from organisms developed by the application of modern biotechnology, the most practical approach to the determination is to consider whether they are substantially equivalent to analogous food products if such exist. The concept of substantial equivalence embodies the idea that existing organisms used as foods, or as a source of food, an be used as the basis for comparison when assessing the safety of human consumption of food or food component that has been modified or is new."

Apart from being vague, this definition is unsound. Foods with Bt toxin genes are not the same as foods without. Herbicide-resistant crops are different from existing varieties because they have new genes for resistance to herbicide. An article by Marc Lappe and others in the Journal of Medicinal Food (1999) has established that Monsanto's Round Up Ready soya beans change the levels of phytoestrogens by 12 to 14 percent. To treat these differences as insignificant when it is a question of safety, and as significant when it is a question of patentability, is totally unscientific. . . .

5. Genetic Contamination Is Inevitable, Co-existence Is Not Possible

In addition to causing harm to public health and ecosystems, GE seeds and crops provide a pathway for corporations to "own" seeds through patents and intellectual property rights (IPRs). Patents provide royalties for the patent holder and corporate monopolies. This translates into super profits for Monsanto. For the farmers this means debt. For example, more than 250,000 Indian farmers have been pushed to suicide in the last decade and a half. Most of the suicides are in the cotton belt where Monsanto has established a seed monopoly through Bt cotton.

At a conference in Washington, D.C. on the Future of Farming, U.S. Secretary of Agriculture, Tom Vilsack, referring to organic farming and GMOs said, "I have two sons, I love them both and I want them to coexist." Filmmaker Debra Grazia responded from the floor "but one of your sons is a bully."

GMOs contaminate non-GE crops. Contamination is inevitable, since cross-pollination is inevitable, within the same species or with close relatives.

The most dramatic case of contamination and genetic pollution is the case of Percy Schmeiser, a Canadian Canola seed grower, whose crop was contaminated by Monsanto's Round-Up Ready Canola. Instead of paying Percy for the damage of contamination in accordance with the "Polluter Pays" principle, Monsanto sued Percy for "Intellectual Property theft."

The contamination of canola in Canada is so severe that 90 percent of certified non-GE Canola seed samples contain GE material.

As Arnold Taylor, Chair of the Organic Agriculture Protection Fund said:

> "There is no organic canola in Canada any more, virtually none, because the seed stock is basically contaminated . . . we've lost that crop."

In the Agriculture Canada study, scientists in Saskatoon found that nearly half of the 70 certified seed samples tested were contaminated with the Roundup Ready gene. Thirty-seven percent had the Liberty Link gene and 59 percent had both.

Another study in the US found that virtually all samples of non-GE corn, soy beans, and canola seed were contaminated by GE varieties. . . .

6. Patents on Seeds and Seed Monopolies

GMOs are intimately linked to seed patents. In fact, patenting of seeds is the real reason why industry is promoting GMOs.

Monopolies over seeds are being established through patents, mergers and cross licensing arrangement.

Monsanto now controls the world's biggest seed company, Scminis, which has bought up [many others]. . . .

Monsanto has cross-licensing arrangements with BASF, Bayer, Dupont, Sygenta and Dow. They have agreements to share patented genetically engineered seed traits with each other. The giant seed corporations are not competing with each other. They are competing with peasants and farmers over the control of the seed supply.

The combination of patents, genetic contamination and the spread of monocultures means that society is rapidly losing its seed freedom and food freedom. Farmers are losing their freedom to have seed and grow organic food free of the threat of contamination by GE crops. Citizens are losing their freedom to know what they are eating, and the choice of whether or not to eat GE free food.

An example of seed monopolies is cotton in India. In a decade, Monsanto gained control of 95 percent of the cotton seed market, and seed prices jumped 8,000 percent. India's Anti-Trust Court, the Monopoly and Restrictive Trade Practices Commission, was forced to rule against Monsanto. High costs of seed and chemicals have pushed 250,000 farmers to suicide with most suicides concentrated in the cotton belt. Monsanto does not just control the seed through patents. It also spreads its control through contamination. After spreading genetic contamination, Monsanto sues farmers as "intellectual property thieves" as it did in the case of Percy Schmeiser. That is why a case has been brought against Monsanto by a coalition of more than 80 groups to stop Monsanto from suing farmers after polluting their crops. (www.pubpat.org/assets/files/seed/OSGATA-v-Monsanto-Complaint.pdf)

Denial of Labeling as the Denial to Consumers of Their Democratic "Right to Know" and "Right to Choose"

In June 1997, the US Trade Representative Charlene Barshefshy warned the European Union Agriculture Commission Franz Fischler not to go through with proposals to require the labeling of genetically modified organisms (GMOs) or their segregation from regular products. The Trade Representative told the Senate Agriculture Committee that the U.S. cannot tolerate a step which would cause a major disruption in US exports to the E.U.

The E.U. Commissioner was under pressure from European Consumers to label GMO foods as their democratic right to inform ation and choice. However, consumer rights were defined by the U.S. trade representative as "arbitrary, politicized and scientifically unjustified" rules. The insistence of consumers to pursue "non-science based restrictions" would lead to a "trade war of major dimensions."

In a letter to the U.S. Secretary on June 12th, 1997, US agribusiness corporations stated the segregation of crops for labeling is both scientifically unjustified and commercially unfeasible.

According to U.S. industry, labeling of foods violates the WTO agreement on free trade. The Sanitary and Phyto-Sanitary measures in WTO are thus viewed by industry as protecting their interests. But the right to information is about democracy and democratic rights cannot be sanctioned by arbitrary technocratic and corporate decision making about what is "sound science" and what is not.

The denial of labelling is one dimension of totalitarian structures associated with the introduction of genetical engineering in food and agriculture. Navdanya filed a case in India demanding labeling of GM foods but the direct intervention by the U.S. embassy prevented the labeling law from being introduced by the Indian Health Ministry.

On July 5, 2011 Codex Alimentarius, the international food safety body, recognized the right of countries to label GMO foods. This ended twenty years of an international struggle. As the Consumer International states: "The new Codex agreement means that any country wishing to adopt GM food labeling will no longer face the threat of a legal challenge from the World Trade Organization (WTO). This is because national measures based on Codex guidance or standards cannot be challenged as a barrier to trade."

We now need to build on this right-to–know principle and ensure GMO labeling in all countries.

GMOs Are an Issue of Food Democracy

This is why GE crops are an issue for democracy. Food democracy is everyone's right and responsibility. We have food democracy when we can exercise our choice to have GMO free seed and food. This choice is being undermined as seed is genetically engineered and patented, as food systems are increasingly controlled by giant corporations, as chemical pollution and genetic pollution spread uncontrolled, making our food unsafe. Each of us must defend our food freedom and urge our governments to protect the rights of their citizens and stop supporting corporate takeover of our seeds and foods. Each of us is vital in creating food democracy. We invite you to join us to defend the most fundamental freedom: our food freedom.

Vandana Shiva is an Indian physicist, environmentalist, and campaigner for sustainability and social justice. She is director/founder of The Research Foundation for Science, Technology and Ecology (RFSTE) and director/founder of Navdanya. She has received many awards, including the Right Livelihood Award and most recently the Sydney Peace Prize. Her most recent book is *Staying Alive: Women, Ecology, and Development* (South End Press, 2010).

EXPLORING THE ISSUE

Are Genetically Modified Foods Safe to Eat?

Critical Thinking and Reflection

1. What does it mean to say that a particular technology is "unnatural"?
2. What is the greatest threat to human health posed by genetically modified (GM) foods?
3. Should tests of GM foods performed by industry scientists be trusted?
4. Should regulation of a new technology be based on demonstrated risks? On potential risks? On the nature of the press coverage?

Is There Common Ground?

The participants in the debate over GM foods agree that it is important to ensure a healthy, safe, and abundant food supply. They differ on whether genetic engineering helps to achieve this aim.

1. It can be instructive to consider other threats to a healthy, safe, and abundant food supply. Among these threats are plant diseases known as rusts and blights. Read Rachel Ehrenberg, "Rust Never Sleeps," *Science News* (September 25, 2010), and discuss the global effects of a massive rust outbreak.
2. List as many other threats to a healthy, safe, and abundant food supply as you can.
3. How many of these threats might be addressed using genetic engineering? Using other technologies?

Additional Resources

Robin Mather, "The Threats from Genetically Modified Foods," *Mother Earth News* (April–May 2012).

Henry I. Miller and Gregory Conko, *The Frankenfood Myth: How Protest and Politics Threaten the Biotech Revolution* (Praeger, 2004).

National Research Council and Committee on the Impact of Biotechnology on Farm-Level Economics and Sustainability, *The Impact of Genetically Engineered Crops on Farm Sustainability in the United States* (National Academies Press, 2010) (www.nap.edu/catalog.php?record_id=12804).

Jeffrey M. Smith, *Seeds of Deception: Exposing Industry and Government Lies about the Safety of the Genetically Engineered Foods You're Eating* (Chelsea Green, 2003).

Create Central

www.mhhe.com/createcentral

Internet References . . .

World Health Organization

The World Health Organization of the United Nations provides links to recent reports and meetings about the safety of GM foods on its Biotechnology page.

www.who.int/foodsafety/biotech/en/

National Institute of Environmental Health Sciences

The National Institute of Environmental Health Sciences studies the health risks of numerous environmental factors, many of which are associated with the use of technology.

www.niehs.nih.gov

Unit 4

UNIT

SPACE

Many interesting controversies arise in connection with technologies that are so new that they may sound more like science fiction than fact. Some examples are technologies that allow the exploration of space, the detection (and perhaps prevention) of space-based threats, and the search for extraterrestrial intelligence. We have capabilities undreamed of in earlier ages, and they raise genuine, important questions about what it is to be a human being, the limits on human freedom in a technological age, the degree to which humans are helpless victims of fate, and the place of humanity in the broader universe. They also raise questions of how we should respond: Should we accept the new devices and abilities offered by scientists and engineers? Or should we reject them? Should we use them to make human life safer and more secure? Or should we remain, as in past ages, at the mercy of the heavens?

Selected, Edited, and with Issue Framing Material by:
Thomas A. Easton, *Thomas College*

ISSUE

Can We Stop an Asteroid or Comet Impact?

YES: Committee to Review Near-Earth-Object Surveys and Hazard Mitigation Strategies Space Studies Board, from "Defending Planet Earth: Near-Earth-Object Surveys and Hazard Mitigation Strategies" (National Academies Press, 2010)

NO: Clark R. Chapman, from "What Will Happen When the Next Asteroid Strikes?" *Astronomy Magazine* (May 2011)

Learning Outcomes

After studying this issue, students will be able to explain:

- Why asteroid and comet impacts are considered a risk to society.
- What options are available to prevent asteroid and comet impacts or mitigate their effects.
- The importance of advance planning to deal with potential disasters such as asteroid and comet impacts.

ISSUE SUMMARY

YES: The Committee to Review Near-Earth-Object Surveys and Hazard Mitigation Strategies Space Studies Board argues that though the probability that a near-Earth object (NEO) will strike Earth in the near future is small, the potential damage is so great that investing in identifying and tracking near-Earth objects (NEOs), and researching ways of preventing impact, is worthwhile. Because the NEO threat is global, there is a need for an international entity to deal with the threat.

NO: Clark R. Chapman argues that though the consequences of an asteroid or comet impact would be catastrophic, efforts to prevent the impact would be futile. It is far more appropriate to incorporate such impact disasters into more conventional disaster planning.

Thomas Jefferson once said that he would rather think scientists were crazy than believe that rocks could fall from the sky. Since then, we have recognized that rocks do indeed fall from the sky. Most are quite small and do no more than making pretty streaks across the sky as they burn up in the atmosphere; they are known as meteors. Some—known as meteorites—are large enough to reach the ground and even to do damage. Every once in a while, the news reports one that crashed through a car or house roof, as indeed one did in January 2007 in New Jersey. Very rarely, a meteorite is big enough to make a crater in the Earth's surface, much like the ones that mark the face of the Moon. An example is Meteor Crater in Arizona, almost a mile across, created some 50,000 years ago by a meteorite 150 feet in diameter. (The Meteor Crater website, www.meteorcrater.com/, includes an animation of the impact.) A more impressive impact is the one that occurred 65 million years ago, when a comet or asteroid 10 kilometers (6 miles) in diameter struck near what is now Chicxulub, Mexico: The results included the extinction of the dinosaurs (as well as a great many other species). Chicxulub-scale events are very rare; a hundred million years may pass between them. Meteor Crater-scale events may occur every thousand years, releasing as much energy as a 100-megaton nuclear bomb and destroying an area the size of a city. And it has been calculated that a human being is more likely to die as the result of such an event than in an airplane crash.

It is not just Hollywood sci-fi, *Deep Impact* and *Armageddon*. Some people think we really should be worried. We should be doing our best to identify meteoroids (as they are called before they become meteors or meteorites) in space, plot their trajectories, tell when they are coming our way, and even develop ways of deflecting them before they cause enormous losses of life and property. In 1984, Thomas Gehrels, a University of Arizona astronomer, initiated the Spacewatch project, which aimed to identify space rocks that cross Earth's orbit. In the early 1990s, NASA workshops considered the hazards of these rocks. NASA now funds the international Spaceguard Survey (http://impact.arc.nasa.gov/intro.cfm), which finds about 25 new near-Earth asteroids every month and has identified more than 600 asteroids over 1 kilometer (2/3 of a mile) in diameter; none seem likely to strike Earth in the next century. On the other hand, in February 2013 an asteroid the size of a skyscraper missed Earth by about 17,000 miles and a 10-ton meteor exploded over Chelyabinsk, Russia (the shock wave broke windows and caused numerous injuries; see Richard Stone, "Siberian Meteor Spurs Dash for Data, Calls for Safeguards," *Science*, March 8, 2013). There are many other large rocks in space, and eventual large impacts on Earth are very likely. According to NASA, there are some 4,700 asteroids more than 100 meters (330 feet) across, of which only 20–30 percent have actually been discovered so far. Greg Easterbrook, "The Sky Is Falling," *Atlantic* (June 2008), argues that human society faces so much risk from asteroid and comet impacts that Congress should place a much higher priority on detecting potential impactors and devising ways to stop them.

In the debate over the risks of near-Earth object (NEO) impacts on Earth, there are a few certainties: They have happened before, they will happen again, and they come in various sizes. As Mike Reynolds says, in "Earth Under Fire," *Astronomy* (August 2006), the question is not whether impacts will happen in the future. "It's just a matter of when and how big the object will be." Many past craters mark the Earth, even though many more have been erased by plate tectonics and erosion. Ivan Semeniuk, "Asteroid Impact," *Mercury* (November/December 2002), says, "If there is one question that best sums up the current state of thinking about the impact hazard, it is this: At what size do we need to act? In the shooting gallery that is our solar system, everyone agrees we are the target of both cannonballs and BBs. The hard part is deciding where to draw the line that separates them. For practical reasons, that line is now set at 1 kilometer. Not only are objects of this diameter a global threat (no matter where they hit, we're all affected to some degree), they are also the easiest to spot." However, as Richard A. Kerr notes, "The Small Ones Can Kill You, Too," *Science* (September 19, 2003). Edward T. Lu, "Stop the Killer Rocks," *Scientific American* (December 2011), argues that "All civilizations that inhabit planetary systems must eventually deal with the asteroid threat, or they will go the way of the dinosaurs." Action is essential.

What if a "killer rock" does present a threat? In September 2002, NASA held a "Workshop on Scientific Requirements for Mitigation of Hazardous Comets and Asteroids," which concluded "that the prime impediment to further advances in this field is the lack of any assigned responsibility to any national or international organization to prepare for a disruptive collision and the absence of any authority to act in preparation for some future collision mitigation attempt" and urged that "NASA be assigned the responsibility to advance this field" and "a new and adequately funded program be instituted at NASA to create, through space missions and allied research, the specialized knowledge base needed to respond to a future threat of a collision from an asteroid or comet nucleus." The results of the workshop appeared as *Mitigation of Hazardous Impacts Due to Asteroids and Comets* (Cambridge University Press, 2004).

The Organization for Economic Cooperation and Development (OECD) Global Science Forum held a "Workshop on Near Earth Objects: Risks, Policies and Actions" in January 2003. It too concluded that more work is needed. In May 2005, the House Science Committee approved a bill to establish and fund a NASA program to detect and assess near-Earth asteroids and comets down to 100 meters in diameter. See also David H. Levy, "Asteroid Alerts: A Risky Business," *Sky & Telescope* (April 2006). NASA's March 2007 "Near-Earth Object Survey and Deflection: Analysis of Alternatives, Report to Congress" argues that although progress is being made, much more would be possible if Congress increased funding.

Given political will and funding, what could be done if a threat were identified? Richard Stone, "Target Earth," *National Geographic* (August 2008), says that "Two facts are clear: Whether in 10 years or 500, a day of reckoning is inevitable. More heartening, for the first time ever we have the means to prevent a natural disaster of epic proportions." There have been numerous proposals, from launching nuclear missiles to pulverize approaching space rocks to sending astronauts (or robots) to install rocket engines and deflect the rocks onto safe paths (perhaps into the sun to forestall future hazards).

At the moment, Europe appears to be taking the lead in the effort to ward off disaster from the skies. In January 2012, the German space agency's (DLR) Institute of Planetary Research in Berlin held the kickoff meeting for Project NEOShield, an international effort to study how to prevent asteroid and comet impacts. See www.neoshield.net/en/index.htm and A. W. Harris, et al., "A Global Approach to Near-Earth Object Impact Threat Mitigation" (http://elib.dlr.de/70019/1/NEOShield_paper_pdc11.pdf).

A December 2008 study by the U.S. Air Force found that we are woefully unprepared for a NEO impact; see David Shiga, "Asteroid Attack: Putting Earth's Defences to the Test," *New Scientist* (September 23, 2009). Not much has changed since Bill Cooke, "Killer Impact," *Astronomy* (December 2004), warned that for the foreseeable future, our only real hope will be evacuation of the target zone. All proposed methods of warding off disaster require a stronger space program than any nation now has. Lacking such a program, knowing that a major rock is on the way would surely be of little comfort. However, given sufficient notice—on the order of decades—a space program might be mobilized to deal with the threat.

In the YES selection, the National Research Council's Space Studies Board's Committee to Review Near-Earth-Object Surveys and Hazard Mitigation

Strategies argues that though the probability that a near-Earth object (NEO) will strike Earth in the near future is small, the potential damage is so great that investing in identifying and tracking NEOs, and researching ways of preventing impact, is worthwhile. Because the NEO threat is global, there is a need for an international entity to deal with the threat. In the NO selection, planetary scientist Clark R. Chapman argues that though the consequences of an asteroid or comet impact would be catastrophic, efforts to prevent the impact would be futile. It is far more appropriate to incorporate such impact disasters into more conventional disaster planning.

YES

Committee to Review Near-Earth-Object Surveys and Hazard Mitigation Strategies Space Studies Board

Defending Planet Earth: Near-Earth-Object Surveys and Hazard Mitigation Strategies

Introduction

Our planet inhabits a hazardous environment. Earth is continually bombarded by cosmic objects. Luckily for its inhabitants, most of these objects are very small and cause no harm to life. Some, however, are large and cause considerable harm. Evidence of these collisions, large and small, is abundant, from the dense defacement of Mercury and the Moon to the craters festooning the surfaces of even small asteroids. Although impacts of cosmic objects on Earth have occurred since its very formation, humanity has been at best dimly aware of these events until very recently. Only two centuries ago it was widely doubted that objects orbiting the Sun could or would collide with Earth.

In general, scientists cannot predict precise times and locations of future impacts but can make statistical statements about the probability of an impact. Objects larger than about 30 meters in diameter probably strike Earth only about once every few centuries, and objects greater than about 300 meters in diameter only once per hundred millennia. Even objects only 30 meters in diameter can cause immense damage. The cosmic intruder that exploded over Siberia in 1908 may have been only a few tens of meters in size, yet this explosion severely damaged a forest of more than 2,000 square kilometers. Had an airburst of such magnitude occurred over New York City, hundreds of thousands of deaths might have resulted.

Assessing risk is difficult primarily because of the lack of sufficient data. . . . For impactor diameters exceeding about 2 to 3 kilometers, worldwide damage is possible, thus affecting all of humanity and its entire living space (the minimum size at which impactors can cause global devastation is still uncertain). While such a collision is exceedingly rare, the consequences are enormous, almost incalculable. This presents the classic "zero times infinity" problem: nearly zero probability of occurrence but nearly infinite devastation per occurrence. Humanity has the capacity to detect and perhaps to counter such an impending natural disaster. This capacity, and interest in exercising it, have developed and sharply increased in the space age, most likely sparked by the discovery in the late 1980s of the approximately 200-kilometer-diameter Chicxulub Crater formed by an impact . . . 65 million years ago in the Yucatan Peninsula. The asteroid or comet that caused this crater is estimated to have been about 10 kilometers in diameter; its impact wrought global devastation, likely snuffing out species, including dinosaurs, in huge numbers. Later, in the 1990s, the collision of comet Shoemaker-Levy 9 with Jupiter emphasized that impacts are currently possible.

To assess the current hazards, surveys were undertaken in the 1970s and were greatly augmented in the 1990s in order to discover and track all NEOs to determine the likelihood that one or more would collide with Earth. These surveys, involving relatively small telescopes whose primary mirrors ranged in diameter from 0.6 to 1.2 meters, were seeking objects with diameters greater than 1 kilometer; also detected were many smaller objects that approached Earth closely enough to be seen.

Congress requested that the National Research Council (NRC) undertake a study, sponsored by NASA, to address two tasks:

Task 1: NEO Surveys

What is the optimal approach to completing the NEO census called for in the George E. Brown, Jr. Near-Earth-Object Survey section of the 2005 NASA Authorization Act to detect, track, catalogue, and characterize the physical . . . characteristics of at least 90 percent of potentially hazardous NEOs larger than 140 meters in diameter by the end of year 2020? Specific issues to be considered include, but are not limited to, the following:

- What observational, data-reduction, and data-analysis resources are necessary to achieve the Congressional mandate of detecting, tracking, and cataloguing the NEO population of interest?
- What physical characteristics of individual objects above and beyond the determination of accurate orbits should be obtained during the survey to support mitigation efforts?
- What role could be played by the National Science Foundation's Arecibo Observatory in characterizing these objects?

- What are possible roles of other ground- and space-based facilities in addressing survey goals, e.g., potential contributions of the Large Synoptic Survey Telescope (LSST) and the Panoramic Survey Telescope and Rapid Response System (Pan STARRS)?

Task 2: NEO Hazard Mitigation

What is the optimal approach to developing a deflection capability, including options with a significant international component? Issues to be considered include, but are not limited to, the following:

- What mitigation strategy should be followed if a potentially hazardous NEO is identified?
- What are the relative merits and costs of various deflection scenarios that have been proposed?

In response to this assignment from Congress, the National Research Council created a steering committee—the Committee to Review Near-Earth-Object Surveys and Hazard Mitigation Strategies—and two panels (one for each task: the Survey/Detection Panel and the Mitigation Panel) to undertake a study to address these issues.

Although the possibility of a large NEO impact with Earth is remote, conducting surveys of NEOs and studying means to mitigate collisions with them can best be viewed as a form of insurance. It seems prudent to expend some resources to prepare to counter this collision threat. Most homeowners, for example, carry fire insurance, although no one expects her or his house to burn down anytime soon. The distinction between insurance for the NEO collision hazard and other "natural" hazards, such as earthquakes and hurricanes, is that the possibility of detecting and preventing most serious collisions now exists. In the case of earthquakes, for example, despite extensive efforts, primarily in China, Japan, and the United States, neither the epoch nor the severity of an earthquake can yet be reliably predicted. Governments do nonetheless fund the analog of an insurance policy through studies of this hazard and through the design and construction of earthquake-resistant structures and in development of plans for response and recovery. The goal is to reduce both the number of fatalities and the damage to property from earthquakes. According to figures from the NRC (2006) report *Improved Seismic Monitoring—Improved Decision-Making: Assessing the Value of Reduced Uncertainty,* the United States alone now spends well in excess of $100 million annually on this suite of earthquake-related efforts. The annual death rate in the United States from earthquakes, averaged over the past two centuries for which data are available, is approximately 20 per year, with 75 percent of that figure attributed to the 1906 San Francisco Earthquake, mostly from related fires. For Japan, both the expenditure and the fatality figures are far larger. China and other parts of Asia have also suffered massive casualties from earthquakes. The September 2009 earthquakes that caused loss of life in Indonesia, Samoa, and American Samoa, and the devastating January 2010 earthquake in Haiti and February 2010 earthquake in Chile, highlight this ongoing threat to human life.

Given the low risk over a period of, say, a decade, how much should the United States invest in NEO insurance? This question requires a political, not a scientific, answer. Yet the question bears on the committee's charge. The committee was asked to recommend the optimal approach for each of the tasks, with the definition of "optimal" left to the committee. A unique characteristic of the "NEO research premiums," which distinguishes them from the usual types of insurance, is that the premiums would be directed entirely toward the prevention of the catastrophe.

In no case, however, is it wise to consider the application of techniques more than a few decades into the future. The technologies available at that time would likely be both more efficient and more effective, rendering present approaches obsolete. However, it is not wise to wait for those future technologies, leaving Earth unaware and threats to Earth unmitigated in the meantime. . . .

Summary

The United States spends about $4 million annually searching for near-Earth objects (NEOs), according to NASA. The goal is to detect those that may collide with Earth. The funding helps to operate several observatories that scan the sky searching for NEOs, but, as explained below, it is insufficient to detect the majority of NEOs that may present a tangible threat to humanity. A smaller amount of funding (significantly less than $1 million per year) supports the study of ways to protect Earth from such a potential collision ("mitigation").

Congress established two mandates for the search for NEOs by NASA. The first, in 1998 and now referred to as the Spaceguard Survey, called for the agency to discover 90 percent of NEOs with a diameter of 1 kilometer or greater within 10 years. An object of this limiting size is considered by many experts to be the minimum that could produce global devastation if it struck Earth. NASA is close to achieving this goal and should reach it within a few years. However, as the recent (2009) discovery of an approximately 2- to 3-kilometer-diameter NEO demonstrates, there are still large objects to be detected.

The second mandate, established in 2005, known as the George E. Brown, Jr. Near-Earth-Object Survey Act, called for NASA to detect 90 percent of NEOs 140 meters in diameter or greater by 2020. As the National Research Council's (NRC's) Committee to Review Near-Earth-Object Surveys and Hazard Mitigation Strategies noted in its August 2009 interim report (NRC, 2009):

Finding: Congress has mandated that NASA discover 90 percent of all near-Earth objects 140 meters in diameter or greater by 2020. The administration has

not requested and Congress has not appropriated new funds to meet this objective. Only limited facilities are currently involved in this survey/discovery effort, funded by NASA's existing budget.

Finding: The current near-Earth-object surveys cannot meet the goals of the 2005 George E. Brown, Jr. Near-Earth Object Survey Act directing NASA to discover 90 percent of all near-Earth objects 140 meters in diameter or greater by 2020.

The Survey and Detection of Near-Earth Objects

The charge from Congress to the NRC committee was stated as two tasks. The first asks for the "optimal approach" to completing the George E. Brown, Jr. Near-Earth-Object Survey. The second asks for the same approach to developing a capability to avert an NEO-Earth collision and for options that include "a significant international component." . . .

Regarding the first task of its charge, the committee concluded that it is infeasible to complete the NEO census mandated in 2005 on the required time scale (2020), in part because for the past 5 years the administration has requested no funds, and the Congress has appropriated none, for this purpose. The committee concludes that there are two primary options for completing the survey:

Finding: The selected approach to completing the George E. Brown, Jr. Near-Earth-Object Survey will depend on nonscientific factors:

- **If the completion of the survey as close as possible to the original 2020 deadline is considered more important, a space mission conducted in concert with observations using a suitable ground-based telescope and selected by peer-reviewed competition is the better approach. This combination could complete the survey well before 2030, perhaps as early as 2022 if funding were appropriated quickly.**
- **If cost conservation is deemed more important, the use of a large ground-based telescope is the better approach. Under this option, the survey could not be completed by the original 2020 deadline, but it could be completed before 2030. To achieve the intended cost-effectiveness, the funding to construct the telescope must come largely as funding from non-NEO programs.**

Multiple factors will drive the decision on how to approach completion of this survey. These factors include, but are not limited to, the perceived urgency for completing the survey as close as possible to the original 2020 deadline, the availability of funds to complete the survey, and the acceptability of the risk associated with the construction and operation of various ground- and space-based options.

Of the ground-based options, the Large Synoptic Survey Telescope (LSST) and the Panoramic Survey Telescope and Rapid Response System, mentioned in the statement of task, and the additional options submitted to the committee in response to its public request for suggestions during the beginning of this study, the most capable appears to be the LSST. The LSST is to be constructed in Chile and has several science missions as well as the capability of observing NEOs. Although the primary mirror for the LSST has been cast and is being polished, the telescope has not been fully funded and is pending prioritization in the astronomy and astrophysics decadal survey of the NRC that is currently underway.

Unless unexpected technical problems interfere, a space-based option should provide the fastest means to complete the survey. However, unlike ground-based telescopes, space options carry a modest launch risk and a more limited lifetime: ground-based telescopes have far longer useful lifetimes and could be employed for continued NEO surveys and for new science projects. (Ground-based telescopes generally have an annual operating cost that is approximately 10 percent of their design and construction costs.)

The committee notes that objects smaller than 140 meters in diameter are also capable of causing significant damage to Earth. The best-known case from recent history is the 1908 impact of an object at Tunguska in the Siberian wilderness that devastated more than 2,000 square kilometers of forest. It has been estimated that the size of this object was on the order of approximately 70 meters in diameter, but recent research indicates that it could have been substantially smaller (30 to 50 meters in diameter), with much of the damage that it caused being due to shock waves from the explosion of the object in Earth's atmosphere. The committee strongly stresses that this new conclusion is preliminary and must be independently validated. Since smaller objects are more numerous than larger ones, however, this new result, if correct, implies an increase in the frequency of such events to approximately once in three centuries.

All told, the committee was struck by the many uncertainties that suffuse the subject of NEOs, including one other related example: Do airbursts from impactors in this size range over an ocean cause tsunamis that can severely damage a coastline? This uncertainty and others have led the committee to the following recommendation:

Recommendation: Because recent studies of meteor airbursts have suggested that near-Earth objects as small as 30 to 50 meters in diameter could be highly destructive, surveys should attempt to detect as many 30- to 50-meter-diameter objects as possible. This search for smaller-diameter objects should not be allowed to interfere with the survey for objects 140 meters in diameter or greater.

In all cases, the data-reduction and data-analysis resources necessary to achieve the congressional mandate would be covered by the survey projects themselves and by a continuation of the current funding of the Smithsonian Astrophysical Observatory's Minor Planet Center.

Characterization and the Arecibo and Goldstone Observatories

Obtaining the orbits and the physical properties of NEOs is known as characterization and is primarily needed to inform planning for any active defense of Earth. Such defense would be carried out through a suitable attack on any object predicted with near certainty to otherwise collide with Earth and cause significant damage. The apparently huge variation in the physical properties of NEOs seems to render infeasible the development of a comprehensive inventory through in situ investigations by suitably instrumented spacecraft: the costs would be truly astronomical. A spacecraft reconnaissance mission might make good sense to conduct on an object that, without human intervention, would hit Earth with near certainty. Such a mission would be feasible provided there was sufficient warning time for the results to suitably inform the development of an attack mission to cause the object to miss colliding with Earth.

In addition to spacecraft reconnaissance missions as needed, the committee concluded that vigorous, ground-based characterization at modest cost is important for the NEO task. Modest funding could support optical observations of already-known and newly discovered asteroids and comets to obtain some types of information on this broad range of objects, such as their reflectivity as a function of color, to help infer their surface properties and mineralogy, and their rotation properties. In addition, the complementary radar systems at the Arecibo Observatory in Puerto Rico and the Goldstone Solar System Radar in California are powerful facilities for characterization within their reach in the solar system, a maximum of about one-tenth of the Earth-Sun distance. Arecibo which has a maximum sensitivity about 20-fold higher than Goldstone's but does not have nearly as good sky coverage as Goldstone can, for example, model the three-dimensional shapes of (generally very odd-shaped) asteroids and estimate their surface characteristics, as well as determine whether an asteroid has a (smaller) satellite or satellites around it, all important to know for planning active defense. Also, from a few relatively closely spaced (in time) observations, radar can accurately determine the orbits of NEOs, which has the advantage of being able to calm public fears quickly (or possibly, in some cases, to show that they are warranted).

Finding: The Arecibo and Goldstone radar systems play a unique role in the characterization of NEOs, providing unmatched accuracy in orbit determination and offering insight into size, shape, surface structure, and other properties for objects within their latitude coverage and detection range.

Recommendation: Immediate action is required to ensure the continued operation of the Arecibo Observatory at a level sufficient to maintain and staff the radar facility. Additionally, NASA and the National Science Foundation should support a vigorous program of radar observations of NEOs at Arecibo, and NASA should support such a program at Goldstone for orbit determination and the characterization of physical properties.

For both Arecibo and Goldstone, continued funding is far from assured, not only for the radar systems but for the entire facilities. The incremental annual funding required to maintain and operate the radar systems, even at their present relatively low levels of operation, is about $2 million at each facility. The annual funding for Arecibo is approximately $12 million. Goldstone is one of the three deep-space communications facilities of the Deep Space Network, and its overall funding includes additional equipment for space communications.

Mitigation

"Mitigation" refers to all means of defending Earth and its inhabitants from the effects of an impending impact by an NEO. Four main types of defense are discussed in this report. The choice of which one(s) to use depends primarily on the warning time available and on the mass and speed of the impactor. The types of mitigation are these:

1. *Civil defense.* This option may be the only one feasible for warning times shorter than perhaps a year or two, and depending on the state of readiness for applying an active defense, civil defense may be the only choice for even longer times.
2. *"Slow-push" or "slow-pull" methods.* For these options the orbit of the target object would be changed so that it avoided collision with Earth. The most effective way to change the orbit, given a constraint on the energy that would be available, is to change the velocity of the object, either in or opposite to the direction in which it is moving (direct deflection—that is, moving the object sideways—is *much* less efficient). These options take considerable time, on the order of decades, to be effective, and even then they would be useful only for objects whose diameters are no larger than 100 meters or so.
3. *Kinetic impactors.* In these mitigation scenarios, the target's orbit would be changed by the sending of one or more spacecraft with very massive payload(s) to impact directly on the target at high speed in its direction, or opposite to its direction, of motion. The effectiveness of this option depends not only on the mass of the target but also on any net enhancement resulting from material being thrown out of the target, in the direction opposite to that of the payload, upon impact.
4. *Nuclear explosions.* For nontechnical reasons, this would likely be a last resort, but it is also the most powerful technique and could take several different forms, as discussed in the report. The nuclear option would be usable for objects up to a few kilometers in diameter.

For larger NEOs (more than a few kilometers in diameter), which would be on the scale that would inflict serious global damage and, perhaps, mass extinctions, there is at present no feasible defense. Luckily such events are exceedingly rare, the last known being about 65 million years ago.

Of the foregoing options, only kinetic impact has been demonstrated (by way of the very successful Deep Impact spacecraft that collided with comet Tempel-1 in July 2006. The other options have not advanced past the conceptual stage. Even Deep Impact, a 10-kilometer-per-second impact on a 6-kilometer-diameter body, was on a scale far lower than would be required for Earth defense for an NEO on the order of 100 meters in diameter, and it impacted on a relatively large—and therefore easier to hit—object.

Although the committee was charged in its statement of task with determining the "optimal approach to developing a deflection capability," it concluded that work in this area is relatively new and immature. The committee therefore concluded that the "optimal approach" starts with a research program.

Further Research

Struck by the significant unknowns in many aspects of NEO hazards that could yield to Earth-based research, the committee recommends the following:

Recommendation: The United States should initiate a peer-reviewed, targeted research program in the area of impact hazard and mitigation of NEOs. Because this is a policy-driven, applied program, it should not be in competition with basic scientific research programs or funded from them. This research program should encompass three principal task areas: surveys, characterization, and mitigation. The scope should include analysis, simulation, and laboratory experiments. . . .

National and International Cooperation

Responding effectively to hazards posed by NEOs requires the joint efforts of diverse institutions and individuals, with organization playing a key role. Because NEOs are a global threat, efforts to deal with them could involve international cooperation from the outset. (However, this is one area in which one nation, acting alone, could address such a global threat.) The report discusses possible means to organize, both nationally and internationally, responses to the hazards posed by NEOs. Arrangements at present are largely ad hoc and informal here and abroad, and they involve both government and private entities.

The committee discussed ways to organize the national community to deal with the hazards of NEOs and also recommends an approach to international cooperation:

Recommendation: The United States should take the lead in organizing and empowering a suitable international entity to participate in developing a detailed plan for dealing with the NEO hazard.

One major concern with such an organization, especially in the area of preparing for disasters, is the maintenance of attention and morale, given the expected exceptionally long intervals between harmful events. Countering the tendency to complacency would be a continuing challenge. This problem would be mitigated if, for example, the civil defense aspects were combined in the National Response Framework with those for other natural hazards.

Recent Near-Earth-Object-Related Events

The U.S. Department of Defense, which operates sensors in Earth orbit capable of detecting the high-altitude explosion of small NEOs, has in the past shared this information with the NEO science community. The committee concluded that this data sharing is important for understanding issues such as the population size of small NEOs and the hazard that they pose. This sharing is also important for validating airburst simulations, characterizing the physical properties of small NEOs (such as their strength), and assisting in the recovery of meteorites.

Recommendation: Data from NEO airburst events observed by the U.S. Department of Defense satellites should be made available to the scientific community to allow it to improve understanding of the NEO hazards to Earth.

In 2008, Congress passed the Consolidated Appropriations Act calling for the Office of Science and Technology Policy to determine by October 2010 which agency should be responsible for conducting the NEO survey and detection and mitigation program. Several agencies are possible candidates for such a role.

During its deliberations the committee learned of several efforts outside the United States to develop spacecraft to search for categories of NEOs. In particular, Canada's Near-Earth Object Surveillance Satellite, or NEOSSat, and Germany's AsteroidFinder are interesting and capable small-scale missions that will detect a small percentage of specific types of NEOs, those primarily inside Earth's orbit. These spacecraft will not accomplish the goals of the George E. Brown, Jr. Near-Earth Object Survey Act of 2005. However, they highlight the fact that other countries are beginning to consider the NEO issue seriously. Such efforts also represent an opportunity for future international cooperation and coordination in the search for potentially hazardous NEOs. In addition, the committee was impressed with the European Space Agency's early development of the Don Quijote spacecraft mission, which would consist of an observing spacecraft and a kinetic impactor. This mission, though not funded, would have value for testing a mitigation technique and could still be an opportunity for international cooperation in this area.

Finally, the committee points out a current estimate of the long-term average annual human fatality rate from impactors: slightly under 100. At first blush, one is inclined to dismiss this rate as trivial in the general scheme of things. However, one must also consider the extreme damage that could be inflicted by a single impact; this presents the classic problem of the conflict between "extremely important" and "extremely rare." The committee considers work on this problem as insurance, with the premiums devoted wholly toward preventing the tragedy. The question then is: What is a reasonable expenditure on annual premiums? The committee offers a few possibilities for what could perhaps be accomplished at three different levels of funding; it is, however, the political leadership of the country that determines the amount to be spent on scanning the skies for potential hazards and preparing our defenses.

The Committee To Review Near-Earth-Object Surveys And Hazard Mitigation Strategies was formed by the Space Studies Board, Aeronautics and Space Engineering Board, Division on Engineering and Physical Sciences, National Research Council of the National Academies, in response to a 2008 request from James L. Green, director, Planetary Science Division, NASA, and Craig Foltz, acting director, Astronomical Sciences Division, National Science Foundation (NSF).

Clark R. Chapman

NO

What Will Happen When the Next Asteroid Strikes?

On October 6, 2008, I was on my way to the Johns Hopkins Applied Physics Laboratory when I turned on the news in the car and could hardly believe my ears: An asteroid discovered late the previous night was predicted to strike Earth in just a few hours—at 2:46 UT on October 7, to be precise. Ground zero would be in Sudan's Nubian Desert, just south of the Egyptian border.

For 2 decades, astronomers had reported minute chances that an asteroid might strike in the distant future, and also about "close calls" as near-Earth asteroids (NEAs) sailed by our planet at distances comparable to that of the Moon. This, however, was the first confident prediction in history of an impending asteroid impact—and it would happen less than 20 hours after discovery.

Fortunately, the incoming rock wasn't dangerous, measuring just 10 to 13 feet (3 to 4 meters) across. But a larger asteroid would cause significant destruction; would we have enough warning?

Collecting Space Rocks

A congressional hearing in 1998 mandated that scientists discover and catalog 90 percent of NEAs larger than 0.6 mile (1 kilometer) wide within 10 years, thus finding them years or decades before one might strike. Immediately after the mandate, astronomers formed the Spaceguard Survey to do just that. (It is a bit behind schedule, having found about 83 percent of them by late 2010.) The hope is we find an NEA on a likely collision course with enough time to do something about it: for example, design and launch a spacecraft mission to tug on the object or run into it. This would nudge it onto a slightly different path, missing Earth.

The Catalina Sky Survey (CSS) telescopes on Mount Bigelow, north of Tucson, Arizona, are part of the Spaceguard Survey, and it was CSS's Richard Kowalski who first noted the moving spot of light October 6, 2008, which scientists later dubbed 2008 TC_3. He immediately reported it to the Minor Planet Center in Cambridge, Massachusetts, which made a preliminary calculation of the asteroid's orbit. This time, there would be no decades of warning—just hours. Luckily, physicists had calculated that objects like 2008 TC_3 would explode brilliantly, but harmlessly, high in the atmosphere. Thus, asteroids smaller than about 100 feet (30m) were nothing to fear, they said.

2008 TC_3 exploded high in the atmosphere, but not exactly harmlessly. Thousands of stone fragments struck the desert beneath its flight path (an area perhaps 20 miles [32 km] long and a few miles across). About 600 pieces have been recovered so far. Ground zero was empty except for a small train station, which scientists named the meteorites after (Almahata Sitta means "Station 6" in Arabic).

A Range of Consequences

2008 TC_3 was a small rock, so what about larger ones? When will the "Big One" hit? (And what defines the "Big One"?) Asteroids tend to travel at similar speeds—about 100 times faster than a jet airliner—so it is primarily their masses that determine their destructive potential when they strike Earth.

The monster object that struck 65 million years ago—eradicating most species of life, including dinosaurs, and paving the way for the emergence of mammals—was a "Big One." It was probably about 6 to 9 miles (10 to 15 km) wide. Its explosive force of a hundred million megatons of TNT disrupted the planet's ecosphere and caused the mass extinction. (Scientists call this collision the K-T boundary event because it represents the sharp change in fossils at the boundary between the Cretaceous [K] and Tertiary [T] periods.) Such an event could happen again this century, but the odds are exceedingly small; the Spaceguard Survey tells us that no NEA even close to that size will hit. Huge objects impact every hundred million years or so.

A large comet, however, could come from the outer solar system and reach Earth in a couple of years, and we could do nothing about it but fearfully await the demise of our species. But the chances of that happening are almost infinitesimally tiny—maybe one in 10 million during this century.

With modest tweaks to CSS observing protocols, or using modest-sized telescopes dedicated to searching for objects on their final plunge to Earth's surface, we could plausibly have advance warning—of tens of hours to weeks—for perhaps half of infalling asteroids larger than a few feet. The other half, coming from the Sun's direction, would still strike without warning.

Notifications of days to weeks provide no chance for a deflection mission. Even attempting to destroy the object as it approaches would risk converting a precisely known ground-zero location into an unpredictable, scattered-shotgun outcome. However, such warnings, just as those for hurricanes, could enable people to evacuate ground zero, potentially saving many lives. In the case of 2008 TC_3, the warning process didn't work perfectly; luckily, there was almost no one in the desert to warn.

The 2008 TC_3 event was mostly good luck: It was the first successful prediction of an asteroid strike (and on such short notice), and the meteorites were recovered (which would have been much less likely if it fell in a swamp or jungle). Largely informal Internet communications enabled many astronomers—professionals and amateurs alike—to observe 2008 TC_3 before it entered Earth's shadow and struck. So, for the first time, we have rocks in our laboratories that we can compare directly with telescopic observations of their progenitor asteroid in space. But 20 hours is extremely short notice. The October 2008 collision showed that we still don't have enough protocols for warning and evacuation in place.

History Shows Collisions

The largest well-documented asteroid impact occurred in 1908. Near the Podkamennaya Tunguska River in Siberia, a multi-megaton atmospheric explosion caused much destruction. Scientists think a roughly 130-foot-wide (40m) asteroid exploded with an energy 30 million times less powerful than the K-T boundary impact. Luckily, the mosquito-infested taiga forest was only sparsely inhabited—the explosion knocked down and burned trees for many miles around. Had the Tunguska blast been over a densely populated region, the natural disaster would have rivaled the worst earthquakes of recent decades. There is a fair chance, maybe one in three or four, that another Tunguska-like impact will happen this century, but it would likely occur over an ocean or a barren desert because a larger percentage of Earth's area is either one of these environments rather than a city.

Asteroids and comets are much more plentiful, but also less damaging, the smaller they are. Although a few K-T-boundary-sized NEAs exist, interplanetary space is voluminous. The chance that such a large cosmic body and Earth would arrive in the same place in our lifetime at the same time is tiny. 2008 TC_3-like impacts are much more likely (we think they occur roughly annually, but we can't see them all). There are hundreds of such NEAs for every Tunguska-sized object, and hundreds of millions for every K-T boundary impactor. And still smaller-sized objects are visible as meteor flashes on any clear, dark night due to countless tiny pebbles and an occasional larger rock burning up harmlessly in the night sky.

Target Earth

A cosmic body vastly more massive and energetic than Tunguska but 100 times less energetic than the K-T boundary event could have serious consequences. It might kill a billion people, destroy the infrastructure of our civilization, and return us to a dark age—but probably not render the human species extinct. Humanity has never experienced a cataclysm more devastating than the Black Plague of the 14th century, so it is difficult to predict the outcome of an impact by such a 1.2- to 1.9-mile-diameter (2 or 3 km) object. Fortunately, the damage would pale before the ecological collapse at the K-T boundary.

Such an impact will happen, although it's much more likely to be millions of years from now rather than during this century. These events have happened in the past, but probably not since human beings first evolved. With objects this size, it won't matter whether the incoming rock strikes the ocean or a desert—the environmental consequences will be enormous worldwide.

Let's play out the scenario. It would start with someone discovering a comet (the Spaceguard Survey has a complete census of large NEAs showing that no asteroid larger than 1.2 miles [2 km] will hit in this century). After a few nights of additional measurements, scientists would calculate a tentative orbit and soon after realize that Earth might be in its path. They would redouble their efforts to observe the comet. Let's say astronomers find that the comet is 1.5 miles (2.4 km) across—rather small as comets go but twice the size of Comet 103P/Hartley, recently visited by NASA's EPOXI mission. They could then calculate the exact date of impact. (Even when the chance of collision is tiny, scientists can determine what date the object would hit, as well as the location of a narrow path across Earth where it would hit.) After weeks and months, the likelihood of an Earth impact would grow.

There might be talk of trying to deflect the comet with a spacecraft—unfortunately for us, that mission would be futile. We couldn't launch enough mass to crash into it. (Engineers have in mind a sphere of metal or rock several tons in mass.) A "gravity tractor" probably wouldn't work either—it moves small bodies large distances, or larger objects small distances. Just conceivably, a large nuclear blast might be energetic enough to boil off the surface on one side of the comet, forcing it to move slightly in reaction. But we couldn't build and launch such a mission in time to intersect the comet years in advance, which is the time needed for nuclear-blast deflection to work. And most comets move unpredictably because of their own outgassing, so it might just as likely nudge the comet toward Earth as away. If we break apart the comet nucleus, smaller pieces with unknown trajectories could pummel our planet.

The Aftermath

I'll leave it to science fiction to describe how individuals, nations, emergency planners, religions, and economic interests worldwide might respond to the ever-more-confident predictions of a cometary calamity as the months pass. But we can estimate what would happen, physically, when the comet struck.

First, we can calculate the immediate damage in the region where the object hits. Planetary scientist Jay Melosh of Purdue University in West Lafayette, Indiana, and his colleagues have a starting place for the calculation: They created a website application called "Impact: Earth" (www.purdue.edu/impactearth) where you can plug in values to simulate collision aftereffects. In our scenario, we have a comet 1.5 miles (2.4 km) in diameter, with a density of 1,000 kilograms per cubic meter (the density of ice). It strikes at 20 miles/second (32 km/s) into a rural area of sedimentary rock.

At 50 miles (80 km) from ground zero, the fireball of the exploding comet—which would appear 60 times bigger than the Sun—would immediately burn us and every flammable thing around us. Surrounding buildings would suffer major damage from the resulting earthquake—nearly as big as the Chilean one of February 2010—that would reach our charred remains about 16 seconds after impact. Some 4 minutes after impact, an enormous airblast with winds approaching 1,200 mph (1,900 km/h) would sweep away anything left standing.

If we were 300 miles (480 km) away from ground zero, we would likely survive, at least initially. Because we know of the impending impact, we could hide in a well-constructed building to avoid burns from the fireball, protect ourselves from falling rocks, and endure the earthquake and airblast. Either the earthquake about 1.6 minutes after impact or the hurricane-force airblast arriving 24.4 minutes after the impact might badly damage ordinary wood-frame houses.

Our best option would be to evacuate far away from ground zero long before the comet approached Earth. But we still wouldn't be safe. What calculations such as "Impact: Earth" don't describe are the global environmental and infrastructure damage, which could disrupt civilization worldwide for months and years to come. For example, as the comet penetrates the atmosphere, chemical reactions would likely destroy Earth's protective ozone layer. Some scientists think there could be an enormous electromagnetic pulse (EMP) that might disable electrical grids around the world and render communications and electronic equipment (including Earth's orbiting satellites) nonfunctional. Unfortunately, we don't know much about the effect; scientists haven't seriously researched impact-induced EMPs.

In addition, Earth would undergo significant climate changes as Sun-blocking dust is launched into the atmosphere after impact. As dust circles the globe during the ensuing weeks, perhaps crossing the equator into the opposite hemisphere, temperatures would cool dramatically, threatening an agricultural growing season and hence the world's food supply.

With more than a year of warning, the international community could mitigate the worst effects before impact: prepare for unprecedented food shortages, the required medical effort, and the possible collapse of the world's economic infrastructure. Maybe humanity could weather the storm without letting fears of the terrible prognosis exacerbate tensions, which would magnify the unfolding tragedy. With foreknowledge, civilization might survive, depending on whether we can stay resilient as we face such a natural disaster.

Closer to Impact

Fortunately, the chance of a 1.5-mile-wide comet striking within the next few centuries is tiny. Instead of worrying about the highly improbable, let's focus on how we will face more 2008 TC_3-sized objects, and even bigger ones like a Tunguska. Civil defense and emergency managers are not yet sufficiently informed about asteroids, nor are communications channels established and tested to reliably warn people near ground zero in time to evacuate.

We must incorporate our future handling of these infrequent events into the "all hazards" methods that nations and localities use when facing the much more frequent floods, tornadoes, and avalanches. The National Research Council, the President's Office of Science and Technology, and NASA's Planetary Defense Task Force published reports about the NEA impact hazard in 2010. Our country, along with the United Nations, is taking the first steps toward becoming more robustly prepared. . . .

Clark R. Chapman is a planetary scientist in the Department of Space Studies at the Southwest Research Institute in Boulder, Colorado.

EXPLORING THE ISSUE

Can We Stop an Asteroid or Comet Impact?

Critical Thinking and Reflection

1. Suppose that astronomers announce that an asteroid big enough to destroy the United States will strike Ohio in 10 years. What could we do about it?
2. Make that 25 years. What could we do about it?
3. Given the inevitability of an eventual asteroid impact, how important is it that we plan ahead? How much should we spend per year on preparations for warding off the impact or recovering afterward?

Is There Common Ground?

No one thinks that if an asteroid or comet struck the Earth, the consequences would be trivial. But because such impacts are rare events, many people are inclined to think they don't need to worry *now,* there is nothing that could be done to stop them, and besides, there are a great many other problems—from malaria to global hunger to climate change—that deserve funding more immediately. As the essays for this issue point out, however, it doesn't take huge amounts of funding to maintain a watch on the skies, inventory potential threats, and plan ahead. There are other potential disasters for which a similar precautionary approach is appropriate. Look up the following terms (begin with the listed URLs) and discuss how people are preparing for future problems.

1. Volcanoes (www.scientificamerican.com/article.cfm?id=volcano-monitoring-jindal)
2. Supervolcanoes (www.nasca.org.uk/supervolcano/supervolcano.html)
3. Tsunamis (www.ess.washington.edu/tsunami/general/warning/warning.html)
4. Earthquakes (http://earthquake.usgs.gov/)

Create Central

www.mhhe.com/createcentral

Additional Resources

Greg Easterbrook, "The Sky Is Falling," *Atlantic* (June 2008).

Edward T. Lu, "Stop the Killer Rocks," Scientific American (December 2011).

National Research Council, *Defending Planet Earth: Near-Earth Object Surveys and Hazard Mitigation Strategies* (National Academies Press, 2010; www.nap.edu/catalog.php?record_id=12842).

Richard Stone, "Target Earth," *National Geographic* (August 2008).

Internet References . . .

National Aeronautics and Space Administration

At this site, you can find out the latest information on the International Space Station, space exploration, and other space-related news.

www.nasa.gov

Close Approaches

NASA's Near-Earth-Object Program lists past and future close approaches to Earth.

http://neo.jpl.nasa.gov/ca/

Near Earth Objects

The Near-Earth-Object Dynamic Site (NEODyS) provides information on all near-earth asteroids (NEAs). Each NEA has its own dynamically generated home page. Note the Risk Page, which presents information on the likelihood of impacts with Earth.

http://newton.dm.unipi.it/neodys/

NEOShield: Preparing to Protect the Planet

The NEOShield project has been set up to carry out a detailed analysis of the open questions relating to realistic options for preventing the collision of a NEO with the Earth.

www.neoshield.net/en/index.htm

Meteor Explodes above Urals

On February 15, 2013, a 10-ton meteor exploded in the air over Chelyabinsk, Russia, breaking windows and injuring hundreds of people. A number of people taped the event and posted the results on Youtube. For one example, see:

www.youtube.com/watch?v=yWTanCmQAxk&noredirect=1

Selected, Edited, and with Issue Framing Material by:
Thomas A. Easton, *Thomas College*

ISSUE

Will the Search for Extraterrestrial Life Ever Succeed?

YES: Seth Shostak, from "When Will We Detect the Extraterrestrials?" *Acta Astronautica* (August 2004)

NO: Peter Schenkel, from "SETI Requires a Skeptical Reappraisal," *Skeptical Inquirer* (May/June 2006)

Learning Outcomes

After studying this issue, students will be able to:

- Explain why it ever seemed reasonable to use radio telescopes to search for extraterrestrial intelligence.
- Explain why some people think, despite the lack of success to date, that it remains worthwhile to search for extraterrestrial intelligence.
- Explain why some people think SETI is not a worthwhile endeavor.
- Discuss the likely consequences of successful SETI.

ISSUE SUMMARY

YES: Radio astronomer and Search for Extraterrestrial Intelligence (SETI) researcher Seth Shostak defends SETI and argues that if the assumptions behind the search are well grounded, signals of extraterrestrial origin will be detected soon, perhaps within the next generation.

NO: Peter Schenkel argues that SETI's lack of success to date, coupled with the apparent uniqueness of Earth's history and suitability for life, suggests that intelligent life is probably rare in our galaxy and that the enthusiastic optimism of SETI proponents should be reined in.

In the 1960s and early 1970s, the business of listening to the radio whispers of the stars and hoping to pick up signals emanating from some alien civilization was still new. Few scientists held visions equal to those of Frank Drake, one of the pioneers of the SETI field. Drake and scientists like him use radio telescopes—large, dish-like radio receiver-antenna combinations—to scan radio frequencies (channels) for signal patterns that would indicate that the signal was transmitted by an intelligent being. In his early days, Drake worked with relatively small and weak telescopes out of listening posts that he had established in Green Bank, West Virginia, and Arecibo, Puerto Rico. See Carl Sagan and Frank Drake, "The Search for Extraterrestrial Intelligence," *Scientific American* (May 1975), and Frank Drake and Dava Sobel, *Is Anyone Out There? The Scientific Search for Extraterrestrial Intelligence* (Delacorte Press, 1992).

There have been more than fifty searches for extraterrestrial (ET) radio signals since 1960. The earliest ones were very limited. Later searches have been more ambitious, using multiple telescopes and powerful computers to scan millions of radio frequencies per second. New technologies and techniques continue to make the search more efficient. See Monte Ross, "The New Search for E.T.," *IEEE Spectrum* (November 2006).

At the outset, many people thought—and many still think—that SETI has about as much scientific relevance as searches for the Loch Ness Monster, Bigfoot, and the Abominable Snowman. However, to SETI fans it seems inevitable that with so many stars in the sky, there must be other worlds with life upon them, and some of that life must be intelligent and have a suitable technology and the desire to search for alien life too.

Writing about SETI in the September–October 1991 issue of *The Humanist*, physicist Shawn Carlson compares visiting the National Shrine of the Immaculate Conception in Washington, D.C., to looking up at the stars and "wondering if, in all [the] vastness [of the starry sky], there is anybody out there looking in our direction. . . . [A]re there planets like ours peopled with creatures like us staring into their skies and wondering about the possibilities of life on other worlds, perhaps even trying to contact it?" That is, SETI arouses in its devotees an almost religious sense of mystery and awe, a craving for contact with the *other.* Success would open up a universe of possibilities, add immensely to human knowledge, and perhaps even provide solutions to problems that our interstellar neighbors have already defeated.

SETI also arouses strong objections, partly because it challenges human uniqueness. Many scientists have objected that life-bearing worlds such as Earth must be exceedingly rare because the conditions that make them suitable for life as we know it—composition and temperature—are so narrowly defined. Others have objected that there is no reason whatsoever to expect that evolution would produce intelligence more than once or that, if it did, the species would be similar enough to humans to allow communication. Still others say that even if intelligent life is common, technology may not be so common, or technology may occupy such a brief period in the life of an intelligent species that there is virtually no chance that it would coincide with Earth scientists' current search. Whatever their reasons, SETI detractors agree that listening for ET signals is futile. Ben Zuckerman, "Why SETI Will Fail," *Mercury* (September/October 2002), argues that the simple fact that we have not been visited by ETs indicates that there are probably very few ET civilizations, and SETI is therefore futile.

Are we in fact alone? Or first? Are the conditions that lead to life and intelligence rare? Are there aliens living in disguise among us? Or are we quarantined? Reservationed? Zooed? Or maybe there is nobody there at all—not even us! (Sure, that could be it—if we are just simulations in some cosmic computer.) In *Where Is Everybody? Fifty Solutions to the Fermi Paradox and the Problem of Extraterrestrial Life* (Copernicus Books, 2002), Stephen Webb describes Fermi and his paradox (if they're out there, why haven't we been visited?) in great detail and offers a variety of answers that have been suggested—most seriously, some a bit tongue-in-cheek—for why the search has not succeeded. His own opinion is on the pessimistic side. The SETI community, however, remains convinced that their effort is worthwhile.

Astronomers have found a great many stars with planets, but so far they have not seen signs of life. Steve Nadis, "How Many Civilizations Lurk in the Cosmos," *Astronomy* (April 2010), discusses how the latest data have improved estimates of the various terms in the Drake equation, which has long guided estimates of how many ET civilizations might exist in the galaxy. Nadis quotes Frank Drake as saying that early estimates may have been much too low. There may be 10,000 such civilizations, and detecting even one may require that we examine 20 million stars. There is, however, an even larger obstacle to success. Paul Davies, *The Eerie Silence* (Houghton Mifflin Harcourt, 2010), notes that our efforts at detection are severely limited by the communications technologies we are familiar with, and ET civilizations may use those technologies for only a brief period in their history, moving on to others that we have not yet thought of and have no way to detect. We need new thinking, meaning that we must look for signals in neutrinos from space, embedded in the genes of viruses, and much more. See also Elizabeth Quill, "Can You Hear Me Now?" *Science News* (April 24, 2010).

What if SETI succeeds? Frank Drake noted in *Is Anyone Out There? The Scientific Search for Extraterrestrial Intelligence* (Delacorte Press, 1992) that positive results would have to be reported to everyone, at once, in order to prevent attempts to suppress or monopolize the discovery. Albert A. Harrison, "Confirmation of ETA: Initial Organizational Response," *Acta Astronautica* (August 2003), focuses on the need for a response to success, but he is skeptical that an effective response is possible; he says, "Foresight and advance preparation are among the steps that organizations may take to prepare for contact, but conservative values, skepticism towards SETI, and competing organizational priorities make serious preparation unlikely." Should our response include sending an answer back to the source of whatever radio signals we detect? H. Paul Schuch, "The Search for Extraterrestrial Intelligence," *Futurist* (May/June 2003), suggests that there may be dangers in such a move. These dangers are addressed by Ivan Almar and H. Paul Schuch in "The San Marino Scale: A New Analytical Tool for Assessing Transmission Risk," *Acta Astronautica* (January 2007); see also Ivan Almar, "SETI and Astrobiology: The Rio Scale and the London Scale," *Acta Astronautica* (November 2011), and Douglas A. Vakoch, "Responsibility, Capability, and Active SETI: Policy, Law, Ethics, and Communication with Extraterrestrial Intelligence," *Acta Astronautica* (February 2011). A few nonscientists have also begun to consider the implications of successful contact. See, for instance, Thomas Hoffman, "Exomissiology: The Launching of Exotheology," *Dialog: A Journal of Theology* (Winter 2004). David Brin, "The Dangers of First Contact," *Skeptic* (vol. 15, no. 3, 2010), argues that because the idea of free and open exchange of information is a historical anomaly here on Earth, any attempts to reply to a signal should not include our most valuable assets—our art, music, science, and other information. Instead, we should seek equal exchange, *quid pro quo*. He does not agree that those scientists are necessarily right who say that ETs must be highly advanced ethically and thus likely to treat us benignly. At the same time, he argues that we should not count on ET messages to solve our problems; it is better that we rely on ourselves.

Have the results of SETI to date been totally blank? Researchers have found nothing that justified any claim of success, but there have been a few "tantalizing signals." T, Joseph W. Lazio and Robert Naeye discuss them in "Hello? Are You Still There?" *Mercury* (May/June 2003).

In the YES selection, Seth Shostak defends SETI and argues that if the assumptions behind the search are reasonable, the search will succeed, perhaps within the next generation. In the NO selection, Peter Schenkel, a retired political scientist, argues that SETI's lack of success to date, coupled with the apparent uniqueness of Earth's history and suitability for life, suggests that intelligent life is probably rare in our galaxy. It is time, he says, "to dampen excessive ET euphoria and to adopt a . . . stand, compatible with facts."

YES

Seth Shostak

When Will We Detect the Extraterrestrials?

Abstract

It has been more than four decades since the first, modern SETI experiment. Many hundreds of star systems have been observed in the radio over wide bandwidth and with impressive sensitivity, and the entire sky has been surveyed in a more restricted mode several times. Optical SETI experiments are underway, and have already scrutinized several thousand nearby stars, looking for nanosecond light pulses.

Still, there is no confirmed signal detection. Given the anticipated improvement in both telescopes and digital electronics applied to SETI, what is the time scale for making such a discovery? In this paper we investigate the rate of stellar surveillance by targeted radio SETI experiments for the foreseeable future, and conclude that it is likely that—if the principal assumptions underlying modern SETI are reasonable—a detection will occur within a single generation.

Introduction

When will SETI succeed is a perennial question which does not, and some would say, cannot, engender reliable answers.* The search has a long history compared with historical exploration efforts, which were typically a decade or so in length—Columbus' four voyages extended over a dozen years, and Cook's reconnaissance of the South Pacific (three voyages) spanned eleven years. In contrast, the first SETI experiment was more than forty years ago (Project Ozma). As has been pointed out, the searches since 1960 have been quite intermittent, and amount to less than two years of continuous observation at sensitivities and spectral coverage comparable to today's experiments. Nonetheless, many SETI researchers are inclined to make the Copernican assumption that our temporal location in the search for signals is mediocre, and that another few decades, or thereabouts, will be necessary for success. Others speak of SETI as a multi-generational project, and encourage a mind-set sympathetic to the "long haul." It is the author's own experience that the most common response by scientists engaged in SETI, when queried as to how long success will take, is to answer with the approximate number of years until their own retirement.

Given the myriad uncertainties of the SETI enterprise, is there any reason to believe that a better prediction could be made, or are such "gut feelings" the best we can hope for? It is the purpose of this brief paper to offer a somewhat more quantitative estimate of when SETI might succeed, based on typical assumptions made by the SETI researchers themselves. Of course, these assumptions could be grossly in error, but the merit of this approach is that the timescales presented here are congruent with SETI's own postulates. To the extent that the arguments made for conducting today's SETI experiments are credible, then the sort of predictions presented here of when a signal might be found are similarly worthy of consideration.

Approach

As for any discovery enterprise, the time required to find a sought-for phenomenon depends on (a) the frequency with which it occurs, and (b) the speed of the reconnaissance. For SETI searches, the first is, crudely, the number of contemporaneous signal generators (transmitters, if you will), and the second is the rapidity with which our telescopes can survey the sky (or, for targeted search strategies, likely locations on the sky) using spectral coverage and sensitivity adequate to find one of these transmitters.

Since the inception of modern SETI, reckoning the number of celestial transmitters has been done using the Drake Equation. The equation computes N, the number of contemporaneous, galactic transmitting sites, as the product of the rate at which intelligent societies arise and the length of time they remain in the transmitting state. As noted, these computations are restricted to our own Galaxy, on the assumption that intelligence in other galaxies would not have the incentive to send signals (or provoke replies) that would be millions of years in transit. In addition, some note that intergalactic messaging, even from nearby nebulae, would require untenable power levels: hundreds to millions of times higher than required for communication over typical intragalactic distances. These arguments have not been considered overly persuasive however, since a number of searches for extragalactic transmitters have been made.

Of possibly greater consequence is the Drake Equation's assumption that searches should be directed to

*To avoid the ambiguity which some researchers ascribe to the word "success" in SETI, we define it as the unambiguous detection of an artificial, extraterrestrial signal.

stellar systems capable of hosting Earth-like worlds. Interstellar travel is difficult but not impossible, and it's unclear whether truly advanced intelligences would remain exclusively, or even principally, confined to the solar system of their birth. If migration away from the home star is common to technological intelligence, then targeted SETI searches, which are the most sensitive, could miss the most advanced (and possibly the most easily detected) transmitters.

Number of Stars to Search

With these caveats in mind, we begin by taking a conservative position, and consider the number of (galactic) transmitters predicted by Drake's Equation. It is not the provenance of this paper to evaluate the individual terms of this equation; we are only interested in their product, N. A compilation of published estimates assembled by Dick yields a (logarithmic) average of $N \sim 10^5$–10^6. (We note that one of Dick's compiled estimates is N = 0.003, which, if correct, would mean that it is overwhelmingly likely that there is nothing and no one to find. Among the SETI research community, this is obviously a minority view.) Drake himself is more conservative, and suggests $N \sim 10^4$. In the discussion that follows, we adopt a range of values for N of 10^4 to 10^6.

With this range estimate for N, and assuming a disk galaxy with diameter of ~90,000 light-years and half-power disk thickness (locally) of ~1,000 light-years, we can conclude that the nearest transmitter is 200–1,000 light-years away.

How many suitable targets lie within this distance? There are $\sim 10^{11}$ stars in the galaxy. Traditionally, 5–10% of these have been considered preferred candidates for harboring intelligence: these comprise, roughly speaking, single F, G or K-type stars at least a few billion years old. The major groups excluded by this historical choice include multiple stars (approximately half of all stars) and M-dwarfs (about 90% of stars). However, recent research has shown that both close double stars and those that are widely separated (tens of AU or more) could host planets in stable orbits. M-dwarfs are presently being reconsidered as SETI targets. It might soon be concluded that only short-lived, massive stars (types A and earlier) can be reliably excluded *ab initio* as SETI targets. Since these comprise only ~1% of all stars, this would mean that virtually the entire stellar complement of the Milky Way would qualify for SETI scrutiny.

However, foreseeable astronomical discoveries may once again narrow the range of interesting stars. The current search for extrasolar planets has shown that ~10% of solar-type stars have detectable worlds, but these are skewed in favor of stars that have higher metallicities. This suggests an obvious target selection criterion. In addition, new space-based interferometers (e.g., NASA's Terrestrial Planet Finder and ESA's Darwin) proposed for deployment in a decade's time will allow not only the direct imaging of Earth-sized worlds, but spectral analyses of their atmospheres. Such techniques could tell us not only which star systems host suitable planets, but could pinpoint worlds that evidence the spectral signatures of life. And, of course, it's still possible that a deeper investigation of the conditions of planets around M-dwarfs could serve to reliably eliminate this very numerous stellar class from consideration.

Consequently, and mindful of this expected progress in our understanding of extrasolar planets, we assume that: (1) for the present decade, all galactic stars remain qualified SETI targets. (2) In the following decade, half of all unobserved stars can be eliminated *a priori* from our SETI target lists, and (3) in the third decade, 90% of unobserved stars can be eliminated. This is, we propose, a conservative projection of progress in choosing which star systems to observe. Indeed, today's experiments often have more restrictive target lists than we are projecting for 2020 and beyond.

Rate of Target Scrutiny

Having estimated (a) the number of galactic transmitters, and (b) the fraction of star systems that need to be searched, we need only consider the rate at which the search is conducted in order to arrive at our goal: an estimate for when a signal will be found.

We first consider radio searches. Note that large swaths of the celestial sphere have been examined in so-called Sky Survey SETI experiments. The failure (so far) of these experiments to discover a signal, assuming such signals exist, could be due to (a) insufficient sensitivity (note that such sky surveys are typically at least an order-of-magnitude less sensitive than targeted searches, which means that the volume of sky sampled at any given sensitivity level is less by a factor of >60), (b) inadequate spectral coverage, or (c) an inability to monitor specific locations for more than a few seconds, with no facility for making immediate follow-up observations. This precludes detection of all but fully continuous signals.

Targeted searches moderate these shortcomings, but have the disadvantage of being a very slow reconnaissance. This is principally due to the fact that the large telescopes favored for SETI research are only intermittently available. The total number of star systems surveyed to date by the SETI Institute's premier radio search, Project Phoenix (which uses the Arecibo radio telescope), is ~500.

This slow pace of targeted radio searches is about to change. The Allen Telescope Array (ATA), a joint project of the SETI Institute and the University of California at Berkeley, will be a highly sophisticated radio antenna that can be used full-time to make SETI observations. It is anticipated that this instrument will be completed within the current decade. This immediately increases by an order of magnitude the amount of telescope time available for the Institute's targeted searches. In addition, an international consortium is planning the construction of an even larger telescope, the Square Kilometer Array (SKA). If built, this instrument could also be partially dedicated to SETI observations. For the purposes of this paper, we assume that this instrument will double the speed of SETI reconnaissance beginning in the (rather uncertain) year of 2015.

Project Phoenix surveys approximately 50–60 stellar systems annually. The ATA will not only have the benefit of ten times as much observing time as this effort, but will also incorporate multiple beams that allow the simultaneous observation of at least three star systems. In addition, efficiencies in follow-up and wider instantaneous spectral coverage will add at least another factor of 2–3 speed improvement. At a minimum, we can say that, once completed, the ATA will increase the rapidity with which nearby stars are checked for signals by at least two orders of magnitude. In its first year, it will observe considerably more stellar systems than the total investigated by Project Phoenix. We will (conservatively) assume this number to be 1,000 systems, applicable to the year 2006.

The ATA is conceived as an instrument whose capabilities can be expanded as the cost of digital computation continues to decline. According to Moore's Law, a fact-of-life in the field of computing hardware for three decades, the density of transistors on commercially available chips doubles every 18 months. In more practical terms, this means that the cost of computing is halved each 1-1/2 years. The speed (not necessarily the efficacy) of SETI experiments has historically followed this law. . . .

We can expect, therefore, that at least the speed of stellar scrutiny using the ATA will grow at this exponential rate, at least so long as Moore's Law continues to hold. How long might that be? Various pundits, including Moore himself, point to the fact that the further exploitation of silicon technology will likely hit a physical "wall" at which the dimensions of the transistors become nearly molecular in size. An additional (and perhaps more formidable) barrier to the continued reign of this law is the economic cost of new fabrication facilities and even of the chips themselves. On the other hand, foreseeing this technological barrier has stimulated research into optical and quantum computing, and these approaches are expected by many to not only sustain the pace of improvement, but perhaps to accelerate it.

For the purposes of this paper, we adopt widespread industry predictions that Moore's Law in its current form will continue to hold until 2015. Thereafter, we conservatively assume a decrease by half: doubling of computational power per dollar will take 36 months, rather than 18. The speed of SETI reconnaissance is postulated to follow this technological growth.

Having considered at some length the speed and expected improvements in radio SETI searches, we note that several optical SETI experiments are also underway. These look for short ($\leq 10^{-9}$ sec) bursts of photons that could be produced by, for example, a pulsed laser deliberately targeting our solar system. While optical SETI experiments are still relatively new, several thousand star systems have already been observed, and an instrument dedicated to an optical sky survey of the two-thirds of the sky visible from the northern hemisphere is currently under construction.

Despite these encouraging developments, we will not incorporate them into our estimate of when extraterrestrial intelligence will be found. This is because of the very real possibility that optical signals might be either highly intermittent or sent to only small numbers of targets. However, with not-unreasonable assumptions, optical SETI might succeed very soon. Consider a simple example: suppose that an extraterrestrial beacon is set up to serially target all $\sim 10^{11}$ galactic star systems, briefly illuminating their inner solar systems with a burst of nanosecond pulses once every 24 hours. (This brute-force approach would provide each star with a daily kilobit of data, which might be adequate to serve as a "pointer" to other information being served up by this transmitting society.) The observation time per beam for the planned Harvard-Princeton optical sky survey is ≥ 48 seconds, so that the chance of a detection for every sweep of the northern sky (estimated to take 150 days) is $\sim 3 \times 10^{-4}$ N, or >1 for all our estimates for N.

This sunny assessment assumes that all transmitters are detectable by the sky survey. In fact, optical searches for signals from star systems at great distance need to be sensitive in the infrared to defeat the attenuating effect of interstellar dust. Such systems are not yet operational, as they must be space-based. However, there is no technical reason to doubt that they could be deployed within a decade or two. On the other hand, very low transmitter duty cycles may dictate that an effective optical SETI search will require the use of multiple, or possibly all-sky, detectors. Given the newness of optical SETI, and the lack of a body of historical "assumptions" regarding optical signaling, we will not factor such searches into our estimate of when a SETI detection will be made. This is obviously a conservative approach, assuming that optical SETI has any chance at all to succeed.

When a Detection Will Take Place

We now have in hand the requisite parameters to estimate the likely date of a (radio) SETI detection. . . . [We can plot] the number of targeted star systems observed using the ATA with, eventually, the addition of the SKA. . . . [We can then calculate] the volume of space (specified by a maximum distance) in which we've observed all suitable target star systems [and date when we will have observed enough star systems to expect successful SETI. If $N = 10^6$, the date will be about 2015. If $N = 10^4$, the date will be about 2027.] . . .

We remark that this span of dates for a predicted SETI detection extends less than two dozen years forward. Although SETI searches are sometimes referred to as multi-generational projects, our estimate suggests that this isn't the case: success is within the foreseeable future. Among other things, this justifies the efforts being made to plan for a detection, as well as to consider society's likely reaction and what would be a suitable response (if any).

We have tried to make conservative assumptions in this presentation. In particular, a reconnaissance of extrasolar planets, which would chart out their size, orbit, and whether or not they evidence spectral biomarkers, will eventually tightly focus the interest of SETI researchers, reducing (substantially, one assumes) the number of suitable target systems. We have only made a crude correction for this highly likely development. We have also made no assumption that SETI observations, particularly those that reach beyond a few hundred light-years, will concentrate their attentions on the galactic plane, thereby increasing the efficiency of the search.

While we have reckoned on an exponential improvement in technology that governs SETI search speed over the next two-and-a-half decades, this extrapolation is based on four decades in which this has been demonstrably true. To be on the safe side, we have assumed a slowing of this growth beginning in 2015. Finally, we have taken no account of the likelihood that a detection will be made with radio sky surveys, or using optical SETI techniques.

On the other hand, there are many possible reasons why our assessment that a detection will be made within a generation might be wrong. We have not considered the luminosity function or duty cycle of extraterrestrial transmitters, but have instead assumed that the N transmitters estimated by the Drake Equation are all detectable by the ATA and SKA. We have not speculated on the possibility that the frequency coverage of our telescopes is inadequate, nor that the signal types to which they are sensitive are the wrong ones. And, indeed, we do not consider that physical laws of which we are still unaware might dictate a completely different approach to interstellar signaling. And, of course, our range of estimates for N are only considered opinion—and some of that opinion [states] that *no* other contemporary, sentient galactic societies exist.

Nonetheless, we reiterate that the intention of this exercise is to improve upon existing "gut feeling" speculation as to when SETI might expect a detection. While there are a myriad uncertainties attendant upon our estimate that this will occur within two dozen years, we have made this prediction using the assumptions adopted by the SETI research community itself. This community builds equipment and uses strategies that it reckons are adequate to find an extraterrestrial signal. It does this based on more than four decades of thought as to how best to prove the presence of extraterrestrial sentience. If such analyses are well grounded, then such proof will not be long in coming.

Seth Shostak is senior astronomer at the SETI Institute. He frequently presents the Institute's work in the media, through lectures, and via the Institute's weekly radio show, *Are We Alone?*

Peter Schenkel **NO**

SETI Requires a Skeptical Reappraisal

The possible existence of extraterrestrial intelligence (ETI) has always stirred the imagination of man. Greek philosophers speculated about it. Giordano Bruno was burnt on the stake in Rome in 1600, mainly [for] positing the likelihood of other inhabited worlds in the universe. Kant and Laplace were also convinced of the multiplicity of worlds similar to ours. In the latter part of the nineteenth century Flammarion charmed vast circles with his books on the plurality of habitable worlds. But all these ideas were mainly philosophical considerations or pure speculations. It was only in the second half of the twentieth century that the Search for Extraterrestrial Intelligence (SETI) became a scientifically underpinned endeavor. Since the late 1950s distinguished scientists have conducted research, attempting to receive intelligent signals or messages from space via radio-telescopes. Hundreds of amateur astronomers, members of the SETI-League in dozens of countries, are scanning the sky, trying to detect evidence of intelligent life elsewhere in our galaxy. SETI pioneers, such as Frank Drake and Carl Sagan, held the stance that the Milky Way is teeming with a large number of advanced civilizations. However, the many search projects to date have not succeeded, and this daring prediction remains unverified. New scientific insights suggest the need for a more cautious approach and a revision of the overly optimistic considerations.

The standard argument for the existence of a multiplicity of intelligent life runs like this: There are about 200 to 300 billion stars in our galaxy and probably hundreds of millions, maybe even billions of planets in our galaxy. Many of these planets are likely to be located in the so-called "habitable zone" in relation [to] their star, enjoying Earth-favorable conditions for the evolution of life. The physical laws, known to us, apply also to the cosmos, and far-away stellar formations are composed of the same elements as our solar system. Therefore, it is assumed, many should possess water and a stable atmosphere, considered to be basic requisites for the development of life. Such planets must have experienced geological and biological processes similar to those on Earth, leading to the development of primitive life organisms. Then, in the course of time, following a similar course of Darwin's theory of natural selection, these evolved into more complex forms, some eventually developing cognitive capacities and—as in our case—higher intelligence.

In other words, it is maintained, our solar system, Earth, and its evolution are not exceptional cases, but something very common in our Milky Way galaxy. Consequently it must be populated by a huge number of extraterrestrial civilizations, many of them older and more advanced than ours.

Considering the enormous number of stars and planets, these seem like fair and legitimate assumptions. It indeed appears unlikely that intelligence should have evolved only on our planet. If many of these civilizations are scientifically and technologically superior to us, contact with them would give mankind a boost in many ways.

These optimistic views are based mainly on the famous Drake formula. . . . It considers the formation of stars in the galaxy, the fraction of stars with planetary systems, the number of planets ecologically suited for life, the fraction of these planets on which life and intelligent life evolves, and those reaching a communicative stage and the length of time of technical civilizations. On the basis of this formula it was estimated that a million advanced civilizations probably exist in the galaxy. The nearest one should be at a distance of about 200 to 300 light-years from Earth. German astronomer Sebastian von Hoerner estimated a number between ten thousand and ten million such civilizations.

But because of many new insights and results of research in a number of scientific fields, ranging from paleontology, geology, biology to astronomy, I believe this formula is incomplete and must be revised. The early optimistic estimates are no longer tenable. A more realistic and sober view is required.

I by no means intend to discredit SETI; the search for extraterrestrial intelligent life is a legitimate scientific endeavor. But it seems prudent to demystify this interesting subject, and to reformulate its claims on a new level, free of the romantic flair that adorns it.

Years ago, I readily admit, I myself was quite taken in by the allegations that intelligence is a very common phenomenon in the galaxy. In books, articles, and on radio and television I advocated the idea that our world, beset by problems, could learn a lot from a civilization more advanced than ours. But, in the meantime, I became convinced that a more skeptical attitude would do reality better justice. There are probably only a few such civilizations in the galaxy, if any at all. The following considerations buttress this rather pessimistic appraisal.

First of all, since project OZMA I in 1959 by Frank Drake, about a hundred radio-magnetic and other searches were conducted in the U.S. and in other countries, and a considerable part of our sky was scanned thoroughly and repeatedly, but it remained disappointingly silent. In forty-six years not a single artificial intelligent signal or message from outer space was received. Some specialists try to downplay this negative result, arguing that so far only a small part of the entire spectrum has been covered, and that more time and more sophisticated equipment is required for arriving at a definite conclusion. Technological and economic criteria may thwart the possibility of extraterrestrial civilizations beaming signals into space over long stretches of time, without knowing where to direct their signals. Or, they may use communication methods unknown to us. Another explanation is that advanced ETI may lack interest in contacting other intelligences, especially those less developed. The argument of the Russian rocket expert Konstantin Tsiolkovski is often quoted: "Absence of evidence is not evidence of absence."

But neither of these arguments, which attempt to explain why we have not received a single intelligent signal from space, is convincing. True, future search projects may strike pay dirt and register the reception of a signal of verified artificial origin. But as long as no such evidence is forthcoming, the possibility of achieving success must be considered remote. If a hundred searches were unsuccessful, it is fair to deduce that estimates of a million or many thousands ETI are unsustainable propositions. As long as no breakthrough occurs, the probability of contact with ETI is near to zero. The argument that advanced extraterrestrials may not be interested in contact with other intelligences is also—as I will show—highly implausible.

Second, as recent research results demonstrate, many more factors and conditions than those considered by the Drake formula need to be taken into account. The geologist Peter D. Ward and the astronomer Donald Brownlee present in their book *Rare Earth* a series of such aspects, which turn the optimistic estimates of ETI upside down.

According to their reasoning, the old assumption that our solar system and Earth are quite common phenomena in the galaxy needs profound revision. On the contrary, the new insights suggest, we are much more special than thought. The evolution of life forms and eventually of intelligent life on Earth was due to a large number of very special conditions and developments, many of a coincidental nature. I'll mention only some that seem particularly important: The age, size, and composition of our sun, the location of Earth and inclination of its axis to it, the existence of water, a stable oxygen-rich atmosphere and temperature over long periods of time—factors considered essential for the evolution of life—and the development of a carbon-based chemistry. Furthermore an active interior and the existence of plate tectonics form the majestic mountain ridges like the Alps, the Himalayas and the Andes, creating different ecological conditions, propitious for the proliferation of a great variety of species. Also the existence of the Moon, Jupiter, and Saturn (as shields for the bombardment of comets and meteorites during the early stages of Earth). Also the repeated climatic changes, long ice ages, and especially the numerous and quite fortuitous catastrophes, causing the extinction of many species, like the one 65 million years ago, which led to the disappearance of dinosaurs but opened the way for more diversified and complex life forms.

Though first primitive life forms on Earth, the prokaryotic bacteria, evolved relatively rapidly, only about 500 million years after the cooling off of Earth's crust and the end of the dense bombardment of meteorites and comets, they were the only life forms during the first two billion years of Earth's 4.6-billion-year history. Mammals—including apes and man—developed much later, only after the extinction of the dinosaurs 65 million years ago. The first human-like being, the Proconsul, emerged in the Miocene Period, just about 18 million years ago. The Australopithecus, our antecessor, dates only 5 to 6 million years. In other words, it took almost 4 billion years, or more than 96 percent of the age of Earth, for intelligence to evolve—an awfully long time, even on the cosmic clock.

In this regard we should note also the caveat of the distinguished biologist Ernst Mayr, who underscored the enormous complexity of human DNA and RNA and their functions for the production of proteins, the basic building blocks of life. He estimated that the likelihood that similar biological developments may have occurred elsewhere in the universe was nil.

The upshot of these considerations is the following: Because of the very special geological, biological, and other conditions which propitiated the evolution of life and intelligence on Earth, similar developments in our galaxy are probably very rare. Primitive life forms, Ward and Brownlee conclude, may exist on planets of other stellar systems, but intelligent life, as ours, is probably very rare, if it exists at all.

Third is the so-called "Fermi Paradox," another powerful reason suggesting a skeptical evaluation of the multiplicity of intelligence in the galaxy. Italian physicist Enrico Fermi posed the annoying question, "If so many highly developed ETIs are out there, as SETI specialists claim, why haven't they contacted us?" I already expressed great doubt about some of the explanations given [for] this paradox. Here I need to focus on two more. The first refers to the supposed lack of interest of advanced aliens to establish contact with other intelligent beings. This argument seems to me particularly untrustworthy. I refer to a Norwegian book, which explains why the Vikings undertook dangerous voyages to far-away coasts in precarious vessels. "One reason," it says, "is fame, another curiosity, and a third, gain!" If the Vikings, driven by the desire to discover the unknown, reached America a thousand years ago with a primitive technology, if we—furthermore—a still scientifically and technically young civilization, search for primitive life on other planets of the solar system and their moons, it is incredible that higher developed extraterrestrial intelligences would not be spurred by likewise interests and yearnings. One of the fundamental traits of intelligence is its unquenchable intellectual curiosity and urge to penetrate the unknown. Elder civilizations, our peers in every respect, must be imbued by the same daring and scrutinizing spirit, because if they are not, they could not have achieved their advanced standards.

A second argument often posited is that distances between stars are too great for interstellar travel. But this explanation also stands on shaky ground. Even our scientifically and technically adolescent civilization is exploring space and sending probes—the Voyager crafts—which someday may reach other stellar systems. We are still far from achieving velocities, near the velocity of light, necessary for interstellar travel. But some scientists predict that in 200 or 300 years, maybe even earlier, we are likely to master low "c" velocities, and once we reach them, our civilization will send manned exploratory expeditions to the nearest stars. Automatic unmanned craft may be the initial attempts. But I am convinced that nothing will impede the desire of man to see other worlds with his own eyes, to touch their soil and to perform research that unmanned probes would not be able to perform. Evidently, civilizations tens of thousands or millions of years in our advance will have reached near c velocities, and they will be able to explore a considerable part of the galaxy. Advanced ETI civilizations would engage in such explorations not only out of scientific curiosity, but in their own interest, for instance for spreading out and finding new habitats for their growing population, or because of the need to abandon their planet due to hazards from their star, and also because with the help of other civilizations it may confront dangers, lurking in the universe, more successfully than alone. The Fermi Paradox should therefore put us on guard, and foster a sound skepticism. Lack of interest in meeting a civilization such as ours is the least plausible reason why we have not heard from ETI.

A little mental experiment illustrates this point. Carl Sagan held once that intelligent aliens would visit Earth at least once every thousand years. But such visits have not taken place. Even extending this period to a million years, we fare no better. Let us assume an extraterrestrial craft landed on Earth any time during the era of the dinosaurs, lasting about 140 million years. It is only logical to assume the aliens would have returned at reasonable intervals to study our world and these fascinating animals, but also to find out if any one of them evolved the capability of reasoning, higher math, and building a civilization. There would have been reason for much surmise. According to paleontologists, Drake stresses, the dinosaur sauronithoides was endowed with such a potential. It was a dinosaur resembling a bird of our size and weight and possessing a mass of brain well above average, and, Drake speculates, if it had survived for an additional ten or twenty million years, it might have evolved into the first intelligent being on Earth. But it didn't happen, because the dinosaurs went extinct due to a cosmic catastrophe. When *Homo australopithecus,* then *Homo faber* and *habilis,* and lastly *Homo sapiens* evolved, shouldn't that have provoked on the part of visiting extraterrestrials a high level of interest? But no such visits are recorded. Only a few mythological, undocumented and highly suspect accounts of alleged visiting aliens exist. It is fair to assume, if advanced aliens had visited Earth during the past 200 million or, at least, during the past 16 million years, they would have left some durable, indestructible and recognizable mark, probably on the moon. But nothing has been detected. The most likely explanation? No such visits took place! There are no advanced extraterrestrial civilizations anywhere in our vicinity. If they existed, they already would have responded to our world's television signals, reaching some 60 light-years into space—another reason invalidating the claim that our galaxy is teeming with intelligence.

Another argument supporting the skeptical point of view sustained here is the fact that none of the detected planets around other stars comes close to having conditions apt for creating and sustaining life. Since Michel Mayor's Swiss group discovered the first planet outside our solar system around the star 51 Pegasi ten years ago, about 130 other planets have been identified within a distance of 200 light-years. Research results show that most are of gaseous composition, some many times the size of Jupiter, some very close to their stars, very hot and with extremely rapid orbital cycles. So far, not one presents conditions favorable for the development of even the most primitive forms of life, not to speak of more complex species. Again it may be argued that only a very tiny fraction of planets were surveyed and future research might strike upon a suitable candidate. This may well be, and I would certainly welcome it. But so far the evidence fails to nourish optimistic expectations. The conditions in our universe are not as favorable for the evolution of life as optimists like to think.

Even if water or fossils of microorganisms should be found underneath the surface of Mars, the importance of such a finding for the theory of a multiplicity of inhabited worlds would be insignificant. Some astronomers think that Titan, the famous moon of Saturn, may have an ocean, possibly of methane. Primitive life forms may exist in it, but this remains to be seen. Even if it does, the evolutionary path from such primitive forms to complex life as human beings is—as we have seen—a long one, studded with a unique sequence of chance and catastrophes.

I am not claiming that we are probably the only intelligent species in our galaxy. Nor do I suggest that SETI activities are a waste of time and money. Though, so far, they have failed to obtain evidence for the existence of ETI, they enrich man's knowledge about the cosmos in many ways. They helped develop sophisticated search techniques, and they contribute decisively to the perception of man's cosmic destiny. Carl Sagan and Frank Drake, the two most distinguished pioneers of SETI, did groundbreaking work. That their efforts and those of other dedicated SETI experts on behalf of this great cause are tinged with a dash of too optimistic expectation is understandable and profoundly human.

However, in the interest of science and sound skepticism, I believe it is time to take the new findings and insights into account, to dampen excessive SETI euphoria and to adopt a more pragmatic and down-to-earth stand, compatible with facts. We should quietly admit that the early estimates—that there may be a million, a hundred thousand, or ten thousand advanced extraterrestrial civilizations in our galaxy—may no longer be tenable. There might not be a hundred, not even ten such civilizations. The optimistic estimates were fraught with too many imponderables and speculative appraisals. What is required is to make contact with a single extraterrestrial intelligence, obtaining irrefutable, thoroughly verified evidence, either via electromagnetic or optical waves or via physical contact, that we are not the only intelligent species in the cosmos. Maybe an alien spacecraft, attracted by our signals, will decide to visit us some day, as I surmised in my novel *Contact: Are We Ready for It?* I would be the first one to react to such a contact event with great delight and satisfaction. The knowledge that we are not alone in the vast realm of the cosmos, and that it will be possible to establish a fruitful dialogue with other, possibly more advanced intelligent beings would mark the biggest event in human history. It would open the door to fantastic perspectives.

But SETI activities so far do not justify this hope. They recommend a more realistic and sober view. Considering the negative search results, the creation of excessive expectations is only grist to the mill of the naysayers—for instance, members of Congress who question the scientific standing of SETI, imputing to it wishful thinking, and denying it financial support. This absolutely negative approach to SETI is certainly wrong, because contrary to the UFO hoax, SETI (as UCLA space scientist Mark Moldwin stressed in a recent issue of this magazine) is based on solid scientific premises and considerations. But exaggerated estimates fail to conform to realities, as they are seen today, tending to backfire and create disappointment and a turning away from this fascinating scientific endeavor. The dream of mankind to find brethren in space may yet be fulfilled. If it is not, man should not feel sorry for his uniqueness. Rather that circumstance should boost the gratitude for his existence and his sense of responsibility for making the most of it.

Peter Schenkel is a retired political scientist interested in the question of what contact with advanced aliens would mean to humanity.

EXPLORING THE ISSUE

Will the Search for Extraterrestrial Life Ever Succeed?

Critical Thinking and Reflection

1. Why do SETI fans think searching for extraterrestrial signals is worth the effort?
2. Why do SETI critics think the effort is wasted?
3. If SETI researchers ever detect extraterrestrial signals, should they reply? If so, what should they say?
4. Why aren't real-life extraterrestrials likely to be much like the ones on TV and in the movies?

Is There Common Ground?

In the debate over this issue, there seems to be little common ground. One side thinks it worth continuing SETI. The other side says, "Forget it." But there are related areas of research, such as the search by astronomers for planets circling other stars, which to many have the ultimate goal of finding life-bearing worlds.

1. What are "exoplanets" and why do astronomers search for them? (http://planetquest.jpl.nasa.gov/; www.superwasp.org/exoplanets.htm)
2. One recent exoplanet discovery was briefly dubbed the "Goldilocks planet." Look up the term and discuss why both the astronomers and the media were excited.
3. To many people, the "Fermi Paradox" is no paradox at all. It posits that we have not been visited by aliens, but what about UFOs, the Roswell incident, alien abductions, and so on? Why don't SETI researchers take such things seriously?

Create Central

www.mhhe.com/createcentral

Additional Resources

Ronald D. Ekers, *SETI 2020: A Roadmap for the Search for Extraterrestrial Intelligence* (SETI Press, SETI Institute, 2002).

Alan Penny, "SETI: Peering into the Future," *Astronomy & Geophysics* (February 2011).

H. Paul Shuch, *Searching for Extraterrestrial Intelligence: SETI Past, Present, and Future* (Springer, 2011).

Douglas A. Vakoch, "Responsibility, Capability, and Active SETI: Policy, Law, Ethics, and Communication with Extraterrestrial Intelligence," *Acta Astronautica* (February 2011).

Internet Reference . . .

SETI Institute

The SETI Institute serves as a home for scientific research in the general field of life in the universe with an emphasis on the search for extraterrestrial intelligence (SETI).

www.seti.org

Selected, Edited, and with Issue Framing Material by:
Thomas A. Easton, *Thomas College*

ISSUE

Do Humans Belong in Space?

YES: Eugene A. Cernan, from Testimony before the U.S. House of Representatives Committee on Science, Space, and Technology hearing on "Spaceflight—Past, Present, and Future: Where Do We Go from Here?" (September 22, 2011)

NO: Neil deGrasse Tyson, from "Delusions of Space Enthusiasts," *Natural History* (November 2006)

Learning Outcomes

After studying this issue, students will be able to:

- Explain the potential benefits of space exploration.
- Argue both in favor of and against sending human beings on space missions.
- Explain how political realities make it difficult to justify manned space exploration.

ISSUE SUMMARY

YES: Eugene A. Cernan, commander of the Apollo XVII mission, argues that manned space exploration is an investment in the future, in technology, jobs, international respect, geopolitical leadership, and the inspiration and education of our youth. It must not be abandoned.

NO: Astronomer Neil deGrasse Tyson argues that large, expensive projects such as space exploration are driven only by war, greed, and the celebration of power. The dream of colonizing space became a delusion as soon as we beat the Russians to the Moon, and it remains so.

The dream of conquering space has a long history. The Russian Konstantin Tsiolkovsky (1857–1935) and the American Robert H. Goddard (1882–1945), the pioneers of rocketry, dreamed of exploring other worlds, although neither lived long enough to see the first artificial satellite, the Soviet *Sputnik*, go up in 1957. That success sparked a race between America and the Soviet Union to be the first to achieve each step in the progression of space exploration. The next steps were to put dogs (the Soviet Laika was the first), monkeys, chimps, and finally human beings into orbit. Communications, weather, and spy satellites were designed and launched. And on July 20, 1969, the U.S. *Apollo* program landed the first man on the moon.

There were a few more *Apollo* landings, but not many. The United States had achieved its main political goal of beating the Soviets to the moon and, in the minds of the government, demonstrating U.S. superiority. Thereafter, the United States was content to send automated spacecraft (computer-operated robots) off to observe Venus, Mars, and the rings of Saturn; to land on Mars and study its soil; and even to carry recordings of Earth's sights and sounds past the distant edge of the solar system, perhaps to be retrieved in the distant future by intelligent life from some other world. (Those recordings are attached to the *Voyager* spacecraft, launched in 1977; published as a combination of CD, CD-ROM, and book, *Murmurs of Earth: The Voyager Interstellar Record,* it is now long out of print.) Humans have not left near-Earth orbit for two decades, even though space technology has continued to develop. The results of this development include communications satellites, space shuttles, space stations, and independent robotic explorers such as the *Mariners* and *Vikings,* the rovers *Spirit* and *Opportunity,* and the polar lander *Phoenix*, which finally found water on Mars in July 2008.

Why has human space exploration gone no further to date? One reason is that robots are now extremely capable. Although some robot spacecraft have failed partially or completely, there have been many grand successes that have added enormously to humanity's knowledge of Earth and other planets. Another is money: Lifting robotic explorers into space is expensive, but lifting people into space—along with all the food, water, air, and other supplies necessary to keep them alive for the duration of a mission—is much more expensive. And there are many people in government and elsewhere who cry that there are many better ways to spend the money on Earth.

Still another reason for the reduction in human space travel seems to be the fear that astronauts will die in space. This point was emphasized by the explosion on takeoff of the space shuttle *Challenger* in January 1986, which killed seven astronauts and froze the entire shuttle program for over two and a half years. The point was reinforced by the breakup of *Columbia* on entry February 1, 2003. After the latter event, the public reaction included many calls for an end to such risky, expensive enterprises. See Jerry Grey, "Columbia—Aftermath of a Tragedy," *Aerospace America* (March 2003); John Byron, "Is Manned Space Flight Worth It?" *Proceedings* (of the U.S. Naval Institute) (March 2003) (and Richard H. Truly's response in the May issue); and "Manned or Unmanned into Space?" *USA Today* (February 26, 2003), among many others. Robert Zubrin, "How Much Is an Astronaut's Life Worth?" *Reason* (February 2012), argues that risk is an inescapable part of manned space flight and the refusal to accept risk has hamstrung the space program. "Human spaceflight vehicles . . . are daring ships of exploration that need to sail in harm's way if they are to accomplish a mission critical to the human future. The mission needs to come first."

In 2004 when President George W. Bush announced his plan to send humans to the Moon and Mars, beginning as soon as 2015, the reaction was immediate. James A. Van Allen asked "Is Human Spaceflight Obsolete?" in *Issues in Science and Technology* (Summer 2004). Andrew Lawler asked "How Much Space for Science?" in *Science* (January 30, 2004). Physicist and Nobel laureate Steven Weinberg, "The Wrong Stuff," *New York Review of Books* (April 8, 2004), argues that nothing needs doing in space that cannot be done without human presence. Until we find something that does need humans on the scene, there is no particular reason to send humans—at great expense—into space. Indeed, the president's Mars initiative may prove to be no more than a ploy to look visionary and force later presidents to face financial realities. John Derbyshire, "Space Is for Science," *National Review* (June 5, 2006), argues that the expense and hazards of putting humans in space do not justify the benefits when much cheaper automated spacecraft (robots) can make all necessary observations. Paul D. Spudis, "Who Should Explore Space? Astronaut Explorers Can Perform Science in Space that Robots Cannot," *Scientific American* (Special Edition, January 2008), argues that there is no substitute for human astronauts in installing and maintaining equipment and in conducting field exploration because humans provide skills that are unlikely to be automated in the foreseeable future. Francis Slakey, "Who Should Explore Space? Unmanned Spacecraft Are Exploring the Solar System More Cheaply and Effectively than Astronauts Are," *Scientific American* (Special Edition, January 2008), argues that NASA sends humans into space chiefly for public relations purposes. Unmanned probes are much cheaper and more effective than astronauts, and many scientific organizations have recommended that space science should instead be done through robotic and telescopic missions. See also Louis D. Friedman and G. Scott Hubbard, "Examining the Vision," *American Scientist* (July/August 2008).

The question of whether robots can do the job is particularly relevant because of the success of the Mars rovers, *Spirit* and *Opportunity*. If robots continue to be successful, it seems likely that efforts to promote manned space travel, even from the White House, will meet resistance. Funding for space exploration remains low largely because problems on Earth (environmental and other) seem to need money more urgently than space exploration projects do. The prospects for manned space expeditions to the moon, Mars, or other worlds seem very dim, although Paul D. Spudis, "Harvest the Moon," *Astronomy* (June 2003), argues that there are four good reasons for putting people at least on the Moon: "The first motivation to revisit the Moon is that its rocks hold the early history of our own planet and the solar system. Next, its unique environment and properties make it an ideal vantage point for observing the universe. The Moon is also a natural space station where we can learn how to live off-planet. And finally, it gives us an extraterrestrial filling station, with resources to use both locally and in near-Earth space." See also Paul D. Spudis, "The New Moon," *Scientific American* (December 2003). Nader Elhefnawy, "Beyond *Columbia*: Is There a Future for Humanity in Space?" *The Humanist* (September/October 2003), says that we cannot ignore the wealth of resources in space. Alex Ellery, "Humans versus Robots for Space Exploration and Development," *Space Policy* (May 2003), argues that "even as robotics and artificial intelligence are becoming more sophisticated, they will not be able to deal with 'thinking-on-one's-feet' tasks that require generalisations from past experience. . . . I submit that there will be a critical role for humans in space for the foreseeable future." Carl Gethmann, "Manned Space Travel as a Cultural Mission," *Poiesis & Praxis* (December 2006), argues that costs should not be used to reject manned space travel as a pointless option. The dream and the effort are part of our culture, and we should pursue them as far as we can afford to. Arthur Woods, "The Space Option," *Leonardo* (vol. 41, no. 4, 2008), argues that space resources are the most realistic way to ensure future human survival and success.

Jeff Foust, "The Future of Human Spaceflight," *Technology Review* (January/February 2010), summarizes the report of the Augustine Commission (*Seeking a Human Spaceflight Program Worthy of a Great Nation*, October 2009, www.nasa.gov/pdf/396093main_HSF_Cmte_FinalReport.pdf) and argues that the ultimate goal of manned space exploration is to "chart a path for human expansion into the solar system." To support that goal will require extending the life of the International Space Station (ISS), providing more funding for mission development, and encouraging the private sector to take over transportation to and from the ISS. At present, human spaceflight is not sustainable. Early in 2010, President Barack Obama announced plans to cancel existing plans for a new launch system that would replace the present space shuttle, shift support missions for the International Space Station to commercial space flight companies, and to start work on a new system that would be able to support missions to asteroids and even Mars; see Andrew Lawler, "Obama Backs New Launcher and Bigger NASA Budget," *Science* (January 1, 2010). In May 2012, the first commercial flight—the unmanned SpaceX Dragon—successfully reached the International Space Station; see "SpaceX Dragon Triumph: Only the Beginning," *CNN online* (May 25, 2012) (http://lightyears.blogs.cnn.com/2012/05/25/spacex-orbital-mission-just-the-beginning/).

In the YES selection, Eugene A. Cernan, commander of the *Apollo XVII* mission, argues that manned space exploration is an investment in the future, in technology, jobs, international respect, geopolitical leadership, and the inspiration and education of our youth. It must not be abandoned. In the NO selection, astronomer Neil deGrasse Tyson argues that large, expensive projects such as space exploration are driven only by war, greed, and the celebration of power. The dream of colonizing space became a delusion as soon as we beat the Russians to the Moon, and it remains so. The *Apollo* program was the end of an era, not the beginning that many hoped it would prove.

YES

Eugene A. Cernan

Testimony Before the U.S. House of Representatives Committee on Science, Space, and Technology Hearing on "Spaceflight—Past, Present, and Future: Where Do We Go from Here?"

The Past

Because the theme of this hearing is "**spaceflight—Past, Present and Future**," and because as you, Mr. Chairman, suggested that there are some on this Committee who might well be a generation or more removed from Apollo, I choose first to address the past because I believe it important to go back in time and re-trace our path through history to the day from which we were destined to become the world's leading space-faring nation. As we now look to the future, I consider the past vital so as to fully understand what it required to become the unchallenged leader in the world of Space Exploration.

Lest we forget, Mr. Chairman, it was a bold and courageous President over a half century ago who started us on a journey to the stars—a journey from which America would never look back—and a journey that challenged the American people at every crossroad to do what most thought couldn't be done. It was a challenge that came in the "terrible 60's," at a time when our nation was shackled by civil strife, campus unrest and the beginning of what became a very unpopular war—and perhaps foremost, it was a challenge to the then Soviet Union's dominance in space. To meet that challenge required all the dedication and personal commitment our nation could muster. And, it was not going to be easy, but hard, and [it] did require sacrifice, just as John F. Kennedy said it would. However, being second best was unacceptable then and being just good today is never going to be good enough for the American people.

JFK did not just challenge us to go to the moon—he believed it was time to take a leading role in space—a role he thought might well hold the key to our future on Earth. So we built upon the uncertainty of Mercury, fabricated Gemini, the bridge to Apollo, and then realized the dream of mankind for eons of time when over 40 years ago we were able to call the moon our home.

But we did not quit there—before the end of Apollo in 1972, Skylab—man's first orbiting laboratory—was ready to fly; the Space Shuttle, perhaps the most capable flying machine ever designed, built and flown by man, was already on the drawing boards; and today the International Space Station, the assembly of which may well go down in history as man's greatest engineering accomplishment of all time, circles the globe sixteen times every day—all in keeping with JFK's challenge to go to the moon "and do the other things." Along the way, thousands of young Americans, who, inspired by what was happening around them, became doctors, engineers, teachers, scientists, and even university Presidents—a "stimulus" for education unparalleled in our history. The above constituted a logical progression with the purpose of achieving and then maintaining our position as the world's leading space-faring nation. And with it came the development of technology which allowed us to satisfy mankind's insatiable quest for knowledge—all on that ocean on which we "set sail" a half century ago. For 50 years, Mr. Chairman, we were caught up in the inertia of growth, where each day brought new revelations about the unknown—our curiosity was overwhelmed with more questions than answers.

The Present

However, today we are on a path of decay. We are seeing the book closed on five decades of accomplishments as the world's leading space-faring nation. As unimaginable as it seems, we have now come full circle and ceded our leadership role in space back to the same country, albeit with a different name, that spurred our challenge five decades ago.

What measures are needed to reverse this inertia of decay? Based upon history the long-term solution appears obvious. One only has to look back and learn from history to understand what it will take to once again be the world's leading space-faring nation. We eventually need an Administration that believes in and understands the importance of America's commitment to regaining its pre-imminence in space. An administration which will provide us with a leader who will once again be bold and challenge our people to do what history has now told us *is possible*. We must have a forward looking independent NASA who can advise the President, manage far-reaching programs, and work with a bi-partisan Congress in moving forward with a space program that benefits all Americans. And a NASA that realizes the importance of looking back in history—learning from our mistakes and building upon the successful culture of a

Cernan, Eugene A. From statement before U.S. House of Representatives, September 22, 2011.

government-private industry partnership that has endured throughout the life of our space program developing safe and cost effective space exploration systems.

The short-term solution is more complex in light of NASA and the present Administration's now obvious agenda to dismantle a space program that has been five decades in the making. First on this agenda was to cancel Constellation—a $10 billion investment five years in development. Embedded in the Constellation architecture was the culture of a long-range building block that could not only service the ISS, extend the life of Hubble, provide national security, but additionally would be capable of carrying us back to the moon and on to Mars. To replace Constellation was a "mission to nowhere" which had no near or long-term goals, time table, specific destination, and no direction for human space flight—and nowhere were there any specific plans for the design and building of hardware should any part of this agenda be overridden by Congress. Then came a decision to subsidize the commercial sector to "whatever extent it might take to make it successful"—a program that appears to have little or no transparency or NASA insight or oversight into existing problems or those that past experience has told us will crop up in the future. My thoughts on the commercial space claims are well-known. I stand behind my assertion that it will be near the end of the decade before these new entrants will be able to place a human safely and cost effectively in Earth orbit. Now we have the termination of the Space Shuttle with, until recently, nothing on the Administration's horizon to replace it. It wasn't but a few months ago we had the most capable operationally proven launch vehicle available far into the future giving us unprecedented personal and payload access to low Earth orbit. Additionally, the Shuttle had the potential of being the catalyst for the assembly and return to Earth for deep space missions resulting in weight and performance advantages. Even if not in future plans to be the primary lift to LEO, the Shuttle certainly provided us with a versatile and redundant operational system. Isn't it ironic that we find ourselves today with no, zero capability to access the ISS? I believe the Shuttle retirement to be a poorly thought out and premature decision. I take no solace in the failure of the last Soyuz booster, but if one examines the recent letter from Dr. Chris Kraft to [NASA Administrator] Charlie Bolden concerning this and other problematic contingencies, serious questions could be asked. This letter requested only that the decision on Shuttle retirement be reconsidered in light of the fact that there was nothing to take its place for some indeterminate time in the future. I find it extremely disrespectful that, to my knowledge, Dr. Kraft has never to this date received a response to his personal letter.

Space Lunch System (SLS)

Of record is the NASA Authorization Act of 2010 in which the plans were outlined to build a heavy lift vehicle with Congressionally appropriated and authorized required funding. Several independent cost assessments as well as NASA itself verified that the program was technically and financially feasible as planned. Until this past week, NASA had continued to disregard, ignore and flaunt the law and the mandate of the Congress while continuing to pursue its own agenda of disabling our nation's space program. It had become obvious that NASA as directed by the Administration has had no interest in following the law and the mandate of Congress in the development of a heavy lift launch vehicle.

It is only now after mandates, requests, investigations, a subpoena, and a stinging rebuke of the Administration by two very prominent Senators that NASA has retreated on its delaying tactics to move forward with the development of a Space Launch System (SLS). This is certainly good news forced upon the Administration by concerned and wiser members of Congress, but this decision could well leave us hostage to Russia for access to the ISS for some time to come. Is it possible that the Administration's delay tactics in committing to the SLS somehow has its origin in the delays anticipated in commercial space's development of the capability to put a human in LEO in the foreseeable future? My assessment of NASA's progress in the development of a heavy lift launch system to enable exploration beyond Earth orbit, as well as provide a capability to service the ISS should a commercial market entrant or our international partners become unavailable, is that it has been deceptive, inadequate and to date non-productive.

The Future

Should the development of the SLS go forward as mandated by Congress along with the Orion Spacecraft as just announced by the Administration, I believe we will have the best and perhaps only opportunity within reach to narrow the gap that now exists between the final Shuttle flight and America's capability to regain access to Earth orbit and the ISS. Access to low Earth orbit should be our primary objective in any plans in the evolutionary development of a new versatile lift vehicle with future deep space missions as a follow on. This, I understand, is the mandate from Congress. Although it is the intent that the "full up" SLS give us the capability of designing a variable set of missions, I firmly believe that the time for a well thought out long term initiative for our nation's role in space, with or without the SLS System, is long overdue. The "Mission to Somewhere" logically points to the moon, thereby building the foundation for a voyage to Mars. Unfortunately, it might well be a generation or more before the U.S. once again exerts its influence in Space Exploration beyond Earth orbit. "If we don't know where we are going, we might end up where we are headed." Nevertheless, since we have apparently decided to relegate the final Shuttle to a place in history, it becomes even more imperative that we move forward quickly and confidently on a LEO derivative of the SLS that can satisfy our urgent near-term requirements to access low Earth orbit.

Risks and Challenges

As a consequence of the cancellation of Constellation, the termination of the Space Shuttle, and NASA's continued unwillingness to accede to Congressional mandates thus causing unnecessary delays over the past two and one-half years, the risks and challenges to NASA and the aerospace community are numerous. My immediate concerns are the deterioration of our technological base, the lack of stability of the NASA budget when considering the present state of the economy, the absence of the Administration's commitment to cooperate with Congress and forge an ambitious program, the question of continued bi-partisan Congressional support, and perhaps the most important risk with lasting effect, is the loss and dismemberment of our skilled workforce.

As a result of these factors, uncertainty and instability abound. Among the thousands of highly educated workers with unique skills developed over generations, once we lose the older, wiser, mature and experienced folks to retirement, who spent in some cases over five decades learning "what they didn't know they didn't know," along with those inspired and enthusiastic young minds of today's generation to other endeavors, inertia takes hold of the downward trend and it is difficult, costly and near impossible to reverse. And those young high school and college students whose dreams were to take their generation back to the moon and beyond are now questioning their plans to seek studies in science, engineering and math in the future. And for those fortunate few still at work within NASA or its contracting team, without a goal or mission, their future is bleak. Under this cloud of uncertainty most are seeking stability for themselves and their families by going elsewhere with their talents. I believe therein is the ongoing risk and challenge this country faces in any potential future development of human space systems. It's important to remember that "technology makes it possible, but people make it happen."

Testimony of May 26, 2010

Very little if anything has changed my assessment of the Administration's space policy since my testimony before this Committee over a year ago. I recounted the words of my colleagues and myself in describing the Administration's plan for the future of Space Exploration—"Devastating," "Slide to mediocrity," "Third-rate stature," "Mission to nowhere." Although with the SLS System we will provide the foundation for designing "missions to somewhere"—they have yet to be defined. So today I stand behind my testimony and convictions of sixteen months ago. Nowhere did I find then nor do I find today one penny in the FY2011 budget proposal in support of Space Exploration. Although I do believe and hope that someday they will succeed, I still assess that those entrepreneurs in the world of commercial space who continue their claims of being able to put humans in space in little more than three years for something less than $5 billion, today still "don't yet know what they don't know." My statement that "the sole reliance on the Commercial Sector without a concurrent or back-up approach could very well lead to the abandonment of our $100 billion, 25 year investment in the ISS" is now more prophetic than ever.

"The space program has never been an entitlement, it's an investment in the future—an investment in technology, jobs, international respect and geo-political leadership, and perhaps most importantly in the inspiration and education of our youth. Those best and brightest minds at NASA and throughout the multitudes of private contractors, large and small, did not join the team to design windmills or redesign gas pedals, but to live their dreams of once again taking us where no man has gone before. If this Administration's agenda continues to override the mandates of Congress, these technicians, engineers, scientists, a generation removed from Apollo, yet re-inspired by the prospect of going back to the moon and on the Mars, will be gone—where I don't know—but gone." Sixteen months later, the absence of a well-defined NASA program has already resulted in the loss of thousands of jobs throughout the aerospace industry.

"America's human space flight program has for a half century risen above partisan differences from Eisenhower to Kennedy to the present day. The challenges and accomplishments of the past were those of a nation—never of a political party or of any individual agenda." Proven to be true today by the overwhelming congressional support and mandates to NASA in support of future space developments.

"We are at a cross road. If we abdicate our leadership in space today, not only is human spaceflight and space exploration at risk, but I believe the future of this country and thus the future of our children and grandchildren as well. Now is the time for wiser heads in the Congress of the United States to prevail. Now is the time to overrule this Administration's *pledge to mediocrity*. Now is the time to be *bold, innovative* and *wise* in how we invest in the future of America. Now is the time to re-establish our nation's commitment *to excellence*."

Mr. Chairman, Ladies and Gentlemen—**it not about space—it's about the country.**

Thank you for your time and patience.
Sincerely, and with respect,

Eugene A. Cernan
Commander, Apollo XVII

Eugene A. Cernan is a retired astronaut and U.S. Navy Captain. He piloted the *Gemini 9A* mission in June 1966, piloted the lunar module of *Apollo 10* in May 1969, and commanded *Apollo XVII*, the last mission to land on the Moon.

Neil deGrasse Tyson **NO**

Delusions of Space Enthusiasts

Sometimes innovation gets interrupted.

Human ingenuity seldom fails to improve on the fruits of human invention. Whatever may have dazzled everyone on its debut is almost guaranteed to be superseded and, someday, to look quaint.

In 2000 B.C. a pair of ice skates made of polished animal bone and leather thongs was a transportation breakthrough. In 1610 Galileo's eight-power telescope was an astonishing tool of detection, capable of giving the senators of Venice a sneak peek at hostile ships before they could enter the lagoon. In 1887 the one-horsepower Benz Patent Motorwagen was the first commercially produced car powered by an internal combustion engine. In 1946 the thirty-ton, showroom-size ENIAC, with its 18,000 vacuum tubes and 6,000 manual switches, pioneered electronic computing. Today you can glide across roadways on in-line skates, gaze at images of faraway galaxies brought to you by the Hubble Space Telescope, cruise the autobahn in a 600-horsepower roadster, and carry your three-pound laptop to an outdoor café.

Of course, such advances don't just fall from the sky. Clever people think them up. Problem is, to turn a clever idea into reality, somebody has to write the check. And when market forces shift, those somebodies may lose interest and the checks may stop coming. If computer companies had stopped innovating in 1978, your desk might still sport a hundred-pound IBM 5110. If communications companies had stopped innovating in 1973, you might still be schlepping a two-pound, nine-inch-long cell phone. And if in 1968 the U.S. space industry had stopped developing bigger and better rockets to launch humans beyond the Moon, we'd never have surpassed the Saturn V rocket.

Oops!

Sorry about that. We haven't surpassed the Saturn V. The largest, most powerful rocket ever flown by anybody, ever, the thirty-six-story-tall Saturn V was the first and only rocket to launch people from Earth to someplace else in the universe. It enabled every Apollo mission to the Moon from 1969 through 1972, as well as the 1973 launch of Skylab I, the first U.S. space station.

Inspired in part by the successes of the Saturn V and the momentum of the Apollo program, visionaries of the day foretold a future that never came to be: space habitats, Moon bases, and Mars colonies up and running by the 1990s. But funding for the Saturn V evaporated as the Moon missions wound down. Additional production runs were canceled, the manufacturers' specialized machine tools were destroyed, and skilled personnel had to find work on other projects. Today U.S. engineers can't even build a Saturn V clone. . . .

What cultural forces froze the Saturn V rocket in time and space?

What misconceptions led to the gap between expectation and reality?

Soothsaying tends to come in two flavors: doubt and delirium. It was doubt that led skeptics to declare that the atom would never be split, the sound barrier would never be broken, and people would never want or need computers in their homes. But in the case of the Saturn V rocket, it was delirium that misled futurists into assuming the Saturn V was an auspicious beginning—never considering that it could, instead, be an end.

On December 30, 1900, for its last Sunday paper of the nineteenth century, the *Brooklyn Daily Eagle* published a sixteen-page supplement headlined "THINGS WILL BE SO DIFFERENT A HUNDRED YEARS HENCE." The contributors—business leaders, military men, pastors, politicians, and experts of every persuasion—imagined what housework, poverty, religion, sanitation, and war would be like in the year 2000. They enthused about the potential of electricity and the automobile. There was even a map of the world-to-be, showing an American Federation comprising most of the Western Hemisphere from the lands above the Arctic Circle down to the archipelago of Tierra del Fuego—plus sub-Saharan Africa, the southern half of Australia, and all of New Zealand.

Most of the writers portrayed an expansive future. But not all. George H. Daniels, a man of authority at the New York Central and Hudson River Railroad, peered into his crystal ball and, boneheadedly predicted:

> It is scarcely possible that the twentieth century will witness improvements in transportation that will be as great as were those of the nineteenth century.

Elsewhere in his article, Daniels envisioned affordable global tourism and the diffusion of white bread to China and Japan. Yet he simply couldn't imagine what might replace steam as the power source for ground transportation, let alone a vehicle moving through the air. Even though he stood on the doorstep of the twentieth century, this manager of the world's biggest railroad system could not see beyond the automobile, the locomotive, and the steamship. . . .

Three years later, almost to the day, Wilbur and Orville Wright made the first-ever series of powered, controlled, heavier-than-air flights. By 1957 the U.S.S.R. launched the first satellite into Earth orbit. And in 1969 two Americans became the first human beings to walk on the Moon.

Daniels is hardly the only person to have misread the technological future. Even experts who aren't totally deluded can have tunnel vision. On page 13 of the *Eagle's* Sunday supplement, the principal examiner at the U.S. Patent Office, W.W. Townsend, wrote, "The automobile may be the vehicle of the decade, but the air ship is the conveyance of the century." Sounds visionary, until you read further. What he was talking about were blimps and zeppelins. Both Daniels and Townsend, otherwise well-informed citizens of a changing world, were clueless about what tomorrow's technology would bring. . . .

Even the Wrights were guilty of doubt about the future of aviation. In 1901, discouraged by a summer's worth of unsuccessful tests with a glider, Wilbur told Orville it would take another fifty years for someone to fly. Nope: the birth of aviation was just two years away. On the windy, chilly morning of December 17, 1903, starting from a North Carolina sand dune called Kill Devil Hill, Orville was the first to fly the brothers' 600-pound plane through the air. His epochal journey lasted twelve seconds and covered 120 feet—a distance just shy of the wingspan of a Boeing 757.

Judging by what the mathematician, astronomer, and Royal Society gold medalist Simon Newcomb had published just two months earlier, the flights from Kill Devil Hill should never have taken place when they did:

> Quite likely the twentieth century is destined to see the natural forces which will enable us to fly from continent to continent with a speed far exceeding that of the bird.
>
> But when we inquire whether aerial flight is possible in the present state of our knowledge; whether, with such materials as we possess, a combination of steel, cloth and wire can be made which, moved by the power of electricity or steam, shall form a successful flying machine, the outlook may be altogether different.

. . . Some representatives of informed public opinion went even further. The *New York Times* was steeped in doubt just one week before the Wright brothers went aloft in the original Wright Flyer. Writing on December 10, 1903—not about the Wrights but about their illustrious and publicly funded competitor, Samuel E. Langley, an astronomer, physicist, and chief administrator of the Smithsonian Institution—the *Times* declared:

> We hope that Professor Langley will not put his substantial greatness as a scientist in further peril by continuing to waste his time, and the money involved, in further airship experiments. Life is short, and he is capable of services to humanity incomparably greater than can be expected to result from trying to fly.

. . . You might think attitudes would have changed as soon as people from several countries had made their first flights. But no. Wilbur Wright wrote in 1909 that no flying machine would ever make the journey from New York to Paris. Richard Burdon Haldane, the British secretary of war, told Parliament in 1909 that even though the airplane might one day be capable of great things, "from the war point of view, it is not so at present." Ferdinand Foch, a highly regarded French military strategist and the supreme commander of the Allied forces near the end of the First World War, opined in 1911 that airplanes were interesting toys but had no military value. Late that same year, near Tripoli, an Italian plane became the first to drop a bomb.

Early attitudes about flight beyond Earth's atmosphere followed a similar trajectory. True, plenty of philosophers, scientists, and sci-fi writers had thought long and hard about outer space. The sixteenth-century philosopher-friar Giordano Bruno proposed that intelligent beings inhabited an infinitude of worlds. The seventeenth-century soldier-writer Savinien de Cyrano de Bergerac portrayed the Moon as a world with forests, violets, and people.

But those writings were fantasies, not blueprints for action. By the early twentieth century, electricity, telephones, automobiles, radios, airplanes, and countless other engineering marvels were all becoming basic features of modern life. So couldn't earthlings build machines capable of space travel? Many people who should have known better said it couldn't be done, even after the successful 1942 test launch of the world's first long-range ballistic missile: Germany's deadly V-2 rocket. Capable of punching through Earth's atmosphere, it was a crucial step toward reaching the Moon.

Richard van der Riet Woolley, the eleventh British Astronomer Royal, is the source of a particularly woolly remark. When he landed in London after a thirty-six-hour flight from Australia, some reporters asked him about space travel. "It's utter bilge," he answered. That was in early 1956. In early 1957 Lee De Forest, a prolific American inventor who helped birth the age of electronics, declared, "Man will never reach the moon, regardless of all future scientific advances." Remember what happened in late 1957? Not just one but two Soviet Sputniks entered Earth orbit. The space race had begun.

Whenever someone says an idea is "bilge" (British for "baloney"), you must first ask whether it violates any well-tested laws of physics. If so, the idea is likely to be bilge. If not, the only challenge is to find a clever engineer—and, of course, a committed source of funding.

The day the Soviet Union launched Sputnik 1, a chapter of science fiction became science fact, and the future became the present. All of a sudden, futurists went overboard with their enthusiasm. The delusion that technology would advance at lightning speed replaced the delusion that it would barely advance at all. Experts went from having much too little confidence in the pace of technology to having much too much. And the guiltiest people of all were the space enthusiasts.

Commentators became fond of twenty-year intervals, within which some previously inconceivable goal would supposedly be accomplished. On January 6, 1967, in a front-page story, *The Wall Street Journal* announced: "The most ambitious U.S. space endeavor in the years ahead will be the campaign to land men on neighboring Mars. Most experts estimate the task can be accomplished by 1985." The very next month, in its debut issue, *The Futurist* magazine announced that according to long-range forecasts by the RAND Corporation, a pioneer think-tank, there was a 60 percent probability that a manned lunar base would exist by 1986. In *The Book of Predictions,* published in 1980, the rocket pioneer Robert C. Truax forecast that 50,000 people would be living and working in space by the year 2000. When that benchmark year arrived, people were indeed living and working in space. But the tally was not 50,000. It was three: the first crew of the International Space Station. . . .

All those visionaries (and countless others) never really grasped the forces that drive technological progress. In Wilbur and Orville's day, you could tinker your way into major engineering advances. Their first airplane did not require a grant from the National Science Foundation: they funded it through their bicycle business. The brothers constructed the wings and fuselage themselves, with tools they already owned, and got their resourceful bicycle mechanic, Charles E. Taylor, to design and hand-build the engine. The operation was basically two guys and a garage.

Space exploration unfolds on an entirely different scale. The first moonwalkers were two guys, too—Neil Armstrong and Buzz Aldrin—but behind them loomed the force of a mandate from an assassinated president, 10,000 engineers, $100 billion, and a Saturn V rocket.

Notwithstanding the sanitized memories so many of us have of the Apollo era, Americans were not first on the Moon because we're explorers by nature or because our country is committed to the pursuit of knowledge. We got to the Moon first because the United States was out to beat the Soviet Union, to win the Cold War any way we could. John F. Kennedy made that clear when he complained to top NASA officials in November 1962:

> I'm not that interested in space. I think it's good, I think we ought to know about it, we're ready to spend reasonable amounts of money. But we're talking about these fantastic expenditures which wreck our budget and all these other domestic programs and the only justification for it in my opinion to do it in this time or fashion is because we hope to beat them [the Soviet Union] and demonstrate that starting behind, as we did by a couple of years, by God, we passed them.

Like it or not, war (cold or hot) is the most powerful funding driver in the public arsenal. When a country wages war, money flows like floodwaters. Lofty goals—such as curiosity, discovery, exploration, and science—can get you money for modest-size projects, provided they resonate with the political and cultural views of the moment. But big, expensive activities are inherently long term, and require sustained investment that must survive economic fluctuations and changes in the political winds.

In all eras, across time and culture, only three drivers have fulfilled that funding requirement: war, greed, and the celebration of royal or religious power. The Great Wall of China; the pyramids of Egypt; the Gothic cathedrals of Europe; the U.S. interstate highway system; the voyages of Columbus and Cook—nearly every major undertaking owes its existence to one or more of those three drivers. Today, as the power of kings is supplanted by elected governments, and the power of religion is often expressed in nonarchitectural undertakings, that third driver has lost much of its sway, leaving war and greed to run the show. Sometimes those two drivers work hand in hand, as in the art of profiteering from the art of war. But war itself remains the ultimate and most compelling rationale.

Having been born the same week NASA was founded, I was eleven years old during the voyage of Apollo 11, and had already identified the universe as my life's passion. Unlike so many other people who watched Neil Armstrong's first steps on the Moon, I wasn't jubilant. I was simply relieved that someone was finally exploring another world. To me, Apollo 11 was clearly the beginning of an era.

But I, too, was delirious. The lunar landings continued for three and a half years. Then they stopped. The Apollo program became the end of an era, not the beginning. And as the Moon voyages receded in time and memory, they seemed ever more unreal in the history of human projects.

Unlike the first ice skates or the first airplane or the first desktop computer—artifacts that make us all chuckle when we see them today—the first rocket to the Moon, the 364-foot-tall Saturn V, elicits awe, even reverence. Three Saturn V relics lie in state at the Johnson Space Center in Texas, the Kennedy Space Center in Florida, and the U.S. Space and Rocket Center in Alabama. Streams of worshippers walk the length of each rocket. They touch the mighty rocket nozzles at the base and wonder how something so large could ever have bested Earth's gravity. To transform their awe into chuckles, our country will have to resume the effort to "boldly go where no man has gone before." Only then will the Saturn V look as quaint as every other invention that human ingenuity has paid the compliment of improving upon.

Neil deGrasse Tyson is the director of the Hayden Planetarium at the American Museum of Natural History. His latest book is *The Sky Is Not the Limit: Adventures of an Urban Astrophysicist* (Prometheus, 2009).

EXPLORING THE ISSUE

Do Humans Belong in Space?

Critical Thinking and Reflection

1. Exploring space is a great idea—but what is in it for us?
2. In a space program dominated by robotic spacecraft and landers, what role remains for human beings?
3. How does the prospect of an asteroid impact on Earth help to justify manned space exploration?
4. How will the U.S. government respond if China puts an astronaut on the Moon?

Is There Common Ground?

Those who argue over the merits of manned space exploration tend to agree that space is worth exploring. They disagree on whether it is necessary to send people into space when robots are already very capable and likely to be much more capable in a few years.

1. Just how capable are robots today? (There is a great deal of material on this question.)
2. Look up "telepresence" (see Tom Simonite, "The New, More Awkward You," *Technology Review* (January/February 2011), www.technologyreview.com/computing/26941/?a=f). Does this technology offer a compromise on the question of using either robots or humans in space?

Create Central

www.mhhe.com/createcentral

Additional Resources

Augustine Commission, *Seeking a Human Spaceflight Program Worthy of a Great Nation* (October 2009) (www.nasa.gov/pdf/396093main_HSF_Cmte_FinalReport.pdf).

Robert Zubrin, "How Much Is an Astronaut's Life Worth?" *Reason* (February 2012).

Internet Reference . . .

The Coalition to Save Manned Space Exploration

The mission of the Coalition to Save Manned Space Exploration is to help rebuild public interest in the space program to result in greater support by Congress and the administration.

www.savemannedspace.com/

Unit 5

UNIT

The Computer Revolution

Fans of computers have long been sure that the electronic wonders offer untold benefits to society. When the first personal computers appeared in the early 1970s, they immediately brought unheard-of capabilities to their users. Ever since, those capabilities have been increasing. Today children command more sheer computing power that major corporations did in the 1950s and 1960s. Computer users are in direct contact with their fellow users around the world. Information is instantly available and infinitely malleable.

Some observers wonder about the purported untold benefits of computers. Specifically, will such benefits be outweighed by threats to children (by free access to pornography and by online predators), civil order (by free access to sites that advocate racism and violence), traditional institutions (will books, for example, become an endangered species?), or to human pride (computers have already outplayed human champions at chess, checkers, and go)? If computers can outthink humans at games, how long will it be before they are as intelligent and even as conscious as we are? What happens to our jobs and careers then? Do we have to worry about cyber-war? And must all software be produced as proprietary product?

Selected, Edited, and with Issue Framing Material by:
Thomas A. Easton, *Thomas College*

ISSUE

Will Robots Take Your Job?

YES: Marshall Brain, from "Robotic Nation" (Summer 2003), http://marshallbrain.com/robotic-nation.htm

NO: Peter Gorle and Andrew Clive, from "Positive Impact of Industrial Robots on Employment," *Metra Martech* (February 21, 2011)

Learning Outcomes

After studying this issue, students will be able to

- Explain what kinds of jobs are now and may soon be suitable for robots.
- Discuss the impact of robotics on their future job prospects.
- Apply their understanding of how robots will affect future jobs in a discussion of career choices.

ISSUE SUMMARY

YES: Marshall Brain argues that by the middle of the twenty-first century, robots will be able to perform nearly any normal job that a human performs today. They will eliminate a huge portion of the jobs currently held by humans. Those humans will be unemployed and—if welfare systems cannot keep up with need—destitute. He insists that "It is time to start rethinking our economy."

NO: Peter Gorle and Andrew Clive argue that robots are not a threat to human employment. Historically, increases in the use of automation almost always increase both productivity and employment. Over the next few years, the use of robotics will generate 700,000–1,000,000 new jobs.

The idea that technology threatens jobs is not new. In the early 1800s, the "Luddites" were textile workers who destroyed new weaving machinery that could be operated by unskilled labor. The movement faded away with the end of the Napoleonic Wars, but its name has continued to be applied to those who oppose industrialization, automation, computerization, and even any new technology. See, for example, Steven E. Jones, *Against Technology: From the Luddites to Neo-Luddism* (CRC Press, 2006).

Not surprisingly, modern computer technology arouses many job-related fears, for computers seem to be growing ever more capable. When IBM's "Watson" won a dramatic victory in the game of "Jeopardy," many wondered if we were finally seeing true artificial intelligence. Kirk L. Kroeker, "Weighing Watson's Impact," *Communications of the ACM* (July 2011), notes that despite many dismissive comments, Watson is an excellent demonstration of the power of machine learning. Future applications of the technology will soon play important roles in medicine (extracting information from vast numbers of medical books and journals), law, education, and the financial industry. Many of these applications do not require that a robot look and act like a human being, but researchers are working on that, too; see Alex Wright, "Robots Like Us," *Communications of the ACM* (May 2012).

"Robocars"—cars that drive themselves, with no human hand at the wheel—have already been demonstrated and their capabilities are improving rapidly; see Sebastian Thrun, "Toward Robotic Cars," *Communications of the ACM* (April 2010), and Alex Wright, "Automotive Autonomy," *Communications of the ACM* (July 2011). Before they can be broadly used, there must be changes in legislation (can you be guilty of OUI if the car drives itself?) and insurance, among other things; see "The Future of the Self-Driving Automobile," *Trends E-Magazine* (December 2010), and John Markoff, "Collision in the Making Between Self-Driving Cars and How the World Works," *New York Times* (January 23, 2012). Given such changes, we can expect to see job losses among taxi drivers and truckers, among others.

Robots may also cost other people their jobs. Jason Borenstein, "Robots and the Changing Workforce," *AI & Society* (2011), notes that robotic workers are going to become ever more common, and though new job opportunities are bound to arise from this, many jobs will disappear and the human workforce will change in many ways—including necessary education and worker income. Judith Aquino, "Nine Jobs that Humans May Lose to Robots," *Business Insider* (March 22, 2011), says the endangered list includes not only drivers, but also pharmacists, lawyers and paralegals, astronauts, store clerks, soldiers, babysitters, rescuers, and sportswriters and other reporters. John Sepulvado asks "Could a Computer Write This Story?" (CNN, May 11, 2012) (http://edition.cnn.com/2012/05/11/tech/innovation/computer-assisted-writing/index.html), and points to a company, Narrative Science (www.narrativescience.com/), that is working on making the answer yes. Farhad Manjoo asks (and answers) "Will Robots Steal Your Job? If You're Highly Educated, You Should Still Be Afraid," *Slate* (September 26, 2011) (www.slate.com/articles/technology/robot_invasion/2011/09/will_robots_steal_your_job.html). "Robots to Take 500,000 Human Jobs . . . for Now," *The Fiscal Times* (December 29, 2011), notes that every industry, from agriculture to the military, will be affected. Martin Ford, "Google's Cloud Robotics Strategy—and How It Could Soon Threaten Jobs," *Huffington Post* (January 3, 2012), says that "nearly any type of work that is on some level routine in nature—regardless of the skill level or educational requirements—is likely to someday be impacted by [robotic] technologies. The only real question is how soon it will happen." This foreboding thought is echoed by Dan Lyons, "Who Needs Humans?" *Newsweek* (July 25, 2011). David J. Lynch is more optimistic: in "It's a Man vs. Machine Recovery," *Bloomberg Businessweek* (January 5, 2012), he notes that businesses are buying machines more than hiring people, but "there's nothing wrong with the labor market that resurgent demand wouldn't fix." There may also be a need to consider the ethics involved, for as more robots enter the workplace, they will bring with them changed expectations (robots are tireless, and they don't need health insurance, retirement plans, vacations, and even pay; will employers expect the same of humans?); this may even mean restricting the use of robots; see Jason Borenstein, "Computing Ethics: Work Life in the Robotic Age," *Communications of the ACM* (July 2010). David Bourne, "My Boss the Robot," *Scientific American* (May 2013), sees a future in which humans and robots collaborate to get jobs done more rapidly and efficiently than either could do alone.

How bad is it going to be? In the YES selection, Marshall Brain argues that by the middle of the twenty-first century, robots will be able to perform nearly any normal job that a human performs today. They will eliminate a huge portion of the jobs currently held by humans. Those humans will be unemployed and—if welfare systems cannot keep up with need—destitute. Brain insists that "It is time to start rethinking our economy." (His ideas are also discussed by Joanna Glasner, "How Robots Will Steal Your Job," *Wired* (August 5, 2003).) In the NO selection, Peter Gorle and Andrew Clive argue that robots are not a threat to human employment. Historically, increases in the use of automation almost always increase both productivity and employment. Over the next few years, the use of robotics will generate 700,000–1,000,000 new jobs.

YES

Marshall Brain

Robotic Nation

I went to McDonald's this weekend with the kids. We go to McDonald's to eat about once a week because it is a mile from the house and has an indoor play area. Our normal routine is to walk in to McDonald's, stand in line, order, stand around waiting for the order, sit down, eat and play.

On Sunday, this decades-old routine changed forever. When we walked in to McDonald's, an attractive woman in a suit greeted us and said, "Are you planning to visit the play area tonight?" The kids screamed, "Yeah!" "McDonald's has a new system that you can use to order your food right in the play area. Would you like to try it?" The kids screamed, "Yeah!"

The woman walks us over to a pair of kiosks in the play area. She starts to show me how the kiosks work and the kids scream, "We want to do it!" So I pull up a chair and the kids stand on it while the (extremely patient) woman in a suit walks the kids through the screens. David ordered his food, Irena ordered her food, I ordered my food. It's a simple system. Then it was time to pay. Interestingly, the kiosk only took cash in the form of bills. So I fed my bills into the machine. Then you take a little plastic number to set on your table and type the number in. The transaction is complete.

We sat down at a table. We put our number in the center of the table and waited. In about 10 seconds the kids screamed, "When is our food going to get here???" I said, "Let's count." In less than two minutes a woman in an apron put a tray with our food on the table, handed us our change, took the plastic number and left.

You know what? It is a nice system. It works. It is much nicer than standing in line. The only improvement I would request is the ability to use a credit card.

As nice as this system is, however, I think that it represents the tip of an iceberg that we do not understand. This iceberg is going to change the American economy in ways that are very hard to imagine.

The Iceberg

The iceberg looks like this. On that same day, I interacted with five different automated systems like the kiosks in McDonald's:

- I got money in the morning from the ATM.
- I bought gas from an automated pump.
- I bought groceries at BJ's (a warehouse club) using an extremely well-designed self-service check out line.
- I bought some stuff for the house at Home Depot using their not-as-well-designed-as-BJ's self-service check out line.
- I bought my food at McDonald's at the kiosk, as described above.

All of these systems are very easy-to-use from a customer standpoint, they are fast, and they lower the cost of doing business and should therefore lead to lower prices. All of that is good, so these automated systems will proliferate rapidly.

The problem is that these systems will also eliminate jobs in massive numbers. In fact, we are about to see a seismic shift in the American workforce. As a nation, we have no way to understand or handle the level of unemployment that we will see in our economy over the next several decades.

These kiosks and self-service systems are the beginning of the robotic revolution. When most people think about robots, they think about independent, autonomous, talking robots like the ones we see in science fiction films. C-3PO and R2-D2 are powerful robotic images that have been around for decades. Robots like these will come into our lives much more quickly than we imagine—self-service checkout systems are the first primitive signs of the trend. Here is one view from the future to show you where we are headed:

> Automated retail systems like ATMs, kiosks and self-service checkout lines marked the beginning of the robotic revolution. Over the course of fifteen years starting in 2001, these systems proliferated and evolved until nearly every retail transaction could be handled in an automated way. Five million jobs in the retail sector were lost as a result of these systems.
>
> The next step was autonomous, humanoid robots. The mechanics of walking were not simple, but Honda had proven that those problems could be solved with the creation of its ASIMO robot at the turn of the century. Sony and other manufacturers followed Honda's lead. Over the course of two decades, engineers refined this hardware and the software controlling it to the point where they could create humanoid bodyforms with the grace and precision of a ballerina or the mass and sheer strength of the Incredible Hulk.

Decades of research and development work on autonomous robotic intelligence finally started to pay off. By 2025, the first machines that could see, hear, move and manipulate objects at a level roughly equivalent to human beings were making their way from research labs into the marketplace. These robots could not "think" creatively like human beings, but that did not matter. Massive AI systems evolved rapidly and allowed machines to perform in ways that seemed very human.

Humanoid robots soon cost less than the average car, and prices kept falling. A typical model had two arms, two legs and the normal human-type sensors like vision, hearing and touch. Power came from small, easily recharged fuel cells. The humanoid form was preferred, as opposed to something odd like R2-D2, because a humanoid shape fit easily into an environment designed around the human body. A humanoid robot could ride an escalator, climb stairs, drive a car, and so on without any trouble.

Once the humanoid robot became a commodity item, robots began to move in and replace humans in the workplace in a significant way. The first wave of replacement began around 2030, starting with jobs in the fast food industry. Robots also filled janitorial and housekeeping positions in hotels, motels, malls, airports, amusement parks and so on.

The economics of one of these humanoid robots made the decision to buy them almost automatic. In 2030 you could buy a humanoid robot for about $10,000. That robot could clean bathrooms, take out trash, wipe down tables, mop floors, sweep parking lots, mow grass and so on. One robot replaced three six-hour-a-day employees. The owner fired the three employees and in just four months the owner recovered the cost of the robot. The robot would last for many years and would happily work 24 hours a day. The robot also did a far better job—for example, the bathrooms were absolutely spotless. It was impossible to pass up a deal like that, so corporations began buying armies of humanoid robots to replace human employees.

The first completely robotic fast food restaurant opened in 2031. It had some rough edges, but by 2035 the rough edges were gone and by 2040 most restaurants were completely robotic. By 2055 the robots were everywhere. The changeover was that fast. It was a startling, amazing transformation and the whole thing happened in only 25 years or so starting in 2030.

In 2055 the nation hit a big milestone—over half of the American workforce was unemployed, and the number was still rising. Nearly every "normal" job that had been filled by a human being in 2001 was filled by a robot instead. At restaurants, robots did all the cooking, cleaning and order taking. At construction sites, robots did everything—Robots poured the concrete, laid brick, built the home's frame, put in the windows and doors, sided the house, roofed it, plumbed it, wired it, hung the drywall, painted it, etc. At the airport, robots flew the planes, sold the tickets, moved the luggage, handled security, kept the building clean and managed air traffic control. At the hospital robots cared for the patients, cooked and delivered the food, cleaned everything and handled many of the administrative tasks. At the mall, stores were stocked, cleaned and clerked by robots. At the amusement park, hundreds of robots ran the rides, cleaned the park and sold the concessions. On the roads, robots drove all the cars and trucks. Companies like Fedex, UPS and the post office had huge numbers of robots instead of people sorting packages, driving trucks and making deliveries.

By 2055 robots had taken over the workplace and there was no turning back.

I know what you are thinking. You are thinking, "This is *impossible*—there will not be humanoid robots in 2055. It is a ridiculous suggestion." But they will be here. Humanoid robots are as inevitable as airplanes.

Imagine this. Imagine that you could travel back in time to the year 1900. Imagine that you stand on a soap box on a city street corner in 1900 and you say to the gathering crowd, "By 1955, people will be flying at supersonic speeds in sleek aircraft and traveling coast to coast in just a few hours." In 1900, it would have been insane to suggest that. In 1900, *airplanes did not even exist*. Orville and Wilbur did not make the first flight until 1903. The Model T Ford did not appear until 1909.

Yet, by 1947, Chuck Yeager flew the X1 at supersonic speeds. In 1954, the B-52 bomber made its maiden flight. It took only 51 years to go from a rickety wooden airplane flying at 10 MPH, to a gigantic aluminum jet-powered Stratofortress carrying 70,000 pounds of bombs halfway around the world at 550 MPH. In 1958, Pan Am started non-stop jet flights between New York and Paris in the Boeing 707. In 1969, Americans set foot on the moon. It is unbelievable what engineers and corporations can accomplish in 50 or 60 short years.

There were millions of people in 1900 who believed that humans would never fly. They were completely wrong. However, I don't think *anyone* in 1900 could imagine the B-52 happening in 54 years.

Over the next 55 years, the same thing will happen to us with robots. In the process, the entire employment landscape in America will change. Here is why that will happen.

Moore's Law

You have probably heard about Moore's law. It says that CPU power doubles every 18 to 24 months or so. History shows Moore's law very clearly. You can see it, for example, by charting the course of Intel microprocessor chips starting with Intel's first single-chip microprocessor in 1971:

- In 1971, Intel released the 4004 microprocessor. It was a 4-bit chip running at 108 kilohertz. It had about 2,300 transistors. By today's standards it was extremely simple, but it was powerful enough to make one of the first electronic calculators possible.

- In 1981, IBM released the first IBM PC. The original PC was based on the Intel 8088 processor. The 8088 ran at 4.7 megahertz (43 times faster clock speed than the 4004) and had nearly 30,000 transistors (10 times more).
- In 1993, Intel released the first Pentium processor. This chip ran at 60 megahertz (13 times faster clock speed than the 8088) and had over three million transistors (10 times more).
- In 2000 the Pentium 4 appeared. It had a clock speed of 1.5 gigahertz (25 times faster clock speed than the Pentium) and it had 42 million transistors (13 times more).

You can see that there are two trends that combine to make computer chips more and more powerful. First there is the increasing clock speed. If you take any chip and double its clock speed, then it can perform twice as many operations per second. Then there is the increasing number of transistors per chip. More transistors let you get more done per clock cycle. For example, with the 8088 processor it took approximately 80 clock cycles to multiply two 16-bit integers together. Today you can multiply two 32-bit floating point numbers every clock cycle. Some chips today even allow you to get more than one floating point operation done per clock cycle.

Taking Moore's law literally, you would expect processor power to increase by a factor of 1,000 every 15 or 20 years. Between 1981 and 2001, that was definitely the case. Clock speed improved by a factor of over 300 during that time, and the number of transistors per chip increased by a factor of 1,400. A processor in 2002 is 10,000 times faster than a processor in 1982 was. This trend has been in place for decades, and there is nothing to indicate that it will slow down any time soon. Scientists and engineers always get around the limitations that threaten Moore's law by developing new technologies.

The same thing happens with RAM chips and hard disk space. A 10 megabyte hard disk cost about $1,000 in 1982. Today you can buy a 250 gigabyte drive that is twice as fast for $350. Today's drive is 25,000 times bigger and costs one-third the price of the 1982 model because of Moore's law. In the same time period—1982 to 2002—standard RAM (Random Access Memory) available in a home machine has gone from 64 kilobytes to 128 megabytes—it improved by of factor of 2,000.

What if we simply extrapolate out, taking the idea that every 20 years things improve by a factor of 1,000 or 10,000? What we get is a machine in 2020 that has a processor running at something like 10 trillion operations per second. It has a terabyte of RAM and one or two petabytes of storage space (a petabyte is one quadrillion bytes). A machine with this kind of power is nearly incomprehensible—there are only two or three machines on the planet with this kind of power today (the monstrous NEC Earth Simulator, with 5,000 separate processor chips working together, is one example). In 2020, every kid will be running their video games on a $500 machine that has that kind of power.

What if we extrapolate another 20 years after that, to 2040? A typical home machine at that point will be 1,000 times faster than the 2020 machine. Human brains are thought to be able to process at a rate of approximately one quadrillion operations per second. A CPU in the 2040 time frame could have the processing power of a human brain, and it will cost $1,000. It will have a petabyte (one quadrillion bytes) of RAM. It will have one exabyte of storage space. An exabyte is 1,000 quadrillion bytes. That's what Moore's law predicts.

The computer power we will have in a home machine around 2050 will be utterly amazing. A typical home computer will have processing power and memory capacity that exceeds that of a human brain. What we will have in 2100 is anyone's guess. The power of a million human brains on the desktop? It is impossible to imagine, but not unlikely.

We need to start thinking about that future today. People are talking optimistically about fielding a team of humanoid robotic soccer players able to beat the best human players in 2050. Imagine a team of C-3POs running and kicking as well as or better than the best human soccer stars, but never getting tired or injured. Imagine that same sort of robot taking 50% of America's jobs. This Honda ad for ASIMO, and the fact that Honda is running it, are telling:

Between 1981 and 2002, the Processing Power, Hard Disk Space and RAM in a Typical Desktop Computer Increased Dramatically Because of Moore's Law. Extrapolating Out to the Years 2021 and 2041 Shows a Startling Increase in Computer Power. The Point Where Small, Inexpensive Computers Have Power Approaching That of the Human Brain Is Just a Few Decades Away.

	1981	2001	2021	2041
Processor	330 thousand ops/sec	1 billion ops/sec	10 trillion ops/sec	10 quadrillion ops/sec
Disk space	10 megabytes	250 gigabytes	1 petabyte	1 exabyte
Memory (RAM)	64 kilobytes	256 megabytes	1 terabyte	1 petabyte

As the ad says, "ASIMO could be quite useful in some very important tasks." One of those very important tasks will be to take your job.

The point is simple. In the 2050 time frame, you can expect to buy a $1,000 home computer that has the computing power and memory of the human brain. Manufacturers will marry that computer with a humanoid robotic chassis like ASIMO, a fuel cell and advanced AI software to create autonomous humanoid robots with startling capabilities. It is not really hard to imagine that we will have robots like C-3PO walking around and filling jobs as early as the 2030 time frame. What's missing from robots right now is brainpower, and by 2030 we will start to have more silicon brainpower than we know what to do with.

The New Employment Landscape

We have no way to understand what is coming or how it will affect us. Keep this fact in mind: the workplace of today is not really that much different from the workplace of 100 years ago. Humans do almost all of the work today, just like they did in 1900. A restaurant today is nearly identical to a restaurant in 1900. An airport, hotel or amusement park today is nearly identical to any airport, hotel or amusement park seen decades ago. Humans do nearly everything today in the workplace, just like they always have. That's because humans, unlike robots, can see, hear and understand language. Robots have never really competed with humans for real jobs because computers have never had the vision systems needed to drive cars, work in restaurants or deliver packages. All that will change very quickly by the middle of the 21st century. As CPU chips and memory systems finally reach parity with the human brain, and then surpass it, robots will be able to perform nearly any normal job that a human performs today. The self-service checkout lines that are springing up everywhere are the first sign of the trend.

The problem, of course, is that all of these robots will eliminate a huge portion of the jobs currently held by human beings. For example, there are 3.5 million jobs in the fast food industry alone. Many of those will be lost to kiosks. Many more will be lost to robots that can flip burgers and clean bathrooms. Eventually they will all be lost. The only people who will still have jobs in the fast food industry will be the senior management team at corporate headquarters.

The same sort of thing will happen in retail stores, hotels, airports, factories, construction sites, delivery companies and so on. All of these jobs will evaporate at approximately the same time, leaving all of those workers unemployed. The Post Office, FedEx and UPS together employed over a million workers in 2002. Once robots can drive the trucks and deliver the packages at a much lower cost than human workers can, those 1,000,000 or so employees will be out on the street.

If you look at the 2000 census figures, you can see the magnitude of the problem. According to the census, there were 114 million employees working for 7 million companies in 2000. The employees brought home almost $4 trillion in wages that year. Here's the breakdown by industry:

U.S. Jobs by Industry According to the 2000 Census.

NAICS	Industry	Employees	Wages ($1,000)
11	Forestry, fishing, hunting, and agriculture supp	183,565	4,682,533
21	Mining	456,128	22,091,246
22	Utilities	655,230	40,650,836
23	Construction	6,572,800	239,910,149
31–33	Manufacturing	16,473,994	643,953,798
42	Wholesale trade	6,112,029	270,122,206
44–45	Retail trade	14,840,775	302,552,506
48–49	Transportation & warehousing	3,790,002	125,592,421
51	Information	3,545,731	209,393,800
52	Finance & insurance	5,963,426	346,805,452
53	Real estate & rental & leasing	1,942,046	59,212,092
54	Professional, scientific & technical services	6,816,216	362,008,229
55	Management of companies & enterprises	2,873,521	211,361,063
56	Admin, support, waste mgt, remediation services	9,138,100	210,281,063
61	Educational services	2,532,324	61,923,347
71	Arts, entertainment & recreation	1,741,497	43,203,906
72	Accommodation & food services	9,880,923	125,581,836
81	Other services (except public administration)	5,293,399	109,876,770
	Total	114,064,976	3,879,430,052

When you look at this chart, it is easy to understand that there will be huge job losses by 2040 or 2050 as robots move into the workplace. For example:

- Nearly every construction job will go to a robot. That's about 6 million jobs lost.
- Nearly every manufacturing job will go to a robot. That's 16 million jobs lost.
- Nearly every transportation job will go to a robot. That's 3 million jobs lost.
- Many wholesale and retail jobs will go to robots. That's at least 15 million lost jobs.
- Nearly every hotel and restaurant job will go to a robot. That's 10 million jobs lost.

If you add that all up, it's over 50 million jobs lost to robots. That is a conservative estimate. By 2050 or so, it is very likely that over half the jobs in the United States will be held by robots.

All the people who are holding jobs like those today will be unemployed.

American society has no way to deal with a situation where half of the workers are unemployed. During the Great Depression at its very worst, 25% of the population was unemployed. In the robotic future, where 50 million jobs are lost, there is the potential for 50% unemployment. The conventional wisdom says that the economy will create 50 million new jobs to absorb all the unemployed people, but that raises two important questions:

- What will those new jobs be? They won't be in manufacturing—robots will hold all the manufacturing jobs. They won't be in the service sector (where most new jobs are now)—robots will work in all the restaurants and retail stores. They won't be in transportation—robots will be driving everything. They won't be in security (robotic police, robotic firefighters), the military (robotic soldiers), entertainment (robotic actors), medicine (robotic doctors, nurses, pharmacists, counselors), construction (robotic construction workers), aviation (robotic pilots, robotic air traffic controllers), office work (robotic receptionists, call centers and managers), research (robotic scientists), education (robotic teachers and computer-based training), programming or engineering (outsourced to India at one-tenth the cost), farming (robotic agricultural machinery), etc. We are assuming that the economy is going to invent an entirely new category of employment that will absorb half of the working population.
- Why isn't the economy creating those new jobs now? Today there are millions of unemployed people. There are also tens of millions of people who would gladly abandon their minimum wage jobs scrubbing toilets, flipping burgers, driving trucks and shelving inventory for something better. This imaginary new category of employment does not hinge on technology—it is going to employ people, after all, in massive numbers—it is going to employ half of today's working population. Why don't we see any evidence of this new category of jobs today?

Labor = Money

Right now, a majority of people in America trade their labor for money, and then they use the money to participate in the economy. Our entire society is built around a simple equation: *labor = money*. This equation explains why any new labor-saving technology is disruptive—it threatens a group of people with joblessness and welfare.

Autonomous humanoid robots will take disruption to a whole new level. Once fully-autonomous, general-purpose humanoid robots are as easy to buy as an automobile, most people in the economy will not be able to make the *labor = money* trade anymore. They will have no way to earn money, and that means they end up homeless and on welfare.

With that many people on welfare, cost control becomes a big issue. We are already seeing the first signs of it today. The January 20, 2003 issue of *Time* magazine notes the trend:

> "Cities have lost patience, concentrating on getting the homeless out of sight. In New York City, where shelter space can't be created fast enough, Mayor Mike Bloomberg has proposed using old cruise ships for housing."

This is not science fiction—this is today's news. What we are talking about here are massive, government-controlled welfare dormitories keeping everyone who is unemployed "out of sight." Homelessness is increasing because millions of people are living on the edge. Millions of working adults and families are trying to make a living from millions of low-paying jobs at places like Wal-Mart and McDonald's. Most of those low-paying jobs are about to evaporate.

This article from the NYTimes sums up our current situation with this quote:

> Jobs have not followed growth, the committee wrote, because of increases in workers' productivity. In fact, Ms. Reaser said, the unemployment rate is unlikely to fall until the economy expands at an annual rate of 3.5 percent or 4 percent, the sort of pace attained in only two quarters since the recovery supposedly began.
>
> With productivity growing at more than 2 percent a year, and the labor force growing about 1 percent a year, she said, the "hurdle rate" of growth for increasing the share of Americans with jobs cannot be less than 3 percent.

The term "worker productivity" in this quote means "robots." We are seeing the tip of the iceberg right now, because robotic replacement of human workers in every employment sector is about to accelerate rapidly. Combine that with a powerful trend pushing high-paying IT jobs to

India. Combine it with the rapid loss of call-center jobs to India. When the first wave of robots and offshore production cut in to the factory workforce in the 20th century, the slack was picked up by service sector jobs. Now we are about to see the combined loss of massive numbers of service-sector jobs, most of the remaining jobs in factories, and many white collar jobs, all at the same time.

When a significant portion of the normal American population is permanently living in government welfare dormitories because of unemployment, what we will have is a third-world nation. These citizens will be imprisoned by unemployment in their own society. If you are an adult in America and you do not have a job, you are flat out of luck. That is how our economy is structured today—you cannot live your life unless you have a job. Many people—perhaps a majority of Americans—will find themselves out of luck in the coming decades.

The arrival of humanoid robots should be a cause for celebration. With the robots doing most of the work, it should be possible for everyone to go on perpetual vacation. Instead, robots will displace millions of employees, leaving them unable to find work and therefore destitute. I believe that it is time to start rethinking our economy and understanding how we will allow people to live their lives in a robotic nation.

Marshall Brain is a writer, national speaker, consultant, and business coach, best known as the founder of "How Stuff Works," a website he started in 1998. In 2007 Discovery Communications purchased HowStuffWorks.com for $250 million. He is also well known as the host of the show "Factory Floor," which appeared on the National Geographic channel.

Peter Gorle and Andrew Clive

NO

Positive Impact of Industrial Robots on Employment

Introduction

Study Aim

The study analyses the impact of the use of robots in the industrialized production of goods on employment. The study covers years 2000 to 2016.

Project Scope

The sectors considered are:

1. The large automotive players as well as the component suppliers.
2. Electronics and its interface with specialist plastics [solar cells, photovoltaics etc or other advanced materials], particularly clean rooms [but not the very specialised microchip manufacturing application].
3. Food and beverage, [health, cleanliness and safety*]
4. Plastics [and Rubber] Industry as such, not only in combination with Electronics, Chemicals and Pharmaceuticals, . . .

Other than the automotive sector, the brief specified that SMEs (Small and Medium Enterprises) up to 250 employees were specified as the target where possible. By agreement, this has been given less emphasis in the project as there is little available information on the use of robots specifically by smaller companies.

Industrial Robots Are the Target

Global markets are covered by the economic background data. The study then focused on six key countries. Brazil, China, Germany, Japan, Republic of Korea and USA.

Method

The project is based largely on analyses of economic data on the six selected countries.This has been combined with the data on Robot use provided by IFR [International Federation of Robotics].

Conclusions were drawn by the Metra Martech team based on economic and industry knowledge. There are considerable gaps in the information available and the main quantifications show orders of magnitude rather than precise numbers. These conclusions have been tested on IFR members in the countries. The testing process involved a two stage set of questions which were responded to by eighteen of these experts. The first question set established the validity of the main assumptions made by Metra Martech; the second was a more detailed set of questions, sent by IFR to selected experts. . . .

The Economic Factors: And Their Effects on the Use of Robotics

Displacement and Re-Employment

Where automation displaces people in manufacturing it almost always increases output. In some cases it allows such an increase in production and related decrease in unit price that it creates a whole new market and generates the need for downstream jobs to get the product to the consumer. It releases employees for other, often new jobs outside manufacturing. Historically, this has always been the case.

An alternative view is that this displacement in the future will be more difficult to place, as service robotics may take over many of the new job opportunities in human tasks such as in banking, fast food chains, and retailing petrol forecourts.

What is likely is that the growth of the production, marketing, selling and maintaining service robots will create the next wave of employment.

The USA has provided a good example, where the total number of people in employment has grown, driven by increase in population, increased participation by women and increased immigrant labour. The long downward trend in manufacturing as a proportion of total employment has been caused by failure to remain competitive in manufacturing as the industrialising countries have grown capacity. . . .

What is driving this trend to fewer employees in manufacturing is that manufacturers have steadily improved manufacturing productivity, largely by increasing the size of production units, automating tasks and sourcing components globally.

. . . [D]oubling use of robots in the past ten years in USA has not affected the trend. By contrast, Germany, which has proportionately many more robots, also doubled the number of robots and has achieved slightly higher growth with almost no reduction in manufacturing employment.

Pressure to increase productivity in the developed countries, has been precipitated by greatly increased competition from overseas manufacturers, and passing of high labour content production to the low labour cost areas.

Pressure to use robotics in the developing countries has been that, despite availability of low cost labour, consistency and accuracy required to compete with or meet the requirements of the developed markets, can sometimes only be achieved by robotics.

Five other economic factors have to be considered:

- Globalisation
- Increasing speed of technology development
- Age and skills profiles
- Wage levels
- Health and safety legislation levels

Globalisation of the Market

There has been very rapid growth of the very large developing markets of China and India.

These are low labour cost countries and while labour costs can be expected to level up around the world, these two countries are likely to be relatively low cost areas for at least 20 years. The markets are so large that they encourage the development of locally grown research and technology. This means the phase when China, for example, largely produced goods to western specifications is passing.

Two defences that the developed countries have to maintain their wealth creating production capacity [without putting up trade barriers] are:

1. To put more money into research and development. The success of the Frauenhofer Institutes in Germany, and the new 150bn Yen FIRST projects [Funding program for world leading Innovative R&D on Science and Technology] in Japan are examples of this.
2. To reduce dependence on high cost labour by introducing automation when it offers an economic alternative.

Increasing Speed of Technology Development

This is about the pace of technological development, and the opportunity which this provides for those who can introduce the new technologies. It results in the shortening of product life cycles. Shorter cycles call for more flexible robotics. The product sectors which are the target for this report are not all affected to the same degree by shortening life cycles. Length of production run is an allied factor. Increasing customisation of products, and the flexibility needed by smaller companies are likely to be met by the next generation of robots.

Age and Skills Profiles

The ageing populations in, for example China, Japan and Germany are often cited as an added reason for adoption of robotics. USA is also affected but to a lesser degree.

A very significant ageing is forecast, but if we consider the workforce, within the timescale of the survey, only Japan is significantly affected, with a projected 5% loss of people of employable age. The German situation will become critical in the following years, but is projected to be less than 2% loss in workforce because of ageing, between now and 2016. Our discussions with robotics experts identify specific problems with ageing workforce in the aerospace sector in USA, but this is outside the scope of the present study.

The existence of skills gaps is reported to be a problem, but this is more a question of education and training regimes than the effect of population ageing.

Several factors are involved in addition to age, the change in population as a whole, the change in people of [currently] employable age, the overall number of people employed and the success of skills training in the country. . . .

Skills Gaps

Even with increasing levels of technology training around the world, reports on the subject show that skills gaps are occurring. The recession has accelerated this. The idea of a jobless recovery [see extract below] favours investment in productivity rather than people. There is another factor connected to this which is the much greater computer and electronic interface skills of the up and coming generation. They also have higher expectations about the type of work they would like to do.

The problem is more of skills mismatch than overall skills availability. This is a structural training problem rather than a consequence of the ageing population.

- jobs are changing
- educational attainment is lagging. . . .

Wage Costs and Availability of Low Cost Labour

One of the arguments against robots, contested by the suppliers, is that they are less flexible in operation and demand more up-front investment than the employment of low cost [often immigrant in the developed countries] labour.

The high labour cost sectors are more likely to use robots.

The differences between the countries are large too, although the interpretation of comparative data is often difficult. . . .

Low Cost Labour

China, and to some extent Brazil, have had access to low cost indigenous labour.

Japan and to a lesser extent Korea have restricted incoming workers.

USA and parts of Europe have until recently allowed this inflow, and both areas have used fewer robots proportionately as a partial result of this, with the exception of Germany. The table shows very large differences in immigration. . . .

Health, Safety [H&S] and Environment

The increasing attention to these factors adds impetus to the employment of robotics in hazardous environments, or those involving great monotony. In the developed countries, H&S is a steadily advancing area; in the developing countries, progress is very sporadic.

According to the International Labor Organization (ILO), 270 million workers fall victim to occupational injuries and illnesses, leading to 2.3 million deaths annually, showing that the problem is significant.

There is pressure from consumer groups to force manufacturers in developing countries to look after their workers to a standard approaching that achieved by the developed world manufacturers, but progress is slow.

However, no specific new initiatives have been identified in the study so far, which would cause a ***step change*** in the current trend to gradual improvement of health and safety practices in the six countries being studied. . . .

Summary

Overall Rise in Employment

Overall paid employment has risen in most countries. In the six considered here, only Japan has seen a decline.

This is driven by increasing participation of women, and increases in population, including immigration in some cases. It is also caused by the increasing demand for services, and the creation of completely new products and markets, often related to the application of electronics to communication.

The statistics mainly point to reduction in employment in manufacturing in the developed countries, but this is often a small reduction. It coincides with an increase in output and an increase in robotics use except in the case of Japan.

The extra number that have gained employment in the years 2000 to 2008 is far greater than the small numbers losing their jobs in manufacturing.

The new jobs have been in:

1. distribution and services, some of the distribution jobs are the result of manufacturers outsourcing their distribution. In the past these jobs would have been classified as part of manufacturing.
2. and also in new manufacturing applications, particularly using technology advances to create new consumer products [mobile phones, computers, games etc].

In the industrialising countries, as could be expected, there has been a sharp rise in employment in manufacturing, as well as increase in output.

Productivity increases are not just caused by automation and robotics, but it is one of three main factors, along with increased size of manufacturing plants and the globalisation of sourcing. *Note: while the IFR numbers provide a clear basis from which to work, it has not always been possible to separate robotics from automation in our analyses.*

Individual countries differ greatly, the importance of manufacturing is only 11% of employment in USA . . . but 24% in Germany and as high as 27% in more recently industrialising countries such as The Republic of Korea.

The level of robotics use has almost always doubled, in all of the six countries [except Japan] in the eight years covered by the study. The proportion of the workforce that is unemployed has hardly changed in this period. . . .

Employment *Directly* Due to the Use of Robotics [World]

The robot industry itself generates on the order of 150,000 jobs worldwide, to which can be added the support staff and operators, another 150,000 people.

There are three other types of application where robotics create or preserve jobs. These are jobs which can only be done by robots.

I Where the product cannot be made to satisfactory precision, consistency and cost, without Robotics.

II Where the conditions under which the current work is done are unsatisfactory [may be illegal in the developed countries], but where a robot will operate.

III Where [particularly] a developed country manufacturing unit with high labour costs is threatened by a unit in a low labour cost area.

Employment *Indirectly* Due to the Use of Robotics

A much larger source of employment, at least partly due to robotics, is the newly created downstream activity necessary to support manufacturing which can only be done by robots. We have been conservative in what we have chosen to include here. Some of the people we have spoken to, for example, would have liked us to have included large parts of the automotive sector sales and distribution employment. Our conclusion was that much of this infrastructure was in place before robots were widely used, and so not resulting from the use of robots.

The best example is the communication and leisure equipment business, from distribution to retailing. In the USA, this part of retailing is of the order of 1 million. In world terms this accounts for 3 to 5 million of jobs which would not exist if automation and robotics had not been developed to allow production of millions of electronic products, from phones to Playstations. . . .

Note that China now produces more cars than USA, but the number of robots used in vehicle manufacture in China is estimated at 28,000 compared with 77,000 in USA.

Robot density in a sector only provides a partial view of employment which is dependent on robotics. For example, use of robotics in the automotive sector does not cover all parts of the industry. However, large parts of the motor vehicle assembly sector would be lost to a country if it did not employ robotics. Probably not the components side, this is often highly automated but less likely to depend on robotics.

In the electronics sector some components could not be made without robotics, or could not be made at a cost which would sell, which would cause job losses not just in manufacture but downstream as well.

Potential for New Job Creation in the Years up to 2016

There are five main areas where new jobs may be created in the next five years by the use of robotics.

I. Continued development of new products based on the development of electronics and communication technology. One of the new areas identified, for example, is the manufacture of service robots. Another is the development and mass adoption of renewable energy technologies.
II. Expansion of existing economies and industries, notably automotive.
III. Greater use of robotics in the SME [small and medium enterprises] sectors, particularly in the developed countries, to protect or win back manufacture from the low cost countries, or to win back production which had been seen as hazardous, but which had been taken up by the developing countries.
IV. Greater use of robotics in the food sector [where current use is low] as processed meals develop, to meet more stringent hygiene conditions.
V. Expansion of the robotics sector itself, to cope with the growth in demand. We have assumed a 15% growth which adds 45,000 people.

Overall Effect

Direct employment due to robotics:

2 to 3 million jobs created in world manufacturing

Considering the world population of industrial robots at just over 1 million, **that is 2 to 3 jobs per robot in use.**

Indirect employment downstream of this more than doubles this number.

For the future, 700,000 to 1 million new jobs to be created by robots in the next five years.

Peter Gorle is the managing director of Metra Martech, a firm specializing in industrial and economic analysis for governments and international organizations.

Andrew Clive is a senior consultant with Metra Martech, a firm specializing in industrial and economic analysis for governments and international organizations.

EXPLORING THE ISSUE

Will Robots Take Your Job?

Critical Thinking and Reflection

1. What are "industrial" robots?
2. What kinds of jobs now held by humans may robots be able to do in the near future?
3. Why do robots threaten more than just industrial jobs?
4. In what ways might robots create jobs?
5. If robots take all the jobs, what will people do?

Is There Common Ground?

Computer technology (including robotics) is a rapidly growing field. Indeed, in the past whenever someone would say "Computers can't do X!" someone else would add "Yet!" They'd be right, too, for computers can now do a great many things their predecessors could not. Surely this applies to robotics as well, and robots have been expanding their presence in the workplace for decades. They will continue to do so, and Marshall Brain and Peter Gorle and Andrew Clive may well agree that there is a fine line between robots taking jobs and—in a faltering economy—robots keeping companies alive without hiring more humans. It is also worth stressing that the YES and NO selections differ in their timelines. Marshall Brain says job loss will be severe by the middle of the twenty-first century. Peter Gorle and Andrew Clive say many (up to 1 million) jobs will be created in the next five years. If they had tried to project further into the future, perhaps they would have agreed with Marshall Brain.

1. Why have employers welcomed robots in the workplace?
2. What jobs seem to you to be out of reach for robots (so far!)?
3. Marshall Brain suggests that it is time to rethink our economy. Where would you begin?

Create Central

www.mhhe.com/createcentral

Additional Resources

Jason Borenstein, "Robots and the Changing Workforce," *AI & Society* (2011)

Kirk L. Kroeker, "Weighing Watson's Impact," *Communications of the ACM* (July 2011).

Alex Wright, "Automotive Autonomy," *Communications of the ACM* (July 2011).

Internet Reference . . .

MIT Computer Science and Artificial Intelligence Laboratory

In hundreds of diverse projects, the MIT Computer Science and Artificial Intelligence Laboratory works to unlock the secrets of human intelligence, extend the functional capabilities of machines, and explore human/machine interactions.

www.csail.mit.edu/

Selected, Edited, and with Issue Framing Material by:
Thomas A. Easton, *Thomas College*

ISSUE

Is Cyber-War or Cyber-Terrorism a Genuine Threat?

YES: Mike McConnell, from "Mike McConnell on How to Win the Cyber-War We're Losing," *The Washington Post* (February 28, 2010)

NO: Maura Conway, from "Privacy and Security Against Cyberterrorism," *Communications of the ACM* (February 2011)

Learning Outcomes

After studying this issue, students will be able to:

- Describe the potential impact of a cyber-war attack on the United States.
- Explain what measures might be taken to prevent cyber-war or cyber-terrorism attacks.
- Explain why cyber-war or cyber-terrorism attacks may be unlikely.

ISSUE SUMMARY

YES: Mike McConnell argues that the United States is already under attack by cyber-warriors, and we are losing. We need to upgrade cyber-defenses and be prepared to counter-attack. This may include requiring the private sector to share more information with government agencies.

NO: Maura Conway argues that even though various cyber-based attacks have been called "cyber-war" and "cyber-terrorism," definitions are crucial. In particular, "cyber-terrorism" fails to qualify as terrorism because it lacks the spectacular public impact of destroying buildings with airliners. "Cyberterrorism . . . is not in our near future."

In June 2010, the Stuxnet worm attacked Iranian nuclear facilities. It used stolen digital certificates to take over control software and interfere with the normal function of nuclear power plants, electrical distribution systems, and oil pipelines. Early reports said the Stuxnet worm was so complex that it must have taken large teams of programmers, millions of dollars in funding, and many months of work to produce it. Iran insisted it had to be an Israeli-American cyber-attack, and on June 1, 2012, David E. Sanger reported in "Obama Order Sped Up Wave of Cyberattacks against Iran," *New York Times*, that interviews with European, U.S., and Israeli officials have revealed that in 2006, President George W. Bush initiated the development of the Stuxnet worm under the code-name Olympic Games. Samuel Greengard, "The New Face of War," *Communications of the ACM* (December 2010), considers this a sign of the way wars will be fought in the future. "The risk of cyber-warfare is growing, and many . . . warn that political leaders aren't entirely tuned into the severity of the threat." It must be taken seriously, for it is only a matter of time before cyber-war is real. Richard A. Clarke and Richard K. Knake, *Cyber War: The Next Threat to National Security and What to Do About It* (HarperCollins, 2010), stress that because society is now totally dependent on telecommunications networks, it is also vulnerable to widespread, long-lasting damage. James P. Farwell and Rafal Rohozinski, "Stuxnet and the Future of Cyber War," *Survival* (February/March 2011), note that cyber-war "offers great potential for striking at enemies with less risk than using traditional means." They also note that many cyber-war techniques are rooted in cyber-crime (viruses, worms, bot-nets, identity theft, hacking, fraud, and more), which has been with us since the dawn of the Internet. John Stone is sure that "Cyber War Will Take Place!" *Journal of Strategic Studies* (February 2013).

The methods of defending against cyber-war and cyber-terrorism are also rooted in the fight against cyber-crime. Few people today do not have antivirus and/or anti-malware software on their computers. The United States government has long sought extensions to digital telephony and the Internet of traditional wiretapping laws that permitted law-enforcement agencies to listen in on the conversations of criminal suspects (see Declan McCullagh, "FBI: We Need Wiretap-Ready Web Sites—Now," *CNET News* (May 4, 2012) (http://news.cnet.com/8301-1009_3-57428067-83/fbi-we-need-wiretap-ready-web-sites-now/)). After September 11, 2001, the War on Terrorism began and every tool that promised to help identify terrorists before or catch them after they committed their dreadful acts was seen as desirable. However, when the Department of Defense's Defense Advanced Research Projects Agency (DARPA) proposed a massive computer system capable of sifting through purchases, tax data, court records, Google searches, emails, and other information from government and commercial databases to seek suspicious patterns of behavior, many people objected that this amounted to a massive assault on privacy and was surely in violation of the Fourth Amendment to the U.S. Constitution (which established the right of private citizens to be secure against unreasonable searches and seizures; "unreasonable" has come to mean "without a search warrant" for physical searches of homes and offices and "without a court order" for interceptions of mail and wiretappings of phone conversations). This Total or Terrorism Information Awareness (TIA) program soon died although many of its components continued under other names; see Shane Harris, "TIA Lives On," *National Journal* (February 25, 2006). Simon Cooper, "Who's Spying on You?" *Popular Mechanics* (January 2005), argues that we are now subject to massively increased routine surveillance and the collection of personal data by both government and business with very few restrictions on how the data are used. Peter Brown, "Privacy in an Age of Terabytes and Terror," *Scientific American* (September 2008), says, "A cold wind is blowing across the landscape of privacy. The twin imperatives of technological advancement and counterterrorism have led to dramatic and possibly irreversible changes in what people can expect to remain of private life." See also Hina Shamsi and Alex Abdo, "Privacy and Surveillance Post-9/11," *Human Rights* (Winter 2011).

Fears of government intrusion were not eased when in July 2008 President Bush signed the revised Foreign Intelligence Surveillance Act, designed to expand the government's warrantless electronic spying activities and ensure retroactive immunity for cooperative telecommunications firms. Nor in 2011 when Congress reapproved the Patriot Act and President Obama signed the bill. Government surveillance programs such as these reflect many fears about the Internet—that it is a place where evil lurks, where technically skilled criminals use their skills to fleece the unsuspecting public, where terrorists plot unseen, where enemy nations plot to destroy industrial infrastructure and bring the nation to its knees, and where technology lends immunity to detection, apprehension, and prosecution. David Talbot, "Moore's Outlaws," *Technology Review* (July/August 2010), notes that the threat is growing rapidly, and sooner or later a cyber-war or cyber-terrorist attack will bring a city or major corporation to its knees. Former Homeland Security official Stewart Baker compared the potential impact to that of the BP oil spill in the Gulf of Mexico; see Pam Benson, "U.S. Vulnerable to Cyber Threats, Experts Warn," *CNN.com* (June 17, 2010) (www.cnn.com/2010/US/06/16/cyber.threats.report/index.html?hpt+C2). Austin Wright, "The Unseen Cyber-War," *National Defense* (December 2009), describes numerous efforts to penetrate the computers of government and defense contractors to steal defense secrets. However, notes Seymour M. Hersh, "The Online Threat," *New Yorker* (November 1, 2010), cyber-espionage is not the same thing as cyber-war.

Does this amount to a real "cyber-terrorism" or "cyber-war" threat? General Keith Alexander, head of the Defense Department's U.S. Cyber Command (www.defense.gov/home/features/2010/0410_cybersec/), is preparing as if it does. However, Howard Schmidt, the Obama administration's cybersecurity chief, says "There is no cyberwar" (see Ryan Singel, "White House Cyber Czar: 'There Is No Cyberwar'," *Wired Online* (March 4, 2010) (www.wired.com/threatlevel/2010/03/Schmidt-cyberwar/). Robert Graham of Errata Security insists "Cyberwar Is Fiction" (June 7, 2010) (http://erratasec.blogspot.com/2010/06/cyberwar-is-fiction.html). Peter Sommer and Ian Brown, "Reducing Systemic Cybersecurity Risk" OECD (Organization for Economic Co-operation and Development)/IFP (International Futures Programme) Project on "Future Global Shocks," 2011), conclude "that very few single cyber-related events have the capacity to cause a global shock. Governments nevertheless need to make detailed preparations to withstand and recover from a wide range of unwanted cyber events, both accidental and deliberate. There are significant and growing risks of localised misery and loss as a result of compromise of computer and telecommunications services." Simson L. Garfinkel, "The Cybersecurity Risk," *Communications of the ACM* (June 2012), argues that the reason why we have not already built more secure computer systems is that "it is more cost-effective to create systems without redundancy or resiliency." Gary McGraw, "Cyber War Is Inevitable (Unless We Build Security In)," *Journal of Strategic Studies* (February 2013), argues that this needs to change.

Robert A. Miller, Daniel T. Kuehl, and Irving Lachow, "Cyber War: Issues in Attack and Defense," *Joint Force Quarterly* (2nd Quarter, 2011), say that some sort of cyber-war is an inevitable component of future conflicts, and dealing with it will not be easy. Ellen Nakashima, "With Plan X, Pentagon Seeks to Spread U.S. Military Might to Cyberspace," *Washington Post* (May 31, 2012), reports that the Defense Advanced Research Projects Agency (DARPA) is now working on developing techniques to launch cyberstrikes against computer-based attacks, as well as survive those attacks. In a debate over whether the cyber-war threat is being exaggerated (Tim Wilson, "In Debate, Audience Finds that the Cyberwar Threat Is Not Exaggerated," *DarkReading* (June 10, 2010) (www.darkreading.com/story/showArticle.jhtml?articleID=225600193)), participants agreed that there has been a great deal of hype about the topic, but the threat is real. On the other hand, many people worry that the worse threat is that posed to civil rights and privacy by efforts to enhance security by monitoring and regulating the Internet. Stephen J. Lukasik, "Protecting Users of the Cyber Commons," *Communications of the ACM* (September 2011), suggests that the best approach may be a bottom-up, community-based threat identification and response system and notes that similar community-based approaches have served the Internet very well in other areas. Others note the need for international treaties; see Scott W. Beidleman, "Defining and Deterring Cyber War," *Military Technology* (2011), and Seung Hyun Kim, et al., "A Comparative Study of Cyber Attacks," *Communications of the ACM* (March 2012).

In May 2011, two security researchers demonstrated that it was possible to create a Stuxnet-type threat with very limited resources—at home, on a laptop computer, and in just a couple of months. According to Shaun Waterman, "Homemade Cyberweapon Worries Federal Officials," *Washington Times* (May 24, 2011), "Officials at the Department of Homeland Security were so distressed by the researchers' findings that they asked the two men to cancel a planned presentation at a computer security conference." They obliged, but the incident raises concerns about how easy it would be for nations, terrorists, or criminals to attack major components of society's infrastructure. In June 2011, the U.S. Department of Defense announced that it was prepared to retaliate against cyber-attacks with conventional weaponry; see David Talbot, "U.S. Aims Missiles at Hackers," *Technology Review Online* (June 2, 2011) (www.technologyreview.com/web/37692/?a=f). However, Jerry Brito and Tate Wilkins recall the Bush administration's lies about Iraq's nuclear threat in "Wired Opinion: Cyberwar Is the New Yellowcake," *Wired Online* (February 14, 2012) (www.wired.com/threatlevel/2012/02/yellowcake-and-cyberwar/). R. Scott Kemp, "Cyberweapons: Bold Steps in a Digital Darkness?" *Bulletin of the Atomic Scientists* (June 7, 2012) (www.thebulletin.org/web-edition/op-eds/cyberweapons-bold-steps-digital-darkness), argues that "We are at a key turning point . . . in which a nation must decide what role cyberweapons will play in its national defense. . . . for the United States and other highly developed nations whose societies are critically and deeply reliant on computers, the safe approach is to direct cyber research at purely defensive applications." According to Richard Stone, "A Call to Cyber Arms," *Science* (March 1, 2013), the U.S. and other governments are putting a great deal of effort not only into devising ways to defend against cyber-espionage and cyber-attacks against industrial, defense, and commercial infrastructure, but also into ways to go on the offensive.

In the YES selection, Mike McConnell, director of the National Security Agency in the Clinton administration and director of national intelligence during President George W. Bush's second term, argues that the United States is already under attack by cyber-warriors, and we are losing. We need to upgrade cyber-defenses and be prepared to counter-attack. This may include requiring the private sector to share more information with government agencies. In the NO selection, Maura Conway argues that even though various cyber-based attacks have been called "cyber-war" and "cyber-terrorism," definitions are crucial. In particular, "cyber-terrorism" fails to qualify as terrorism because it lacks the spectacular public impact of destroying buildings with airliners. "Cyberterrorism . . . is not in our near future."

YES

Mike McConnell

Mike McConnell on How to Win the Cyber-War We're Losing

The United States is fighting a cyber-war today, and we are losing. It's that simple. As the most wired nation on Earth, we offer the most targets of significance, yet our cyber-defenses are woefully lacking.

The problem is not one of resources; even in our current fiscal straits, we can afford to upgrade our defenses. The problem is that we lack a cohesive strategy to meet this challenge.

The stakes are enormous. To the extent that the sprawling U.S. economy inhabits a common physical space, it is in our communications networks. If an enemy disrupted our financial and accounting transactions, our equities and bond markets or our retail commerce—or created confusion about the legitimacy of those transactions—chaos would result. Our power grids, air and ground transportation, telecommunications, and water-filtration systems are in jeopardy as well.

These battles are not hypothetical. Google's networks were hacked in an attack that began in December and that the company said emanated from China. And recently the security firm NetWitness reported that more than 2,500 companies worldwide were compromised in a sophisticated attack launched in 2008 and aimed at proprietary corporate data. Indeed, the recent Cyber Shock Wave simulation revealed what those of us involved in national security policy have long feared: For all our war games and strategy documents focused on traditional warfare, we have yet to address the most basic questions about cyber-conflicts.

What is the right strategy for this most modern of wars? Look to history. During the Cold War, when the United States faced an existential threat from the Soviet Union, we relied on deterrence to protect ourselves from nuclear attack. Later, as the East-West stalemate ended and nuclear weapons proliferated, some argued that preemption made more sense in an age of global terrorism.

The cyber-war mirrors the nuclear challenge in terms of the potential economic and psychological effects. So, should our strategy be deterrence or preemption? The answer: both. Depending on the nature of the threat, we can deploy aspects of either approach to defend America in cyberspace.

During the Cold War, deterrence was based on a few key elements: attribution (understanding who attacked us), location (knowing where a strike came from), response (being able to respond, even if attacked first) and transparency (the enemy's knowledge of our capability and intent to counter with massive force).

Against the Soviets, we dealt with the attribution and location challenges by developing human intelligence behind the Iron Curtain and by fielding early-warning radar systems, reconnaissance satellites and undersea listening posts to monitor threats. We invested heavily in our response capabilities with intercontinental ballistic missiles, submarines and long-range bombers, as well as command-and-control systems and specialized staffs to run them. The resources available were commensurate with the challenge at hand—as must be the case in cyberspace.

Just as important was the softer side of our national security strategy: the policies, treaties and diplomatic efforts that underpinned containment and deterrence. Our alliances, such as NATO, made clear that a strike on one would be a strike on all and would be met with massive retaliation. This unambiguous intent, together with our ability to monitor and respond, provided a credible nuclear deterrent that served us well.

How do we apply deterrence in the cyber-age? For one, we must clearly express our intent. Secretary of State Hillary Rodham Clinton offered a succinct statement to that effect last month in Washington, in a speech on Internet freedom. "Countries or individuals that engage in cyber-attacks should face consequences and international condemnation," she said. "In an Internet-connected world, an attack on one nation's networks can be an attack on all."

That was a promising move, but it means little unless we back it up with practical policies and international legal agreements to define norms and identify consequences for destructive behavior in cyberspace. We began examining these issues through the Comprehensive National Cybersecurity Initiative, launched during the George W. Bush administration, but more work is needed on outlining how, when and where we would respond to an attack. For now, we have a response mechanism in name only.

The United States must also translate our intent into capabilities. We need to develop an early-warning system to monitor cyberspace, identify intrusions and locate the source of attacks with a trail of evidence that can support diplomatic, military and legal options—and we must be able to do this in milliseconds. More specifically, we need to reengineer the Internet to make attribution, geolocation, intelligence analysis and impact assessment—who did it, from where, why and what was the result—more manageable. The technologies are already available from public and private sources and can be further developed if we have the will to build them into our systems and to work with our allies and trading partners so they will do the same.

Of course, deterrence can be effective when the enemy is a state with an easily identifiable government and location. It is less successful against criminal groups or extremists who cannot be readily traced, let alone deterred through sanctions or military action.

There are many organizations (including al-Qaeda) that are not motivated by greed, as with criminal organizations, or a desire for geopolitical advantage, as with many states. Rather, their worldview seeks to destroy the systems of global commerce, trade and travel that are undergirded by our cyber-infrastructure. So deterrence is not enough; preemptive strategies might be required before such adversaries launch a devastating cyber-attack.

We preempt such groups by degrading, interdicting and eliminating their leadership and capabilities to mount cyber-attacks, and by creating a more resilient cyberspace that can absorb attacks and quickly recover. To this end, we must hammer out a consensus on how to best harness the capabilities of the National Security Agency, which I had the privilege to lead from 1992 to 1996. The NSA is the only agency in the United States with the legal authority, oversight and budget dedicated to breaking the codes and understanding the capabilities and intentions of potential enemies. The challenge is to shape an effective partnership with the private sector so information can move quickly back and forth from public to private—and classified to unclassified—to protect the nation's critical infrastructure.

We must give key private-sector leaders (from the transportation, utility and financial arenas) access to information on emerging threats so they can take countermeasures. For this to work, the private sector needs to be able to share network information—on a controlled basis—without inviting lawsuits from shareholders and others.

Obviously, such measures must be contemplated very carefully. But the reality is that while the lion's share of cybersecurity expertise lies in the federal government, more than 90 percent of the physical infrastructure of the Web is owned by private industry. Neither side on its own can mount the cyber-defense we need; some collaboration is inevitable. Recent reports of a possible partnership between Google and the government point to the kind of joint efforts—and shared challenges—that we are likely to see in the future.

No doubt, such arrangements will muddy the waters between the traditional roles of the government and the private sector. We must define the parameters of such interactions, but we should not dismiss them. Cyberspace knows no borders, and our defensive efforts must be similarly seamless.

Ultimately, to build the right strategy to defend cyberspace, we need the equivalent of President Dwight D. Eisenhower's Project Solarium. That 1953 initiative brought together teams of experts with opposing views to develop alternative strategies on how to wage the Cold War. The teams presented their views to the president, and Eisenhower chose his preferred approach—deterrence. We now need a dialogue among business, civil society and government on the challenges we face in cyberspace—spanning international law, privacy and civil liberties, security, and the architecture of the Internet. The results should shape our cybersecurity strategy.

We prevailed in the Cold War through strong leadership, clear policies, solid alliances and close integration of our diplomatic, economic and military efforts. We backed all this up with robust investments—security never comes cheap. It worked, because we had to make it work.

Let's do the same with cybersecurity. The time to start was yesterday.

Mike McConnell was the director of the National Security Agency in the Clinton administration and the director of national intelligence during President George W. Bush's second term. A retired Navy vice admiral, he is executive vice president of Booz Allen Hamilton, which consults on cybersecurity for the private and public sector.

Maura Conway

NO

Privacy and Security Against Cyberterrorism

Like the 2007 cyber attacks on Estonia, the October 2010 Stuxnet botnet attack on Iranian nuclear facilities made cyber-based attacks global news. The Estonian attacks were largely labeled a cyberwar by journalists, although some did invoke the concept of cyberterrorism. The Stuxnet attack, on the other hand, has been very widely described as cyberterrorism, including by the Iranian government.

Cyberterrorism is a concept that appears recurrently in contemporary media. It is not just reported upon in newspapers and on television, but is also the subject of movies (such as 1990's *Die Hard II* and 2007's *Die Hard IV: Live Free or Die Hard*) and popular fiction books (for example, Winn Schwartau's 2002 novel *Pearl Harbor Dot Com*). This coverage is particularly interesting if one believes, as I do, that no act of cyberterrorism has ever yet occurred and is unlikely to at any time in the near future. Having said that, it is almost always portrayed in the press as either having already occurred or being just around the corner. As an academic, I'm not alone in arguing that no act of cyberterrorism has yet occurred and, indeed, some journalists agree; most, however, seem convinced as to the salience of this threat. Why?

I can only surmise that, just as a large amount of social psychological research has shown, the uncertain and the unknown generally produce fear and anxiety. This is the psychological basis of an effective movie thriller: the fear is greatest when you suspect something, but you're not certain what it is. The term "cyberterrorism" unites two significant modern fears: fear of technology and fear of terrorism. Fear of terrorism, though the likelihood of any one of us being the victim of terrorism is statistically insignificant, has become perhaps normalized; but fear of technology? In fact, for those unfamiliar with the workings of complex technologies, these are perceived as arcane, unknowable, abstract, and yet increasingly powerful and ubiquitous. Many people therefore fear that technology will become the master and humankind the servant. Couple this relatively new anxiety with age-old fears associated with apparently random violence and the result is a truly heightened state of alarm. Many journalists—although fewer technology journalists than others—have succumbed, like members of the general population, to these fears, to which the journalists have then added further fuel with their reporting.

The Definition Issue

The second stumbling block for journalists is that just as the definition of terrorism is fraught, so too is the definition of cyberterrorism. My preference is to distinguish between cyberterrorism and terrorist use of the Net. This is the distinction FBI Director Robert Mueller seemed implicitly to be drawing in a March 2010 speech in which he stated that "the Internet is not only used to plan and execute attacks; it is a target in and of itself . . . We in the FBI, with our partners in the intelligence community, believe the cyber terrorism threat is real, and it is rapidly expanding." Where the FBI Director and I diverge is in the efficacy of the cyberterrorist threat as opposed to that of everyday terrorist use of the Net (that is, for radicalization, researching and planning, financing, and other purposes).

Dorothy Denning's definitions of cyberterrorism are probably the most well known and respected. Her most recent attempt at defining cyberterrorism is: ". . . [H]ighly damaging computer-based attacks or threats of attack by non-state actors against information systems when conducted to intimidate or coerce governments or societies in pursuit of goals that are political or social. It is the convergence of terrorism with cyberspace, where cyberspace becomes the means of conducting the terrorist act. Rather than committing acts of violence against persons or physical property, the cyberterrorist commits acts of destruction or disruption against digital property."

Analyses of cyberterrorism can be divided into two broad categories on the basis of where the producers stand on the definition issue: those who agree broadly with Denning versus those who wish to incorporate not just use, but a host of other activities into the definition. The literature can also be divided on the basis of where the authors stand on the magnitude of the cyberterrorism threat. Dunn-Cavelty uses the term "Hypers" to describe those who believe a cyberterrorist attack is not just likely, but imminent, and the term "De-Hypers" to describe those who believe such an attack is unlikely. Most journalists are hypers, on the other hand I'm emphatically a de-hyper. In this column, I lay out the three major reasons why.

Three Arguments Against Cyberterrorism

In my opinion, the three most compelling arguments against cyberterrorism are:

- The argument of Technological Complexity;
- The argument regarding 9/11 and the Image Factor; and
- The argument regarding 9/11 and the Accident Issue.

The first argument is treated in the academic literature; the second and third arguments are not, but ought to be. None of these are angles to which journalists appear to have devoted a lot of thought or given adequate consideration.

In the speech mentioned earlier, FBI Director Mueller observed "Terrorists have shown a clear interest in pursuing hacking skills. And they will either train their own recruits or hire outsiders, with an eye toward combining physical attacks with cyber attacks." That may very well be true, but the argument from Technological Complexity underlines that "wanting" to do something is quite different from having the ability to do the same. Here's why:

Violent jihadis' IT knowledge is not superior. For example, in research carried out in 2007, it was found that of a random sampling of 404 members of violent Islamist groups, 196 (48.5%) had a higher education, with information about subject areas available for 178 individuals. Of these 178, some 8 (4.5%) had trained in computing, which means that out of the entire sample, less than 2% of the jihadis came from a computing background. And not even these few could be assumed to have mastery of the complex systems necessary to carry out a successful cyberterrorist attack.

Real-world attacks are difficult enough. What are often viewed as relatively unsophisticated real-world attacks undertaken by highly educated individuals are routinely unsuccessful. One only has to consider the failed car bomb attacks planned and carried out by medical doctors in central London and at Glasgow airport in June 2007.

Hiring hackers would compromise operational security. The only remaining option is to retain "outsiders" to undertake such an attack. This is very operationally risky. It would force the terrorists to operate outside their own circles and thus leave them ripe for infiltration. Even if they successfully got in contact with "real" hackers, they would be in no position to gauge their competency accurately; they would simply have to trust in same. This would be very risky.

So on the basis of technical know-how alone cyberterror attack is not imminent, but this is not the only factor one must take into account. The events of Sept. 11, 2001 underscore that for a true terrorist event spectacular moving images are crucial. The attacks on the World Trade Center were a fantastic piece of performance violence; look back on any recent roundup of the decade and mention of 9/11 will not just be prominent, but pictures will always be provided.

The problem with respect to cyberterrorism is that many of the attack scenarios put forward, from shutting down the electric power grid to contaminating a major water supply, fail on this account: they are unlikely to have easily captured, spectacular (live, moving) images associated with them, something we—as an audience—have been primed for by the attack on the World Trade Center on 9/11.

The only cyberterrorism scenario that would fall into this category is interfering with air traffic control systems to crash planes, but haven't we seen that planes can much more easily be employed in spectacular "real-world" terrorism? And besides, aren't all the infrastructures just mentioned much easier and more spectacular to simply blow up? It doesn't end there, however. For me, the third argument against cyberterrorism is perhaps the most compelling; yet it is very rarely mentioned.

In 2004, Howard Schmidt, former White House Cybersecurity Coordinator, remarked to the U.S. Senate Committee on the Judiciary regarding Nimda and Code Red that "we to this day don't know the source of that. It could have very easily been a terrorist." This observation betrays a fundamental misunderstanding of the nature and purposes of terrorism, particularly its attention-getting and communicative functions.

A terrorist attack with the potential to be hidden, portrayed as an accident, or otherwise remain unknown is unlikely to be viewed positively by any terrorist group. In fact, one of the most important aspects of the 9/11 attacks in New York from the perpetrators viewpoint was surely the fact that while the first plane to crash into the World Trade Center could have been accidental, the appearance of the second plane confirmed the incident as a terrorist attack in real time. Moreover, the crash of the first plane ensured a large audience for the second plane as it hit the second tower.

Alternatively, think about the massive electric failure that took place in the northeastern U.S. in August 2003: if it was a terrorist attack—and I'm not suggesting that it was—but *if it was*, it would have been a spectacular failure.

Conclusion

Given the high cost—not just in terms of money, but also time, commitment, and effort—and the high possibility of failure on the basis of manpower issues, timing, and complexity of a potential cyberterrorist attack, the costs appear to me to still very largely outweigh the potential publicity benefits. The publicity aspect is crucial for potential perpetrators of terrorism and so the possibility that an attack may be apprehended or portrayed as an accident, which would be highly likely with regard to cyberterrorism, is detrimental. Add the lack of spectacular moving images and it is my belief that cyberterrorism, regardless of what you may read in newspapers, see on television, or obtain via other media sources, is not in our near future.

So why then the persistent treatment of cyberterrorism on the part of journalists? Well, in this instance, science fiction-type fears appear to trump rational calculation almost every time. And I haven't even begun to discuss how the media discourse has clearly influenced the pronouncements of policymakers.

Maura Conway is lecturer in international security in the School of Law and Government at Dublin City University in Dublin, Ireland.

EXPLORING THE ISSUE

Is Cyber-War or Cyber-Terrorism a Genuine Threat?

Critical Thinking and Reflection

1. Is there a difference between "cyber-war" and "cyber-terrorism"?
2. Is all the talk of "cyber-war" and "cyber-terrorism" just hype?
3. The Defense Department is talking of retaliating against cyber-attackers with conventional weapons. Why will it be difficult to find the cyber-attackers?

Is There Common Ground?

There are many reasons to keep intruders out of computer networks. Criminal hackers use malware to take control of home (and other) computers to steal private information—usernames and passwords, in particular—so they can steal from bank accounts, use credit cards, and steal identity. Spies want to steal secret files. Cyber-warriors may wish to disrupt electricity generation, shut down factories, shut down the Internet, or perhaps just mess with a city's traffic lights to cause traffic jams (among other things). In other words, it may be less about cyber-war than about cyber-security.

1. How do you protect your own computer (passwords, firewalls, encryption, etc.)?
2. Visit your campus IT department and ask how it protects the campus network from intruders.
3. Do you think similar measures would work against a cyber-war or cyber-terrorist attack?

Create Central

www.mhhe.com/createcentral

Additional Resources

Richard A. Clarke and Richard K. Knake, *Cyber War: The Next Threat to National Security and What to Do About It* (HarperCollins, 2010).

James P. Farwell and Rafal Rohozinski, "Stuxnet and the Future of Cyber War," *Survival* (February/March 2011).

Samuel Greengard, "The New Face of War," *Communications of the ACM* (December 2010).

R. Scott Kemp, "Cyberweapons: Bold Steps in a Digital Darkness?" *Bulletin of the Atomic Scientists* (June 7, 2012) (www.thebulletin.org/web-edition/op-eds/cyberweapons-bold-steps-digital-darkness).

Internet Reference . . .

United States Department of Defense, U.S. Cyber Command

The U.S. Cyber Command is a unit of the Department of Defense (DoD) that defends information networks and prepares to conduct military cyberspace operations to ensure U.S./Allied freedom of action in cyberspace and deny the same to adversaries.

www.defense.gov/home/features/2010/0410_cybersec/

Selected, Edited, and with Issue Framing Material by:
Thomas A. Easton, *Thomas College*

ISSUE

Does Endorsing Open Source Software Fail to Respect Intellectual Property?

YES: International Intellectual Property Alliance (IIPA), from *Indonesia: 2010 Special 301 Report on Copyright Protection and Enforcement* (February 12, 2010)

NO: Michael Tiemann, from "The OSI Categorically Rejects IIPA's Special Pleadings Against Open Source," *Open Source Initiative* (May 3, 2010)

Learning Outcomes

After studying this issue, students will be able to:

- Explain the concept of "open source."
- Explain the purpose of copyright and patent law.
- Discuss whether the International Intellectual Property Alliance (IIPA) is more interested in protecting intellectual property or income.
- Explain how copyright protections are essential to open source products.

ISSUE SUMMARY

YES: The International Intellectual Property Alliance (IIPA) argues that Indonesia should be put on the United States Trade Representative's "Special 301" watchlist because, in part, Indonesia's attempt to promote open source solutions "encourages a mindset that does not give due consideration to the value of intellectual creations."

NO: Michael Tiemann of Open Source Initiative objects strenuously, arguing that open source software is just as much an intellectual creation as proprietary software, it depends just as much on copyright protections, and because open source preferences have been promoted in several states, as well as portions of the federal government, the IIPA's position amounts to an attack on the United States itself.

To understand the Open Source movement and the opposition toward it, it helps to understand a bit of the history of the computer industry. It had its roots in academia at a time when the reward structure was *not* the same as in the corporate world. Historically, academics have not seen their score in the game of life in terms of money, but rather in terms of respect or prestige. To gain such respect or prestige, they made their ideas, investigations, discoveries, and conclusions freely available (much as described in this book's Introduction, under the "Communication" part of the scientific method). In the last few decades, academics have found numerous opportunities to patent their discoveries and start-up businesses, and the profit motive has entered academia. To some, it has polluted the purity of the older reward system.

The first computers were built with government money for government (often military) purposes. Corporations such as IBM played an important role in developing large commercial computers (mainframes) and their software. During the 1950s and 1960s, computers became common on college and university campuses, and programming languages became easier to use. A great many students graduated with computer experience, programming skills, and the then-standard academic value system. Many became computer hobbyists and played a major part in the development of the personal computer. Since they were hobbyists, money was not always the point. From the beginning, some PC software was commercial, but by the 1970s and 1980s, "shareware" (pay if you like it) and "freeware" (it's free!) were common. Some software still fits this model, to a degree; AVG antivirus software (http://free.avg.com/us-en/homepage), for instance, provides a free version that does the basic job and a pay version that does more.

To oversimplify, in the beginning the corporate world just didn't see how big the computer revolution was going to be. But that changed. "Payware" became much more common, moving as it did so through a number of copy-protection schemes (some of which were as simple as saying (untruthfully), "Cheat, and your computer will stop working!"). There were some efforts to tarnish the image of freeware and shareware, but they were not successful. In time the Open Source movement took form. Some Open Source software programs are free (think of the Firefox browser and the OpenOffice productivity suite). Some ask for donations. Some are packaged for sale with manuals, consulting, and support (various Linux distributions). The defining feature is that the source code for the software is available for users to modify, with good modifications feeding back into the distributed software (see Chris DiBona and Sam Ockman, *Open Sources* (O'Reilly, 1999)). In other words, Open Source software is community-built and community-supported software. Its proponents argue that this gives Open Source software immense advantages even beyond the low up-front cost.

There are of course opponents of Open Source as well as proponents. Many are opponents because they see the advantages of Open Source costing them sales. In 2010, one of those opponents, the International Intellectual Property Alliance (IIPA), made headlines by seeking to have the U.S. Trade Representative put several countries on its "Special 301" Watchlist—which is used to pressure countries into handling international trade in ways more satisfactory to U.S. interests—in part because of their approval of Open Source Software.

Michael Tiemann of Open Source Initiative wrote the response to the IIPA, which is reprinted in the NO selection. But this essay was by no means the only objection. He also wrote "OSFA Refutes IIPA's Attack on Open Source Software" for Open Source for America (http://opensourceforamerica.org/opensource-attack). The title of Bobbie Johnson's *Guardian* blogpost, "When Using Open Source Makes You an Enemy of the State" (www.guardian.co.uk/technology/blog/2010/feb/23/opensource-intellectual-property) says it all. Under the headline "Encouraging Open Source Could Land You in Trouble" (www.technollama.co.uk/encouraging-open-source-could-land-you-in-trouble) Andres Guadamuz, law lecturer at the University of Edinburgh, concluded that "It is nice to know where the IIPA stands. Only commercial intellectual property is worthy of protection, everything else is as bad as piracy." (Is piracy that bad? On April 12, 2010, the U.S. Government Accountability Office released *Intellectual Property: Observations on Efforts to Quantify the Economic Effects of Counterfeit and Pirated Goods* [GAO-10-423]. The basic point is that the numbers often cited by the IIPA and other groups "cannot be substantiated due to the absence of underlying studies." Piracy is a sizeable problem, but we do not have the numbers to say how bad it really is.)

Despite the objections, the IIPA's position apparently swayed the U.S. Trade Representative, which on April 30, 2010, released the 2010 Watchlist. According to the press release (www.ustr.gov/about-us/press-office/press-releases/2010/april/ustr-releases-2010-special-301-report-intellectual-p): "Trading partners on the Priority Watch List do not provide an adequate level of IPR protection or enforcement, or market access for persons relying on intellectual property protection. China, Russia, Algeria, Argentina, Canada, Chile, India, Indonesia, Pakistan, Thailand, and Venezuela are on the Priority Watch List. These countries will be the subject of particularly intense engagement through bilateral discussion during the coming year."

It is worth noting that the Open Source approach is by no means limited to computer software. Kate Greene, "Open Up and Say Eureka," *Technology Review* (November/December 2008), describes a number of efforts to make gadgets as hackable as software and notes that "technology companies . . . are recognizing that embracing openness doesn't amount to giving away the store. If they aim to provide a platform for other designers rather than trying to design the best product for everyone . . . they are freed to focus on what large companies are uniquely equipped to do: namely, high-volume production, customer service, and brand marketing."

Both Open Source software and hardware play important parts in the development of home 3D printers such as Fab@Home (http://fabathome.org/) and RepRap (http://reprap.org/wiki/Main_Page), which proponents say are roughly where the home PC was in the mid-70s. In two decades, the PC created an economic and social revolution, and they expect 3D printing will too. See Thomas A. Easton, "The Design Economy: A Brave New World for Businesses and Consumers," *The Futurist* (January–February 2009).

In related news, in June 2010, the American Society of Composers, Authors and Publishers (ASCAP) and National Music Publishers Association (NMPA) attacked the "Free Culture Movement," as represented by organizations such as Creative Commons, the Electronic Frontier Foundation, and Public Knowledge, on the grounds that they support a different version of copyright that would permit artists to allow free access to their work. This is the same version of copyright that supports Open Source software, and its proponents have fired back at ASCAP and NMPA with vigor. See Drew Wilson, "Copyright War Escalates with NMPA Joining ASCAP's Attack on Free Culture," Zeropaid.com (June 29, 2010) (www.zeropaid.com/news/89600/copyright-war-escalates-with-nmpa-joining-ascaps-attack-on-free-culture/). For more about "Free Culture," just Google on the term, preferably using your Open Source Firefox browser. You will even find a free copy of Lawrence Lessig's *Free Culture: The Nature and Future of Creativity* (Penguin, 2004).

In the YES selection, the International Intellectual Property Alliance's (IIPA's) discussion of Indonesia in its appeal to the U.S. Trade Representative makes explicit its view that Open Source software and intellectual property are incompatible concepts. It argues that Indonesia's attempt to promote Open Source solutions "encourages a mindset that does not give due consideration to the value of intellectual creations." In the NO selection, Michael Tiemann of Open Source Initiative objects strenuously, arguing that Open Source software is just as much an intellectual creation as proprietary software, it depends just as much on copyright protections, and because Open Source preferences have been promoted in several states, as well as portions of the federal government, the IIPA's position amounts to an attack on the United States itself.

YES

International Intellectual Property Alliance (IIPA)

Indonesia: 2010 Special 301 Report on Copyright Protection and Enforcement

Special 301 Recommendation

IIPA recommends that Indonesia remain on the Priority Watch List.

Executive Summary

IIPA congratulates Indonesian President Susilo Bambang Yudhoyono, his Vice President, and his new Cabinet on re-election in July 2009 for a second term (running until 2014). As a result of this election, IIPA hopes that the momentum of May 2009 Trade and Investment Framework Agreement (TIFA) discussions between USTR Ambassador Kirk and Indonesian Trade Minister Mari Pangestu, which included intellectual property rights issues, can be carried forward into 2010. With the establishment of a new Cabinet in October 2009, IIPA also hopes the Indonesian government can follow through on the promise to protect copyright and open the copyright market in Indonesia. WIPO reports that a study is under way to evaluate the contribution of creativity to Indonesia's economy. Other studies in the region have shown high output by creative industries both in terms of contribution to gross domestic product and good jobs. Those studies support the proposition that adequate and effective protection of intellectual property in a country, as well as adequate market access to foreign companies, are vital to ensure continued positive contributions to real and human capital in the country.

Unfortunately, in Indonesia, piracy problems, including end-user piracy of business software, mall piracy including mobile device piracy and CD-R and DVD-R burning, book piracy, illegal camcording, pay TV piracy, some factory optical disc piracy, and emerging Internet-based piracy cause serious economic harm to right holders. In many instances, organized criminal groups engaged in other criminal behavior are suspected of or have been detected engaging in piracy. Piracy levels in Indonesia remained among the highest in the world in 2009. In terms of enforcement, key government enforcement agencies assisted industry in certain respects, for example, with several raids as part of a National IP Campaign instituted against those engaged in end-user piracy of business software. In September 2009, the Task Force extended this National IP Campaign to other sectors, making visits to mall owners and warning them that distribution or fostering distribution of infringing goods could lead to actions against them in 2010. However, IIPA members do not report that this increased focus of attention on piracy problems has led to significant deterrent enforcement actions against all kinds of piracy, increased prosecutions, improvements to the court system, or fighting corruption.

Worse yet, instead of focusing attention on piracy and solutions to the problem, the government retained onerous market access barriers, including the requirement to locally manufacture film prints and home videos in Indonesia (which had been suspended throughout 2009) and added new restrictions. For example, in March 2009, the Ministry of Administrative Reform (MenPAN) issued Circular Letter No. 1 of 2009 to all central and provincial government offices including State-owned enterprises, endorsing the use and adoption of open source software within government organizations. While the government issued this circular in part with the stated goal to "reduc[e] software copyright violation[s]," in fact, by denying technology choice, the measure will create additional trade barriers and deny fair and equitable market access to software companies. In September 2009, a new Film Law was enacted which would impose a local film quota and strict censorship requirements on local and foreign films. The Film Law is so badly conceived that no one in the film industry to our knowledge, including local and foreign industry, has come out in its support.

Priority Actions Requested in 2010

IIPA requests that the government of Indonesia take the following actions, which would result in the most significant near term commercial benefits to the copyright industries:

Market Access and Related Issues

- Rescind March 2009 MenPAN circular letter endorsing the use and adoption of open source software which threatens to create additional trade barriers and deny fair and equitable market access to software companies.
- Repeal Film Law that imposes a local film quota and strict censorship requirements on local and foreign films.

- Immediately lift market access restrictions on the 1) requirement to locally replicate all theatrical prints and home video titles released in Indonesia; 2) direct distribution of audiovisual products; and 3) ban on the broadcast of most foreign programming in Indonesia.

Enforcement Issues

- Follow through on the National IP Task Force's "Campaign" to take deterrent action against piracy, including:
  - Corporate end-user piracy, to protect the local and international business software industry from the use of unlicensed business software for any commercial purpose.
  - Retail and mall piracy, including imposition of landlord liability for mall owners.
  - Mobile device piracy.
  - Illegal camcording of movies in cinemas.
  - Signal theft, i.e., those who engage in decrypting encrypted television or cable/satellite signals, or those that transmit or retransmit signals (whether decrypted with or without authorization).
  - Book piracy, to address and bring enforcement actions against illegal photocopying on and near university campuses, print piracy, and unauthorized translations.
- Bring and conclude more high-profile deterrent criminal piracy cases, including distributors, warehouses, factories, and high-profile cases involving end-user piracy of business software.
- Commit to expand Commercial Courts in Medan, Jakarta, Semarang, Surabaya, and Makassar to adjudicate copyright cases, establish special IP courts for criminal cases, and take steps to improve judicial processes by developing a cadre of well-qualified, IP-literate judges and prosecutors.
- Address corruption and transparency issues, for example, by creating a database viewable by right holders on all commenced raid actions and status reports on such cases.
- Expedite the establishment by the Directorate General of IPR (DGIPR) of a "Directorate of Investigation" so that Civil Servant Investigators are authorized to enforce all IP laws.

Legislative Issues

- Enact a modern copyright law fully implementing the WIPO Copyright Treaty (WCT) and WIPO Performances and Phonograms Treaty (WPPT) and providing for effective enforcement, including, among other necessary changes:
  - maintaining *ex officio* powers to raid upon suspicion of infringement;
  - codifying in the copyright law explicit liability against mall landlords;
  - providing minimum criminal penalties for all kinds of copyright infringement, including sellers of pirate goods and pirate end-users of business software;
  - ensuring appropriate cybercrime provisions are in place against Internet-based infringements, and creating incentives for service providers to help enforce against Internet and mobile copyright piracy;
  - criminalizing the act of camcording in cinemas;
  - properly protecting sound recordings under the law;
  - extending term of protection.
- Ensure copyright infringement is included in larger fight against organized criminal behavior (i.e., that infringement is a predicate ground for broader criminal investigation, seizure/freezing of assets, etc.).
- Make optical disc regulations more effective by 1) making inspections routine, unannounced and off-hours; 2) enforcing against SID Code violations, including gouging off or non-use of source identification codes; 3) providing transparency in raids and results; and 4) ensuring that the Department of Industry collects exemplars.

Market Access and Related Issues

In 2009, the government of Indonesia took backward steps by further closing a market already considered to be one of the least open in the world for copyright businesses. As of 2008, the government had already essentially closed the market to entertainment companies, severely limiting investment in media businesses, and imposing strict restrictions on the kind of foreign content that could be broadcast in the country. The situation considerably worsened in 2008 due to the imposition of a local manufacturing requirement for the replication of film prints and home video/DVDs released in Indonesia. In 2009, the government issued a Circular announcing a government procurement policy for public sector software usage that would if implemented deny software companies of a level-playing field with the public sector and set a very poor example in terms of technology choice and procurement practices for the private sector, and enacted an ill-conceived Film Law which imposes an onerous quota for local film production and strict censorship restrictions that foreign and even local film companies oppose.

Government Procurement Preference Denies U.S. Software Companies a Level Playing Field: The government of Indonesia, under its Ministry of Administrative Reform (MenPAN), officially sent to all central and provincial government offices, including state-owned enterprises in Indonesia, Circular Letter No. 1 of 2009 issued on March 30, 2009, endorsing the use and adoption of open source software within government organizations. More specifically, the MenPAN letter, concerning the "Utilization of Legal Software and Open Source Software (OSS)," encourages government agencies to use "FOSS" (Free Open Source Software) with a view toward implementation by the end of 2011, which the Circular states will result in the use of legitimate open source and FOSS software and a reduction in overall costs of software. The letter was followed by subsequent clarification documents, including an April 2009 State Ministry of Research & Technology (RISTEK) document regarding the "Migration to Open Source in Government Agencies."

While IIPA has no issue with one of the stated goals of the circular, namely, "reducing software copyright violation," the Indonesian government's policy as indicated in the circular letter instead simply weakens the software industry and undermines its long-term competitiveness by creating an artificial preference for companies offering open source software and related services, even as it denies many legitimate companies access to the government market. Rather than fostering a system that will allow users to benefit from the best solution available in the market, irrespective of the development model, it encourages a mindset that does not give due consideration to the value to intellectual creations. As such, it fails to build respect for intellectual property rights and also limits the ability of government or public-sector customers (e.g., State-owned enterprise) to choose the best solutions to meet the needs of their organizations and the Indonesian people. It also amounts to a significant market access barrier for the software industry. The "Principles for Technology Choice Pathfinder," adopted by APEC in 2006 (furthering the 2002 "Statement to Implement APEC Policies on Trade and the Digital Economy," to which Indonesia was a participant), recognize that procurement preferences can close markets and stifle innovation and economic development. By implementing this government procurement preference policy, the Indonesian government is not adopting an effective approach to drive down piracy rates, but rather, is creating an additional trade barrier and denying fair and equitable market access to software companies worldwide, which is inconsistent with the APEC Principles.

Rather than start down this path away from innovation and to further promote respect for copyright, the government should abandon the Circular's approach and follow a realistic policy framework that includes adequate education and effective enforcement of IP rights and non-discrimination in business choice, software development, and licensing models. The government of Indonesia promised to legalize the public sector's use of software, e.g., in the January 13, 2006 Indonesian Ministry of Communication and Information (MOCI) and Microsoft Memorandum of Understanding (MOU) in which the government undertakes to legalize government use of its products on government computers. We strongly urge USTR to consider the implications that Indonesia's open source preference policy has on IP protection and access to Indonesia's market for U.S. goods and services. . . .

Piracy and Enforcement Challenges in Indonesia

Indonesia Ranks in World's Top 12 Highest Business Software End-User Piracy Rates, But Enforcement Cooperation Remains Generally Good: The willful use of unlicensed or pirate software in the workplace continues to cause the greatest losses to business software companies in Indonesia. The software piracy rate in Indonesia rose slightly, from 85% to 86%, between 2008 and 2009 and still exceeds the Asia regional average (which was 61% in 2008). For 2008, Indonesia ranked 12th highest in the world in terms of global piracy rate, and 19th highest in the world in terms of global losses. Failure to deal with software piracy harms not only U.S. (and other foreign) software companies but harms Indonesia's local economy. A January 2008 study done by the International Data Corporation (IDC) with the Business Software Alliance (BSA) concluded that decreasing Indonesia's software piracy rate by ten percent over a four year period to 2011 would add US$1.8 billion to Indonesia's economy, create 2,200 new high-wage high-tech jobs and generate an additional $90 million in tax revenue.

Overall, enforcement against end-user software infringements in businesses did not improve much in 2009. Some police commands who signed memoranda of understanding (MOUs) have been very cooperative when identifying and following through on cases of end-user infringement. The police are normally taking *ex officio* actions, although in many cases the police take these actions without notifying right holders and administer fines without consulting the industry. This lack of transparency raises obvious concerns and also diminishes the deterrent value of such actions. In 2009, there were 42 overall actions against end-user piracy of business software, with police initiating 13 corporate end-user raids based on BSA complaints, and 29 police-initiated raids.

Further exacerbating the end-user software piracy problem in Indonesia has been a generally ineffective judicial system to combat piracy. It often takes an unusually lengthy period for a case to be finalized and there is no indication that IPR cases (especially criminal prosecutions) are being prioritized. In 2009, we understand that criminal trials against corporate end-user piracy in the country were concluded (one decided by the Semarang District Court in Central Java, and two others decided by the South Jakarta District Court). This follows seven criminal convictions in 2008. In the South Jakarta cases, the police successfully investigated and prosecuted two IT managers for using unlicensed software for business purposes. In November 2009, these two defendants were found guilty for end-user piracy by the South Jakarta District Court. They were both sentenced to six months imprisonment, suspended for 10 months probation, and fined IDR10 million (about US$1,050), which may be substituted with 2 months imprisonment. This sentence was shocking to the local software industry due to the extremely low, non-deterrent fines imposed. . . .

Training and Public Awareness

Various Industry Trainings Provide Capacity Building Assistance in 2009: In 2009, as in previous years, the copyright industries conducted and participated in various training and public awareness activities in Indonesia. Training has been carried out with police, although more needs to be done. For example, in October 2009, BSA spoke to about a dozen police officers from West Java Regional Police and about 100 students from the Faculty of Law, University of Padjajaran in Bandung, West Java, about legal aspects of corporate end-user piracy. In addition, BSA and the U.S. Commercial Services hosted a mini "software asset management" (SAM) seminar targeting 63 companies in Jakarta in May 2009. IIPA understands that some enforcement seminars have taken place in Lampung, Medan and Bali as part of the National IP Campaign in February 2009. The Motion Picture Association provided training throughout the year for approximately 180 theater employees on anti-camcording investigation and enforcement techniques.

U.S. Department of Justice Program Lends Positive Support to Industry: IIPA members continue to support the training program from the United States, the "International Criminal Investigative Training Assistance Program" (ICITAP) which commenced in October 2006. This program, comprising an anti-piracy enforcement initiative and an optical disc piracy initiative, has led in the past to some concrete positive results in terms of facilitating better enforcement against copyright infringements. It also helped build capacity, mentored, and provided technical assistance to optical disc factory inspection teams that include officials from the Department of Industry (DOI), Police, Customs, the Department of Trade and the Directorate General of Intellectual Property Rights in implementing the provisions of the optical disc regulations.

Copyright Law and Related Issues

Copyright Law Implementing Regulations Still Have Not Been Issued: Copyright protection in Indonesia is governed by the Law of the Republic of Indonesia, Number 19 Year 2002 Regarding Copyright (Copyright Law) (effective July 29, 2003) (Undang-Undang RI No. 19 Thn 2002 Tentang Hak Cipta). Regulations dealing with "rights management information" (RMI) were finalized in 2005, but implementing regulations regarding technological protection measures (TPMs) (as covered in Article 27 of the Copyright Law) are still missing and are needed to fully implement the WCT and the WPPT. Indonesia joined the WCT on June 5, 1997 (in force March 6, 2002), and the WPPT on February 15, 2005.

Copyright Law Amendments Needed to Modernize Protection: Reform of the Copyright Law has been in the works for a several years, and IIPA understands that a draft set of amendments emerged in 2008 and is currently in the legislative queue. IIPA encourages the Indonesian government to ensure that any proposed changes are open for public consultation and comment. The following issues should be dealt with in any amendment, to ensure that the law meets the needs of the modern copyright system and keeps abreast of the latest in international and WCT and WPPT obligations:

- **Provide Minimum Criminal Penalties for All Kinds of Copyright Infringement:** There is a continuing need to provide a minimum criminal penalty clause as to all copyright infringements. The current Copyright Law provides minimum criminal penalties only for the production or manufacture of pirate goods (see Article 72(1) of the Copyright Law). For future amendments, it would be vital to provide minimum criminal penalties for sellers of pirate goods as well as those who engage in corporate end-user piracy, especially in view of the low fines we have seen imposed by the courts. The law should also maintain current maximum sentencing provisions. We understand there is a draft criminal code being considered, but IIPA has not been given an opportunity to review such a draft (and it may be that the minimum penalties will be dealt with directly in the copyright law).
- **Maintain Ex Officio Powers to Raid Upon Suspicion of Infringement:** It is important that, for the next amendment of the Copyright Law, copyright infringement must remain a state offense. Any change from this could result in a significant decrease in the numbers of raids and decrease the efficacy of enforcement in Indonesia.
- **Provide for Landlord Liability:** Landlords that do not directly infringe but control infringement of tenants and financially benefit from such infringement should be held liable in Indonesia. This would ensure that all mall owners would be responsible for ridding their premises of piracy. Articles 55 and 56 of the Penal Code provide for criminal liability for one who forces others to commit or jointly commits a criminal act (Article 55(1)) or one who providing "opportunity" or "intentionally 'persuades' others" to commit a criminal act. We understand the government is considering codifying such liability for criminal copyright infringements as to mall landlords who have infringing activity occurring on their premises. IIPA supports this move.
- **Cover Copyright Infringement Under Cybercrime Law, and Provide Incentives for Service Providers to Cooperate, Including Notice and Takedown:** With Internet piracy, including P2P downloading, increasing in Indonesia, it is imperative that the laws adequately address computer-based infringements. The government of Indonesia has reportedly just enacted a new Cyber Law. IIPA has not had an opportunity to review this law, but looks forward to doing so to compare it against the Council of Europe Cybercrime Convention. Reportedly, the law requires some technical implementing regulations including those related to ISP liability, although it is already apparently being employed to prosecute cases involving online pornography or distribution of false information through Internet media, although unfortunately not involving copyright piracy. The law

should be used to combat IP-related cybercrime including copyright infringements. It is also very important to ensure that proper incentives are put into place to ensure service providers cooperate with right holders to curtail such infringing activities. Service providers need to be reminded of potential liability for infringements occurring over their networks, and mechanisms need to be available to ensure removal of infringing content, including notice and takedown as well as effective and fair policies in place by ISPs as to potential termination of repeat infringers, and to ensure assistance to right holders in identifying and removing infringing content and P2P piracy. . . .

Generalized System of Preferences

Indonesia currently participates in the Generalized System of Preferences (GSP) program, a U.S. trade program, which offers preferential trade benefits to eligible beneficiary countries. One of the discretionary criteria of this program is that the country provides "adequate and effective protection for intellectual property rights." In 2008, almost $2.2 billion worth of Indonesian goods entered the U.S. under the duty-free GSP code, accounting for almost 13.8% of its total imports to the U.S. During 2009, almost $1.5 billion worth of Indonesian goods, or almost 11.3% of Indonesia's total imports to the U.S., entered the U.S. under the duty-free GSP code. Indonesia needs to continue to endeavor to meet the adequate and effective test under the statute to remain eligible to continue to receive favorable treatment under the GSP program.

The International Intellectual Property Alliance (IIPA) is a coalition of trade associations (the Association of American Publishers, the Business Software Alliance, the Entertainment Software Association, the Independent Film & Television Alliance, the Motion Picture Association of America, the National Music Publishers' Association, and the Recording Industry Association of America). It works to improve international protection and enforcement of copyrighted materials and open up foreign markets closed by piracy and other market access barriers.

Michael Tiemann

NO

The OSI Categorically Rejects IIPA's Special Pleadings Against Open Source

Introduction

Moore's Law, Disk Law, and Fiber Law have created an economic engine for growth, promising exponentially improving computing, storage, and networking performance for the foreseeable future. And yet according to a 2003 UNCTAD report, "there has been no Moore's Law for software," and indeed it is because of software that computer systems have become more expensive, more complex, and less reliable. The global economy spent $3.4T USD on Information and Communication Technologies in 2008, of which we estimate $1T USD was wasted on "bad software." And reconfirming the 2003 report and our own numbers updated for 2010, others have estimated losses of at least $500B and as much as $6T USD (meaning that for every dollar spent on ICT, that dollar and almost one more went down the drain). Whether the annual loss number is $500B, $1T, or $6T, all represent an unsustainable cost and undeniable evidence that something in the dominant design of the proprietary software industry is deeply flawed.

Open source software is an alternative approach to software development that allows, rather than prohibits, users and developers to collaborate and innovate together. It encourages, rather than threatens, transparency and accountability. It rewards meritorious behavior and it routes around bottlenecks caused by concentration of power and control. Open source software was the catalyst that helped effect the revolution of the World Wide Web, where for the first time in history, the promise of the freedom of the press was available to anybody with a computer and an Internet connection. Indeed, open source software was, and remains, the technology of the whole Internet itself. When Thomas Friedman claimed that open source is the most powerful and disruptive of the ten flattening forces described in the best-selling book *The World Is Flat,* it was no surprise to us. But now a consortium of industry trade associations, the International Intellectual Property Alliance (IIPA), has launched an attack against open source, and so we must stand up, defend our position, and explain how the use of open source leads to the continued progress of the 21st century economy.

The successes of open source software are too numerous to mention in a single article. A few examples establish that open source has become the most reliable and sustainable software with virtually unlimited upside potential. The interests of the State, be they security, accountability, transparency, or economic opportunity, are advanced by open source. The NSA's SE Linux project singlehandedly restored the economic viability of a highly secure platform able to securely run a growing range of innovative applications. Its protections have resulted in an operating system kernel that has suffered zero critical security vulnerabilities in more than four years of commercial availability. The US Department of Defense issued a memo in 2009 stating "To effectively achieve its missions, the Department of Defense must develop and update its software-based capabilities faster than ever, to anticipate new threats and respond to continuously changing requirements. The use of Open Source Software (OSS) can provide advantages in this regard . . ." The Executive Office of the President has been collaborating with the Sunlight Foundation and others to provide greater transparency into US Federal spending, using open source software to collect, index, and publish hundreds of billions of dollars worth of Federal procurements and contracts. And open source software is the fastest growing segment of the software industry, registering double-digit organic growth compared to zero-to-negative growth of the industry as a whole. It is little wonder that in the State of California, considered by most to be the epicenter of America's technology industry, Chief Information Officer Terri Takai published ITPL-10-01, which serves to "formally establish the use of Open Source Software (OSS) in California state government as an acceptable practice."

Other nations, seeing the success of open source in US and State governments, industry, and R&D, have initiated their own investigations into open source software, and many have liked what they have found. The CSIS Open Source Policy report documents the progress of hundreds of open source policies around the world, and open source policy research studies . . . show that open source adoption positively correlates with the Human Development Index. By contrast, rates of software piracy have no correlation whatsoever with that index. Moreover, objective quality metrics (published in reports sponsored by the Department of Homeland Security) show not only that Open Source Software has achieved a hundredfold higher quality than typical proprietary software (as measured by defect density per 1000 lines of source code), but open source continues to improve its quality metrics by double digits per year while proprietary software remains static in its (not very good) defect density. The fact that open source software has achieved such a quality differential should be sufficient for open source to win in a neutral competitive bidding process—and it does as shown by its revenue and market share growth. But software is not merely a commodity to be consumed, it is an investment whose value can increase with proper stewardship. Customers who buy software with the rights and community necessary to effect continuous improvement get good value for their money. Governments who seek those rights are being smart about the dollars they spend today without artificially limiting the adaptations they may need to make tomorrow. This is one reason why governments are not only seeking best value for today's dollar, but the freedoms to make today's investment more valuable tomorrow, and why open source has become an explicit consideration in policies, procurements, and discussions of best practices.

Open Source Provides Long-Term Value Beyond Proprietary Alternatives

Unlike proprietary software, whose value diminishes over time as it become obsolete (if it was ever useful in the first place), open source software, as a knowledge commons, permits a kind of compound interest to accrue to its intellectual capital base. (The theory underlying this discovery won a Nobel Prize in economics for 2009.) It should therefore be no surprise that open source software should be one of the key drivers in advancing national technology objectives among all nations, whether developing or developed. Anyone who has seen the progress and the potential of open source software, should be surprised by an information infrastructure built on software that prohibits independent improvement, frustrates interoperabilty, criminalizes collaboration, and defeats Moore's Law. And yet this is the heart of the IIPA's recommendation. But it is not only the heart of that recommendation that is rotten.

Attacks by the IIPA Are Unjust

A recent blog posting at *The Guardian* about the IIPA's recommendation, and its influence over US "Special 301" rules, suggests that there is something well hidden from review: a secret trial to which neither the accused nor any jury are invited to attend. Andres Guadamuz has done the digging to reveal that guilt has been read out in a Star Chamber. Orders have been handed down that are not only unjust, but entirely arbitrary. An excerpt from Wikipedia provides the following definition and explanation of the term "Selective Enforcement" as follows:

> Selective enforcement is the ability that executors of the law (such as police officers or administrative agencies, in some cases) have to arbitrarily select choice individuals as being outside of the law. The use of enforcement discretion in an arbitrary way is referred to as selective enforcement or selective prosecution.
>
> Historically, selective enforcement is recognized as a sign of tyranny, and an abuse of power, because it violates rule of law, allowing men to apply justice only when they choose. Aside from this being inherently unjust, it almost inevitably must lead to favoritism and extortion, with those empowered to choose being able to help their friends, take bribes, and threaten those they desire favors from.

Singling out a single country like Indonesia for policies that can be found across the European Union (not to mention within US civilian, academic, military, and intelligence communities) is a blatant case of selective enforcement, one which hides the absurdity of the claims by the narrowness of their application. The sheer hypocrisy of the claims made by the IIPA should cause anybody to doubt the merits of those claims, such as this:

> While IIPA has no issue with one of the stated goals of [the Ministry of Administrative Reform (MenPAN) . . . Circular Letter No. 1 of 2009 issued on March 30, 2009, endorsing the use and adoption of open source software within government organizations], namely, "reducing software copyright violation," the Indonesian government's policy as indicated in the circular letter instead simply weakens the software industry and undermines its long-term competitiveness by creating an artificial preference for companies offering open source software and related services, even as it denies many legitimate companies access to the government market. Rather than fostering a system that will allow users to benefit from the best solution available in the market, irrespective of the development model, it encourages a mindset that does not give due consideration to the value to intellectual creations. As such, it fails to build respect for intellectual property rights and also limits the ability of government or public-sector customers (e.g., State-owned enterprise) to choose the best solutions to meet the needs of their organizations and the Indonesian people. It also amounts to a significant market access barrier for the software industry.

The IIPA complains that the open source community does not respect intellectual property. "Intellectual property" conflates trade secrets, patents, copyrights, and trademarks. By pretending as if these separate domains are all one common thing, and then arguing by analogy how all should be understood, the concept of "intellectual property" has taken on a meaning that has no actual basis in law. Worse, this meaning has been construed to actually contradict the original purpose that was enshrined into the US Constitution, which was "To promote the

Progress of Science and useful Arts, by securing for limited Times to Authors and Inventors the exclusive Right to their respective Writings and Discoveries." The copyright clause speaks not at all to any natural rights of Authors and Inventors, but only to the goal of progress. If there were any invention worthy of protection by law, it would be the invention of how to make more progress in science and the useful arts. Which is precisely what open source software now appears to be doing.

But even if one does not believe that open source is a better way of doing things, there is no question that open source is equally dependent—no more, no less—than proprietary software on the strong protections of copyright law. Open source depends on the strong ability to grant rights to those who wish to copy our work—a true copy right!—and thus we respect copyright at least as much as those who don't trust it enough to call it by its real name. If anything, the ones guilty of not respecting copyright are those who invent new terms like "intellectual property" and then write up and promote their own legal theories: as to how such stuff is supposed to work, who should be rewarded for buying into their system, and who should be punished if they do not.

Open source software is today a part of every commercial software solution. IIPA's assertion that expecting use of open source software "denies many legitimate companies access to the government market" is a desperate distortion of the truth. It requires a suspension of belief in core suppliers like IBM, Oracle, Red Hat, Microsoft, HP—and most others—all of whom have already integrated open source into their business in one of the ways Gartner describes. To say it "undermines [the software market's] long-term competitiveness" beggars belief, given the enormous competitive impetus the industry has received from the relaxation of lock-in and the introduction of new competitive innovation from open source. Far from being "a significant market access barrier," an open source requirement corrects the power a small number of suppliers have been able to derive from lock-in and the exercise of monopoly—in some cases illegally and unremedied.

Further, IIPA's position represents a direct attack on the very government to which it is making a recommendation. If expecting the presence of open source did indeed "simply weaken the software industry," the US government itself would be culpable since the Department of Defence has issued and clarified clear guidance preferring open source software for most purposes. By their logic, it would be justifiable for foreign governments to embargo the USA.

The greatest outrage arose from the assertion that "it fails to build respect for intellectual property rights," which compresses into a few words both an inversion of the truth and a dishonest, self-serving conceptual framing. Open source software has no impact on the use of trademarks, patents or trade secrets, so the stew of "intellectual property" here actually refers only to copyright. To say that open source fails to build respect for copyright is ridiculous. Open source licensing is copyright licensing and thus depends upon and promotes the greatest possible respect for copyright. Without that respect, open source software would be impossible. One suspects the comment is derived more from a desire to mislead government for commercial purposes by associating open source with file sharing in order to smear and discredit it from the worldview of the RIAA (Recording Industry Association of America).

Open Source Supports Business

Open Source was not parachuted in from an alternate universe. It is a result of the ordinary business decision to build versus buy. Businesses purchase some software and write some other software themselves. They have found that they can reduce their cost of writing software by sharing it with the public. They turn the software into a commodity, available at minimal cost. Inevitably, this is going to annoy the people who would rather that software be a scarce economic good only available through certain vendors (themselves). Of course they have the right to make their case, as they have. But their case must be clearly identified as special pleading designed to advance their own ends, not a general defense of business interests.

Conclusion

The entire position taken by IIPA is unbalanced. It relies on outdated definitions, special interests, and a fear of innovation and new business model opportunities. It blends them together to abuse an outdated mechanism of the US government with a condemnation that applies to the US itself. America has a role in defending free markets around the world. The IIPA's stance does not support that role, and should not be respected.

We call on national organizations, such as Open Source for America, to take action by representing the large and growing open source community.

Michael Tiemann is vice president of Open Source Affairs at Red Hat, Inc., as well as president of the Open Source Initiative.

EXPLORING THE ISSUE

Does Endorsing Open Source Software Fail to Respect Intellectual Property?

Critical Thinking and Reflection

1. What does "open source" mean?
2. Does any business or other institution have a right to continue its operations as it is accustomed to doing?
3. What is the purpose of copyright and patent law?
4. In what sense does endorsing the use of open source software help to prevent copyright infringement?

Is There Common Ground?

Both sides of this debate agree that copyright law is important. The Open Source and Free Culture movements, however, use it differently from the IIPA. There are many different open source "licenses"; see www.opensource.org/docs/osd and www.opensource.org/licenses/index.html. After studying the definitions here, answer the following questions:

1. Does any open source license permit piracy or theft of software?
2. Does any open source license fail to permit software buyers to share the software with others?
3. Does any open source license fail to permit for-profit distribution of software?

Create Central

www.mhhe.com/createcentral

Additional Resources

Intellectual Property: Observations on Efforts to Quantify the Economic Effects of Counterfeit and Pirated Goods (U.S. Government Accountability Office, April 12, 2010) (GAO-10-423).

Lawrence Lessig, *Free Culture: The Nature and Future of Creativity* (Penguin, 2004).

Internet References . . .

Sourceforge

Sourceforge is a comprehensive guide to available Open Source software.

http://sourceforge.net/

Open Source Initiative

The Open Source Initiative (OSI) advocates for the benefits of open source and builds bridges among different constituencies in the open source community.

www.opensource.org/

Unit 6

UNIT

Ethics

Society's standards of right and wrong have been hammered out over millennia of trial, error, and (sometimes violent) debate. Accordingly, when science and technology offer society new choices to make and new things to do, debates are renewed over whether or not these choices and actions are ethically acceptable. Today there is vigorous debate over such topics as the use of animals in research; cloning of both stem cells and whole organisms; and enhancing the human form with genetic engineering, electronic accessories, and even mechanical aids.

Selected, Edited, and with Issue Framing Material by:
Thomas A. Easton, *Thomas College*

ISSUE

Is "Animal Rights" Just Another Excuse for Terrorism?

YES: John J. Miller, from "In the Name of the Animals: America Faces a New Kind of Terrorism," *National Review* (July 3, 2006)

NO: Steven Best, from "Dispatches from a Police State: Animal Rights in the Crosshairs of State Repression," *International Journal of Inclusive Democracy* (January 2007)

Learning Outcomes

After studying this issue, students will be able to:

- Explain why animals are used in research.
- Explain why alternatives to the use of animals in research are sought.
- Describe the difference between "animal welfare" and "animal rights."
- Explain why society chooses to restrain extreme protests.

ISSUE SUMMARY

YES: Journalist John Miller argues that animal rights extremists have adopted terrorist tactics in their effort to stop the use of animals in scientific research. Because of the benefits of such research, if the terrorists win, everyone loses.

NO: Professor Steven Best argues that the new Animal Enterprise Protection Act is excessively broad and vague, imposes disproportionate penalties, endangers free speech, and detracts from prosecution of real terrorism. The animal liberation movement, on the other hand, is both a necessary effort to emancipate animals from human exploitation, and part of a larger resistance movement opposed to exploitation and hierarchies of any and all kinds.

Modern biologists and physicians know a great deal about how the human body works. Some of that knowledge has been gained by studying human cadavers and tissue samples acquired during surgery and through "experiments of nature." Some knowledge of human biology has also been gained from experiments on humans, such as when patients agree to let their surgeons and doctors try experimental treatments.

The key word here is *agree*. Today it is widely accepted that people have the right to consent or not to consent to whatever is done to them in the name of research or treatment. In fact, society has determined that research done on humans without their free and informed consent is a form of scientific misconduct. However, this standard does not apply to animals, experimentation on which has produced the most knowledge of the human body.

Although animals have been used in research for at least the last 2000 years, during most of that time, physicians who thought they had a workable treatment for some illness commonly tried it on their patients before they had any idea whether or not it worked or was even safe. Many patients, of course, died during these untested treatments. In the mid-nineteenth century, the French physiologist Claude Bernard argued that it was sensible to try such treatments first on animals to avoid some human suffering and death. No one then questioned whether or not human lives were more valuable than animal lives. In the twentieth century, Elizabeth Baldwin, in "The Case for Animal Research in Psychology," *Journal of Social Issues* (vol. 49, no. 1, 1993), argued that animals are of immense value in medical, veterinary, and psychological research, and they do not have the same moral rights as humans. Our obligation, she maintains, is to treat them humanely.

Today geneticists generally study fruit flies, roundworms, and zebra fish. Physiologists study mammals, mostly mice and rats but also rabbits, cats, dogs, pigs, sheep, goats, monkeys, and chimpanzees. Experimental animals are often kept in confined quarters, cut open, infected with disease organisms, fed unhealthy diets, and injected with assorted chemicals. Sometimes the animals suffer. Sometimes the animals die. And sometimes they are healed, albeit often of disease or injuries induced by the researchers in the first place.

Not surprisingly, some observers have reacted with extreme sympathy and have called for better treatment of animals used in research. This "animal welfare" movement has, in turn, spawned the more extreme "animal rights" movement, which asserts that animals—especially mammals—have rights as important and as deserving of regard as those of humans. Thus, to kill an animal, whether for research, food, or fur, is the moral equivalent of murder. See Steven M. Wise and Jane Golmoodall, *Rattling the Cage: Toward Legal Rights for Animals* (Perseus, 2000), and Roger Scruton and Andrew Tayler, "Do Animals Have Rights?" *The Ecologist* (March 2001).

As the idea that people must give informed consent to what is done to them in the name of research gained currency, along with the related idea that whatever is done should aim to benefit them, some people have tried to extend these ideas to animals. They say that just as scientists cannot do whatever they wish to humans, they cannot do whatever they wish to animals. Harriet Rivo, "Toward a More Peaceable Kingdom," *Technology Review* (April 1992) says that the animal rights movement "challenges the ideology of science itself . . . forcing experimenters to recognize that they are not necessarily carrying out an independent exercise in the pursuit of truth—that their enterprise, in its intellectual as well as its social and financial dimensions, is circumscribed and defined by the culture of which it is an integral part."

Among books that are pertinent to this issue are F. Barbara Orlans, *In the Name of Science: Issues in Responsible Animal Experimentation* (Oxford University Press, 1993); Rod Strand and Patti Strand, *The Hijacking of the Humane Movement* (Doral, 1993); Deborah Blum, *The Monkey Wars* (Oxford University Press, 1994); Tom Regan, *Empty Cages: Facing the Challenge of Animal Rights* (Rowman and Littlefield, 2005); and Paul Waldau, *Animal Rights: What Everyone Needs to Know* (Oxford University Press, 2011). Adrian R. Morrison provides a guide to responsible animal use in "Ethical Principles Guiding the Use of Animals in Research," *American Biology Teacher* (February 2003). Barry Yeoman, "Can We Trust Research Done with Lab Mice?" *Discover* (July 2003), notes that the conditions in which animals are kept can make a huge difference in their behavior and in their responses to experimental treatments.

The same research that leads to treatments for human illness also enhances the treatment tools of veterinarians. Thus Damon Linker, in "Rights for Rodents," *Commentary* (April 2001), can say, "Can anyone really doubt that, were the misanthropic agenda of the animal-rights movement actually to succeed, the result would be an increase in man's inhumanity, to man and animal alike? In the end, fostering our age-old 'prejudice' in favor of human dignity may be the best thing we can do for animals, not to mention for ourselves." An editorial in *Lancet*, "Animal Research Is a Source of Human Compassion, Not Shame" (September 4, 2004), insists that the use of animals in biomedical research is both an essentially humanistic endeavor and necessary. University of Pittsburgh assistant professor of anesthesiology and radiology Stuart Derbyshire writes in "Vivisection: Put Human Welfare First," *Spiked-Online* (June1, 2004), that the use of animals in research is justified by the search for knowledge, not just the search for medical treatments, and reflects a moral choice to put humans first. Josie Appleton, "Speciesism: A Beastly Concept: Why It Is Morally Right to Use Animals to Our Ends," *Spiked-Online* (February 23, 2006), contends that the development of human civilization has been marked by increasing separation from animals. Humans come first, and it is entirely moral to use animals for own ends. Torturing animals is wrong, but mostly because it reflects badly upon the torturer. Wesley J. Smith, *A Rat Is a Pig Is a Dog Is a Boy: The Human Cost of the Animal Rights Movement* (Encounter, 2010), defends the stance that human interests must come before those of animals; granting rights to animals is an attack on human dignity.

Animal-rights extremists defend the opposing view vigorously, even going so far as to firebomb researchers' homes and cars; see Greg Miller, "Scientists Targeted in California Firebombings," *Science* (August 8, 2008). John Hadley, "Animal Rights Extremism and the Terrorism Question," *Journal of Social Philosophy* (Fall 2009), questions whether such extremist actions really fall under the "terrorism" label, but most people seems to have no trouble using the label. P. Michael Conn and James V. Parker of the Oregon National Primate Research Center describe in *The Animal Research War* (Palgrave Macmillan, 2008) how animals are used and protected in research and the benefits of their use, while also detailing the movement of terrorist tactics from the United Kingdom to the United States. In their view, "It is extremely important that an informed public know what is really going on and how it impacts on the future of health care and medical advances."

Yet the idea that animals have rights too continues to gain ground. Steven M. Wise finds in *Drawing the Line: Science and the Case for Animal Rights* (Perseus, 2002) that there is a spectrum of mental capacities for different species, which supports the argument for rights. Niall Shanks, in "Animal Rights in the Light of Animal Cognition," *Social Alternatives* (Summer 2003), considers the moral/philosophical justifications for animal rights and stresses the question of consciousness. Jim Motavalli, in "Rights from Wrongs," *E Magazine* (March/April 2003), describes with approval the movement toward giving animals legal rights (though not necessarily human rights). Jeffrey Stinson, "Activists Pursue Basic Legal Rights for Great Apes," *USA Today* (July 15, 2008), describes current efforts to grant such rights to the great apes. Paul Starobin, "Animal Rights on the March," *National Journal* (May 22, 2010), notes that the animal rights movement is shifting toward legislative efforts to meet their goals. In India, the use of live animals in most research has been banned;

see Linah Baliga, "Govt Bans Use of Live Animals for Education, Research," *Times of India* (April 17, 2012).

The animal welfare movement has led to important reforms in the treatment of animals, to the development of several alternatives to using animals in research, and to a considerable reduction in the number of animals used in research. See, for example, Robert A. Coleman, "Human Tissue in the Evaluation of Safety and Efficacy of New Medicines: A Viable Alternative to Animal Models?" *ISRN Pharmaceutics* (special section) (2011); Alan Dove, "The Search for Animal Alternatives," *Drug Discovery & Development* (May 2010); and Manfred Liebsch, et al., "Alternatives to Animal Testing: Current Status and Future Perspectives," *Archives of Toxicology* (August 2011). There is also a scientific Journal, ALTEX: Alternatives to Animal Experimentation (http://altweb.jhsph.edu/altex/index.html). However, it has also led to hysterical objections to in-class animal dissections, terrorist attacks on laboratories, the destruction of research records, and the theft of research materials (including animals).

The Animal Enterprise Protection Act (AEPA) was designed to prevent attacks on laboratories and researchers, and since its passage, such attacks indeed have diminished. Yet critics do object that it may have a chilling effect on legitimate protest; see Michael Hill, "United States v. Fullmer and the Animal Enterprise Terrorism Act: 'True Threats' to Advocacy," *Case Western Reserve Law Review* (Spring 2011), and Dara Lovitz, *Muzzling a Movement: The Effects of Anti-Terrorism Law, Money, and Politics on Animal Activism* (Lantern Books, 2010). One lawsuit was dismissed in March 2013 for failure to show that such "chilling" actually existed; see Rose Bouboushian, "Terror Fears of Animal Rights Group Tossed," *Courthouse News* (March 21, 2013).

In the YES selection, Journalist John J. Miller argues that animal rights extremists have adopted terrorist tactics in their effort to stop the use of animals in scientific research. Because of the benefits of such research, if the terrorists win, everyone loses. In the NO selection, Professor Steven Best argues that new laws against animal rights "terrorism" represent the efforts of animal exploitation industries that seek immunity from criticism. The new Animal Enterprise Protection Act is excessively broad and vague, imposes disproportionate penalties, endangers free speech, and detracts from prosecution of real terrorism. The animal liberation movement, on the other hand, is both a necessary effort to emancipate animals from human exploitation and part of a larger resistance movement opposed to exploitation and hierarchies of any and all kinds.

YES

John J. Miller

In the Name of the Animals: America Faces a New Kind of Terrorism

Six days after the World Trade Center was destroyed, the New York Stock Exchange rang its opening bell and traders sang "God Bless America" from the floor: They wanted to send a loud-and-clear message to the world that al-Qaeda could not shut down the U.S. economy. Even though the Dow suffered its biggest one-day point-loss in history, the mere fact that buying and selling could resume so quickly marked an inspiring day for capitalism and against terrorism.

On September 7, 2005, however, terrorists struck again, and the NYSE still hasn't recovered. This time, they didn't target a couple of skyscrapers near the exchange, but rather a company called Life Sciences Research (LSR). It had recently qualified for a NYSE listing and its senior management had gathered on Wall Street to celebrate the occasion. Just a few minutes before the first trades were set to occur, NYSE president Catherine Kinney informed her guests that their listing would be postponed. It was immediately obvious to everyone from LSR what had happened: "A handful of animal extremists had succeeded where Osama bin Laden had failed," Mark Bibi, the company's general counsel, would say in congressional testimony the next month.

LSR is better known by the name of its operating subsidiary, Huntingdon Life Sciences (HLS), which is in the business of testing products on animals to assess their safety and comply with government regulations. Most people probably don't like to think about what goes on in these labs—vivisections of monkeys, for instance—but they also appreciate the importance of research whose ultimate goal is the protection and enhancement of human health. About 95 percent of all lab animals are rats and mice, but for animal-rights extremists who believe that "a rat is a pig is a dog is a boy" (as Ingrid Newkirk of People for the Ethical Treatment of Animals once said), the whole endeavor is deeply immoral. And some of them have decided that because the traditional practices of honest persuasion and civil disobedience haven't changed many hearts or minds, they must now adopt a different strategy—something they euphemistically call "direct action." These are efforts to intimidate and harass animal researchers and everyone who comes into contact with them. In recent years, hardcore activists have embraced property destruction and physical assaults. "This is the number-one domestic terrorist threat in America," says Sen. James Inhofe, an Oklahoma Republican. Keeping LSR off the Big Board probably represents their greatest achievement yet.

Red in Tooth and Claw

The animal-rights movement may be wrongheaded, but there's no denying that most of its members are motivated by genuine compassion for animals and a sincere commitment to preventing cruelty. There's also no denying that violence in their name has become a significant problem. Just as the pro-life movement is haunted by the murderers of abortion doctors, the environmental and animal-rights movements are cursed by their own packs of fierce radicals. A year ago, the FBI said that 35 of its offices were conducting more than 150 investigations into "animal rights/ecoterrorist activities." The number of illegal incidents involving these activities has risen sharply, from 220 in the 1980s and 1990s to 363 in just the last five years, according to a recent report by the Foundation for Biomedical Research, an association of businesses and universities that conduct animal research. (By contrast, abortion-clinic violence appears to be subsiding.)

"Other groups don't come close in terms of the financial damage they've done," says John Lewis, an FBI agent who until recently coordinated federal efforts against domestic terrorism. Not even militants in the mold of Timothy McVeigh, the man behind the Oklahoma City bombing in 1995? "We have an acute interest in all of these groups, but when the rubber meets the road, the eco- and animal-rights terrorists lately have been way out in front." Lewis estimates that they've caused around $100 million in damage, mostly property destruction affecting businesses, much of it from arson. This fall, eleven defendants will face trial in Oregon for causing an estimated $20 million in damage in five states.

Although animal-rights terrorism is fundamentally barbaric, its execution has assumed increasingly sophisticated forms. The campaign against Huntingdon Life Sciences began in the United Kingdom seven years ago with the formation of a group called Stop Huntingdon Animal Cruelty, or SHAC. Soon after, SHAC recruited members in the United States to focus on an HLS facility in New Jersey, using methods that were deployed to great effect in the U.K. A federal trial earlier this year—perhaps the most important trial ever held involving animal-rights extremism—put the group's methods on full display.

Many of SHAC's efforts targeted HLS directly. An electronic attack in 2002, for instance, caused the HLS server to overload. But other confrontations involved HLS employees away from work: cars vandalized in driveways, rocks tossed through the windows of homes, and graffiti messages such as "PUPPY KILLER" spray-painted on houses. Descriptions of these incidents were dutifully posted on SHAC's own website, often with an unnerving sense of glee. After a tire-slashing visit to the home of one HLS employee, for example, the SHACtivists seemed pleased that "his wife is reportedly on the brink of a nervous breakdown and divorce." These messages were meant to generate publicity, build a sense of momentum, and serve as models for activists spread across the country. In Britain, one top HLS employee was attacked by a group of hooded men wielding ax handles. "It's only a matter of time before it happens in the United States," warns Frankie Trull, head of the Foundation for Biomedical Research. "Everything they do over there eventually comes over here."

Intimidating employees in their private lives places pressure on HLS itself. But SHAC's harassment didn't stop with HLS employees. They also engaged in "tertiary targeting"—i.e., taking aim at companies with ties to HLS, plus their workers. Dozens of firms decided that doing business with HLS simply wasn't worth it. Deloitte & Touche, which had audited the HLS books, ended its relationship. Lawn gardeners quit. Even a security company that provided services to HLS succumbed to the abuse.

SHAC's methods certainly can be menacing, as transcripts from the trial make clear. One of SHAC's main targets was Marsh, a company that sold insurance to HLS. There was a smoke-bomb attack at an office in Seattle, forcing the evacuation of a high-rise building. In San Antonio, SHAC members glued the locks to a Marsh office and plastered the windows and doors of the building with pictures of a mutilated dog. Once they even stormed inside, screaming threats: "You have the blood of death on your hands! . . . We know where you live! You cannot sleep at night! We will find you!"

And they made good on these threats. Marsh employees were repeatedly harassed at home. There were late-night phone calls: "Are you scared? Do you think the puppies should be scared?" Other calls were more menacing: "We know where you live. You shouldn't sleep at night. You shouldn't rest until the puppies rest." Marion Harlos, who was managing director for Marsh in San Antonio, said that people went through her mail, ordered magazine subscriptions in her name, and rang her doorbell and dashed off in a kind of never-ending Devil's Night. Sometimes protesters would gather in front of her house, banging drums and hollering into megaphones. "They proceeded to parade the neighborhood, shout my name, that of my children," she said. "I was petrified. I was petrified for my children." The kids were kept indoors: "We did not know what was going to take place. Would someone be in the front yard? Would someone be in the back yard? Would someone come up and talk to them? Would someone try and take them?" To make a bad situation even worse, a neighbor threatened to sue Harlos, claiming that the ongoing presence of protesters was hurting property values. Harlos eventually moved.

Sally Dillenback, a Marsh employee in Dallas, had a similarly harrowing experience. A SHAC website published private information, some of it probably obtained by going through her trash: her home address, her car's license-plate number, and even her auto-insurance policy number. Most unsettling, however, was the information about her children: their names, the names of their schools and teachers, and descriptions of their after-school activities. "I felt that my family might be threatened with that kind of information being posted," she testified. The activists certainly didn't leave her alone; they plastered pictures on the side of her house, her mailbox, and her sidewalk. A SHAC website described the strategy: "Let the stickers serve to remind Marsh employees and their neighbors that their homes are paid for in the blood, the blood of innocent animals." On other occasions, animal-rights radicals held protests outside her home with drums and bullhorns. They followed her to church. The scariest moment may have been when Dillenback read an e-mail: "It asked how I would feel if they cut open my son . . . and filled him with poison the way that they, Huntingdon, [were] doing to animals." Her husband bought a semi-automatic shotgun, even though Mrs. Dillenback doesn't like guns: "He was wanting to protect the family."

Pundits in Black Ski Masks

Marsh employees were by no means the only tertiary victims of abuse. Two bombs went off at a California office of Chiron, a biotech company. Nobody was hurt, but the second explosion was delayed—a tactic sometimes used by terrorists to kill first responders. Workers at GlaxoSmithKline, a pharmaceutical company, also had their windows smashed and mail stolen. In one case, SHAC posted information about the spouse of a GSK employee who was undergoing treatment for alcoholism. Another employee was summoned to the Baltimore morgue to identify a dead relative—but when she arrived, she learned the call was a hoax.

Sometimes, the connections between SHAC targets and HLS were so tenuous as to be almost nonexistent. Elaine Perna, a housewife who is married to an executive who retired from the Bank of New York—another company with ties to HLS—confronted SHAC when protesters appeared on her porch. "When I opened the door, they were yelling at me through the bullhorn. One spat at my face through the screen and yelled obscenities at me, about me, about my husband." A defense lawyer's attempt to minimize the incident—"All Ms. Gazzola did was she screamed through the bullhorn, didn't she?"—irritated Perna: "They were yelling at me through a bullhorn, they were calling me effing this and my husband effing that and spitting in my face through a screen. Now, if you think that 'that's all,' you know, you can call it 'that's all.' But to me, it wasn't 'that's all.'" The mayhem didn't stop until the police arrived.

On March 2, a jury convicted six members of SHAC (at press time, sentencing had not yet occurred). This is an important victory, but animal-rights extremism isn't going away—groups such as Hugs for Puppies and Win Animal Rights are now on the scene, continuing their perverse crusade. They certainly don't lack for true believers. In Senate testimony last fall, Jerry Vlasak of the North American Animal Liberation Press Office announced that violence against HLS was "extensional self-defense" in behalf of "non-human animals." Recently, a mysterious full-page advertisement appeared in the *New York Times* and the *Wall Street Journal*. It featured the image of a man in a black ski mask, alongside the words "I Control Wall Street" and a short account of the NYSE fiasco. "Nobody knows who paid for it," says Trull. One theory proposes that a group of institutional investors are responsible; another claims that it's a backhanded attempt by animal-rights activists to raise anxieties even further. HLS still isn't listed.

Several members of Congress have tried to address this species of domestic terrorism by proposing legislation that would toughen the Animal Enterprise Protection Act, a law that was passed before the advent of "tertiary targeting." At the recent trial, prosecutors secured convictions against SHAC only because they were able to rely on anti-stalking laws. "They had to scour the federal code, looking for violations," says Brent McIntosh, a deputy assistant attorney general at the Department of Justice. "This is an enormous, surreptitious, and interstate conspiracy. We need to strengthen laws against it." Bills to do so have been introduced in both the House and the Senate, but a crowded legislative calendar probably means they won't be debated until a new Congress convenes next year.

The stakes are high. "Five years from now, we don't want to count up another $100 million in losses," says the FBI's Lewis. That's true, although the real costs of animal-rights terrorism aren't really quantifiable: They come in the form of medical discoveries that are delayed or never made, products that aren't approved, and careers that aren't started. Whatever the real price tag, one thing is certain: Each time an animal-rights terrorist wins, people lose.

John J. Miller is *National Review's* national political reporter. His latest book is *A Gift of Freedom: How the John M. Olin Foundation Changed America* (Encounter Books, 2005).

Steven Best

NO

Dispatches from a Police State: Animal Rights in the Crosshairs of State Repression

Welcome to the post-constitutional America, where defense of animal rights and the earth is a terrorist crime.

In the wake of 9/11, and in the midst [of] the neoliberal attack on social democracies, efforts to grab dwindling resources, and crush dissent of any kind, the US has entered a neo-McCarthyist period rooted in witch-hunts and political persecution. The terms and players have changed, but the situation is much the same as the 1950s: the terrorist threat has replaced the communist threat, Attorney General Alfred [*sic*] Gonzalez dons the garb of Sen. Joseph McCarthy, and the Congressional Meetings on Eco-Terrorism stand in for the House Un-American Activities Committee. The Red Scare of communism has morphed into the *Green Scare* of ecoterrorism, where the bad guy today is not a commie but an animal, environmental, or peace activist. In a nightmare replay of the 1950s, activists of all kinds today are surveilled, hassled, threatened, jailed, and stripped of their rights. As before, the state conjures up dangerous enemies in our midst and instills fear in the public, so that people willingly forfeit liberties for an alleged security that demands secrecy, non-accountability, and centralized power. . . .

The bogus "war on terror" has served as a highly-effective propaganda and bullying device to ram through Congress and the courts a pro-corporate, anti-environmental, authoritarian agenda. Using vague, catch-all phrases such as "enemy combatants" and "domestic terrorists," the Bush administration has rounded up and tortured thousands of non-citizens (detaining them indefinitely in military tribunals without right to a fair trial) and surveilled, harassed, and imprisoned citizens who dare to challenge the government or corporate system it protects and represents.

"The Animal Enterprise Protection Act"

While dissent in general has become ever-more criminalized in the dark days of the Bush Reich, animal rights activists especially have been caught in the crosshairs of state repression, targeted by "anti-terrorist" legislation that subverts First Amendment rights to protect the blood money of corporate exploiters. This is because the animal rights/liberation movement is not only one of the most dramatic forms of resistance alive today (such as [is] evident in the dramatic raids, rescues, sabotage, and arson attacks of the Animal Liberation Front, a global movement), but also is an economic threat to postindustrial capital which is heavily rooted in science and research, and therefore dependent upon (it believes) animal experimentation.

In 1992, a decade before the passage of the USA PATRIOT Act, animal exploitation groups such as the National Association for Biomedical Research successfully lobbied Congress to pass a federal law called the Animal Enterprise Protection Act (AEPA). This legislation created the new crime of "animal enterprise terrorism," and laid out hefty sentences and fines for any infringement. The law applies to anyone who "intentionally damages or causes the loss of any property" of an "animal enterprise" (research facilities, pet stores, breeders, zoos, rodeos, circuses, furriers, animal shelters, and the like), or who causes an *economic loss* of any kind. The AEPA defines an "animal rights or ecological terrorist organization" as "two or more persons organized for the purpose of supporting any politically motivated activity intended to obstruct or deter any person from participating in any activity involving animals or an activity involving natural resources." The act criminalizes actions that obstruct "any lawful activity involving the use of natural resources with an economic value."

Like the category of "domestic terrorism" that is a keystone in the USA PATRIOT Act attack on civil liberties, the frightening thing about the AEPA is its strategic vagueness that subsumes any and every form of protest and demonstration against exploitative industries to a criminal act, specifically, to a *terrorist* act. Thus, the actions of two or more people can be labeled terrorist if they leaflet a circus, protest an experimental lab, block a road to protect a forest, do a tree-sit, or block the doors of a fur store. Since, under the purview of the AEPA, any action that interferes with the profits and operations of animal and environmental industries, even boycotts and whistle-blowing could be criminalized and denounced as terrorism. On the sweeping interpretations of such legislation, Martin Luther King, Mahatma Gandhi, and Cesar Chavez would today be vilified and imprisoned as terrorists, since the intent of their principled boycott campaigns was precisely to cause "economic damage" to unethical businesses. And since the AETA, like the legal system in general, classifies animals as "property," their "theft" (read: *liberation*) is unequivocally defined as a terrorist offense.

There already are laws against sabotage and property destruction, so isn't the AEPA just a redundant piece of legislation? No—not once [one] understands its hidden agenda which strikes at the heart of the Bill of Rights. The real purpose of the AEPA is to protect animal and earth exploitation industries from protest and criticism, not property destruction and "terrorism." The AEPA redefines vandalism as ecoterrorism, petty lawbreakers as societal menaces, protestors and demonstrators as domestic terrorists, and threats to their blood money as threats to national security. Powerful economic and lobbying forces, they seek immunity from criticism, to intimidate anyone contemplating protest against them, and to dispatch their opponents to prison.

Free Speech on Trial: The SHAC 7

Hovering over activists' heads like the sword of Damocles for over a decade, the AEPA dropped in March, 2006, with the persecution and conviction of seven members of a direct action group dedicated to closing down the world's largest animal-testing company, Huntingdon Life Sciences (HLS). Exercising their First Amendment rights, activists from the Stop Huntingdon Animal Cruelty (SHAC) campaign ran a completely legal and highly effective campaign against HLS, driving them to the brink of bankruptcy. Since 1999, SHAC activists in the UK and US have waged an aggressive direct action campaign against HLS, notorious for extreme animal abuse (torturing and killing 500 animals a day) and manipulated research data. SHAC roared onto the historical stage by combining a shrewd knowledge of the law, no nonsense direct action tactics, and a singular focus on one corporation that represents the evils of the entire vivisection industry. From email and phone blockades to raucous home demonstrations, SHACtivists have attacked HLS and pressured over 100 companies to abandon financial ties to the vivisection firm. By 2001, the SHAC movement drove down HLS stock values from $15/share to less than $1/share. Smelling profit emanating from animal bloodshed, investment banking firm Stephens Inc. stepped in to save HLS from bankruptcy. But, as happened to so many companies before them, eventually Stephens too could not withstand the intense political heat and so fled the SHAC kitchen. Today, as HLS struggles for solvency, SHAC predicts its imminent demise.

Growing increasingly powerful through high-pressure tactics that take the fight to HLS and their supporters rather than to corrupt legislatures, the SHAC movement poses a clear and present danger to animal exploitation industries and the state that serves them. Staggered and driven into the ropes, it was certain that SHAC's opponents would fight back. Throwing futile jabs here and there, the vivisection industry and the state recently teamed up to mount a major counterattack.

Alarmed indeed by the new form of animal rights militancy, HLS and the biomedical research lobby commanded special sessions with Congress to ban SHAC campaigns. On May 26, 2004, a police dragnet rounded up seven prominent animal rights activists in New Jersey, New York, Washington, and California. Hordes of agents from the FBI, Secret Service, and other law agencies stormed into the activists' homes at the crack of dawn, guns drawn and helicopters hovering above. Handcuffing those struggling for a better world, the state claimed another victory in its phony "war against terror." Using the AEPA, HLS successfully prosecuted the "SHAC 7," who currently are serving prison sentences up to six years.

After the SHAC 7 conviction, David Martosko, the noxious research director of the Center for Consumer Freedom and a fierce opponent of animal rights, joyously declared: "This is just the starting gun." Indeed, corporations and legislators continue to press for even stronger laws against animal rights and environmental activism, as the Bush administration encloses the nation within a vast web of surveillance and a militarized garrison.

In September 2006, the US senate unanimously passed a new version of the AEPA (S3990), significantly renamed the "Animal Enterprise *Terrorism* Act" (AETA). To prevent critical discussion, the Senate fast-tracked the bill without hearings or debate, and just before adjourning for the election recess. In November 2006, the House approved the bill (HR 4239), and President Bush obligingly signed it into law. Beyond the portentous change in name, the new and improved version extends the range of legal prosecution of activists, updates the law to cover Internet campaigns, and enforces stiffer penalties for "terrorist" actions. Created to stop the effectiveness of the SHAC-style tactics that biomedical companies had habitually complained about to Congress, the AETA makes it a criminal offense to interfere not only with so-called "animal enterprises" directly, but also with third-party organizations such as insurance companies, law firms, and investment houses that do business with them.

Thus, the Senate version of the bill expands the law to include "any property of a person or entity having a connection to, relationship with, or transactions with an animal enterprise." The chain of relations, like the application of the law, extends possibly to the point of infinity. As journalist Will Potter notes, "The clause broadens the scope of legislation that is already overly broad." This problem is compounded further with additional vague concepts such as criminalize actions that create "reasonable fear" in the targets of protest, making actions like peaceful home demonstrations likely candidates for "ecoterrorism."

As the Equal Justice Alliance aptly summarizes the main problems with the AETA:

- "It is excessively broad and vague.
- It imposes disproportionately harsh penalties.
- It effectively brands animal advocates as 'terrorists' and denies them equal protection.

- It effectively brands civil disobedience as 'terrorism' and imposes severe penalties.
- It has a chilling effect on all forms of protest by endangering free speech and assembly.
- It interferes with investigation of animal enterprises that violate federal laws.
- It detracts from prosecution of real terrorism against the American people."

ACLU Betrayal

A sole voice of dissent in Congress, Representative Dennis Kucinich (D-Ohio) stated that the bill compromises civil rights and threatens to "chill" free speech. Virtually alone in examining the issue from the perspective of the victims rather than victimizers, Kucinich said: "Just as we need to protect people's right to conduct their work without fear of assault, so too this Congress has yet to address some fundamental ethical principles with respect to animals. How should animals be treated humanely? This is a debate that hasn't come here."

One of the most unfortunate aspects of the passing of this bill was the failure of the American Civil Liberties Union to challenge it. The ACLU did indeed write a letter to Congress about the passing of the AETA, to caution against conflating illegal and legal protest, but the organization failed to challenge the real terrorism perpetuated by animal and earth exploitation industries, and ultimately consented to their worldview and validity.

In an October 30, 2006, letter to Chairman of the House Judiciary Committee F. James Sensenbrenner and Ranking Member John Conyers, the ACLU writes that it "does not oppose this bill, but believes that these minor changes are necessary to make the bill less likely to chill or threaten freedom of speech." Beyond proposed semantic clarifications, the ACLU mainly warns against broadening the law to include legal activities such as boycotts: "Legitimate expressive activity may result in economic damage. . . . Care must therefore be taken in penalizing economic damage to avoid infringing upon legitimate activity."

Thus, unlike dozens of animal protection groups who adamantly reject the AETA *en toto,* the ACLU "does not oppose the bill." In agreement with corporate interests, the ACLU assures the government it "does not condone violence or threats." It thereby dodges the complex question of the legitimacy of sabotage against exploitative industries. The ACLU uncritically accepts (1) the corporate–state definition of "violence" as intentional harm to *property,* (2) the legal definition of animals as "property," and (3) the use of the T-word to demonize animal liberationists rather than animal exploiters. Ultimately, the ACLU sides with the government against activists involved in illegal forms of liberation or sabotage, a problematic alliance in times of global ecocide. The ACLU thereby defends *the property rights* of industries to torture and slaughter billions of animals over the *moral rights* of animals to bodily integrity and a life free from exploitation and gratuitous violence.

The ACLU failed to ask the tough questions journalist Will Potter raised during his May 23, 2006 testimony before the House Committee holding a hearing on the AETA, and to follow Potter in identifying key inconsistencies in bill. Does the ACLU really think that their proposed modifications would be adequate to guarantee that the AETA doesn't trample on legal rights to protest? Are they completely ignorant and indifferent to the fact that the AEPA was just used to send the SHAC 7 to jail for the crime of protesting fraudulent research and heinous killing? And just where was the ACLU during the SHAC 7 trial, one of the most significant First Amendment cases in recent history? Why does the ACLU only recognize violations of the Constitution against human rights advocates? Do they think that animal rights activists are not citizens? Do they not recognize that tyrannical measures used against animal advocates today will be used against all citizens tomorrow? How can the world's premier civil rights institution [be] blatantly speciesist and bigoted toward animals? *Why will they come to the defense of the Ku Klux Klan but not the SHAC 7?* The ACLU's silence in the face of persecution of animal rights activists unfortunately is typical of most civil rights organizations that are too bigoted and myopic to grasp the implications of state repression of animal rights activists for human rights activists and all forms of dissent.

Animal Liberation as a New Social Movement

Corporate exploiters and Congress have taken the US down a perilous slippery slope, where it becomes difficult to distinguish between illegal and legal forms of dissent, between civil disobedience and terrorism, between PETA and Al Qaeda, and between liberating chickens from a factory farm and flying passenger planes into skyscrapers. The state protects the corporate exploiters who pull their purse strings and stuff their pockets with favors and cash.

The right to free speech ends as soon as you begin to exercise it. As the politics of nature—the struggle for liberation of animals and the earth—is the most dynamic fight today, one that poses a serious threat to corporate interests, animal and earth liberationists are under ferocious attack. The growing effectiveness of direct action anti-vivisection struggles will inevitably bring a reactionary and retaliatory response by the corporate–state complex to crack down on democratic political freedoms to protest, as well as new Draconian laws that represent a concerted effort by power brokers to crush the movement for animal liberation.

In the "home of the brave, land of the free," activists are followed by federal agents; their phone conversations and computer activity [are] monitored, their homes are raided, they are forced to testify before grand juries and pressured to "name names," they are targets of federal round ups, they are jailed for exercising constitutionally protected rights and liberties. Saboteurs receive stiffer prison sentences than rapists, bank robbers, and murderers.

There has never been freedom of speech or action in the US, but in the post-9/11 climate, where the USA PATRIOT Act is the law of the land, not the Constitution and Bill of Rights, activists are demonized as terrorists—not just the Animal Liberation Front (ALF), Earth Liberation Front (ELF), and SHAC, but also completely legal and peaceful groups like Food Not Bombs and vegan outreach organizations.

The massive police resources of the US state are being used far more to thwart domestic dissent than to improve homeland insecurity. While Big Brother is obsessed with the email, conversations, and meetings of people who know a thing or two about the duties of citizenship, the airlines, railways, subways, city centers, and nuclear power plants remain completely vulnerable to an attack, which, according to the elites, is imminent.

The contemporary animal liberation movement is an *extension of the new social movements,* and as such issues "post-materialist" demands that are not about higher wages but the end to hierarchy and violence, and a new relation with the natural world.

Second, it is a *postindustrial movement,* operating within a global postindustrial society where the primary aspects of the economy no longer center on processing of physical materials as much as information, knowledge, science, and research. Transnational corporations such as Monsanto, pharmaceutical industries such as GlaxoSmithKline, AstraZeneca, Novartis, and Pfizer, and drug testing corporations such as Huntingdon Life Sciences show the importance of science and research for the postindustrial economy, and thus the relevance of the animal liberation movement.

This movement also is an *anti-globalization* movement in that the corporations it attacks often are transnational and global in scope, part of what I call the Global Vivisection Complex (GVC). The GVC is comprised of pharmaceutical industries, biotechnology industries, medical research industries, universities, and testing laboratories, all using animal experimentation to test and market their drugs. As animals are the gas and oil for these corporate science machines, the animal liberation movement has disrupted corporate supply chains, thwarted laboratory procedures, liberated captive slaves, and attacked the legitimacy of biomedical research as an effective scientific paradigm.

Fourth, the animal liberation movement is an *abolitionist movement,* seeking empty cages not bigger cages, demanding rights not "humane treatment" of the slaves, opposing the greatest institution of domination and slavery ever created—the empire of human supremacy over millions of species and billions of animal slaves.

To an important degree, the historical and socioeconomic context for the emergence of the animal advocacy movement (in all its diverse tendencies and aspects) is the industrialization of animal exploitation and killing. This is dramatically evident with the growth of slaughterhouses at the turn of the 20th century, the emergence and globalization of factory farming after World War II, and the subsequent growth of research capital and animal experimentation. To this, one would have to add expanding human population numbers, the social construction of carnivorous appetites, and the rise of fast food industries which demand the exploitation and massacre of ever-growing numbers of animals, now in the tens of billions on a global scale. Along with other horrors and modes of animal exploitation, the industrialization, mechanization, and globalization of animal exploitation called into being an increasingly broad, growing, and powerful animal liberation movement.

Animal liberation builds on the great abolitionist struggle of past centuries and is the abolitionist movement of our day. Animal liberationists are waging war against the oldest and last form of slavery to be formally abolished—the exploitation of nonhuman animals. Just as the modern economy of Europe, the British colonies in America, and the United States after the Revolutionary War were once entirely dependent on the trafficking in human slaves, so now the current global economy would crash if all animal slaves were freed from every lab, cage and other mode of exploitation. Animal liberation is in fact the anti-slavery movement of the present age and its moral and economic ramifications are as world-shaking, possible more so, than the abolition of the human slavery movement (which of course itself still exists in some sectors of the world in the form of sweatshops, child sex slavery, forced female prostitution, and the like).

The animal liberation movement is a profound threat to the corporate–state complex and hierarchical society in two ways.

First, it is a serious economic threat, as the planetary capitalist system thrives off animal exploitation with the meat/dairy and biomedical research industries. In the UK, for instance, where the animal rights movement has been particularly effective, drug-makers are the third most important contributor to the economy after power generation and oil industries. The animal rights movement has emerged as a powerful anti-capitalist and anti-(corporate) globalization force in its ability to monkeywrench the planetary vivisection machine and challenge transnational corporations such as HLS, GlaxoSmithKline, and Novartis.

Second, the animal rights movement is a potent ideological and psychological threat. The fight for animal liberation demands radical transformations in the habits, practices, values, and mindset of all human beings as it also entails a fundamental restructuring of social institutions and economic systems predicated on exploitative practices. The philosophy of animal liberation assaults the identities and worldviews that portray humans as conquering Lords and Masters of nature, and it requires entirely new ways of relating to animals and the earth. Animal liberation is a direct attack on the power human beings—whether in premodern or modern, non-Western or Western societies—have claimed over animals, since at least the dawn of agricultural society ten thousand years ago.

Total Liberation

As the dynamics that brought about global warming, rainforest destruction, species extinction, and poisoning of communities are not reducible to any single factor or cause—be it agricultural society, the rise of states, anthropocentrism, speciesism, patriarchy, racism, colonialism, industrialism, technocracy, or capitalism—all radical groups and orientations that can effectively challenge the ideologies and institutions implicated in domination and ecological destruction have a relevant role to play in the global social-environmental struggle. While standpoints such as deep ecology, social ecology, ecofeminism, animal liberation, Black liberation, and the Earth Liberation Front are all important, none can accomplish systemic social transformation by itself. Working together, however, through a diversity of critiques and tactics that mobilize different communities, a flank of militant groups and positions can drive a battering ram into the structures of power and domination and open the door to a new future.

Although there is diversity in unity, there must also be unity in diversity. Solidarity can emerge in recognition of the fact that all forms of oppression are directly or indirectly related to the values, institutions, and *system* of global capitalism and related hierarchical structures. To be unified and effective, however, anti-capitalist and anti-imperialist alliances require mutual sharing, respectful learning, and psychological growth, such that, for instance, black liberationists, ecofeminists, and animal liberationists can help one another overcome racism, sexism, and speciesism.

The larger context for current dynamics in the animal liberation movement involves the emergence of the neoliberal project (as a response to the opening of the markets that was made necessary by the continuous expansion of transnational corporations in the post-war period) which was crucial in the elites' effort to destroy socialism and social democracy of any kind, to privatize all social structures, to gain total control of all resource markets and dwindling resources, and to snuff out all resistance. The animal rights/liberation movement has come under such intense fire because it has emerged as a threat to operations and profits of postindustrial capital (heavily rooted in research and therefore animal experimentation) and as a significant form of resistance. The transnational elite want the fire crushed before its example of resistance becomes a conflagration.

Conversely, the animal liberation movement is most effective not only as a single-issue focus to emancipate animals from human exploitation, but to join a larger resistance movement opposed to exploitation and hierarchies of any and all kinds. Clearly, SHAC and the ALF alone are not going to bring down transnational capitalism, pressuring HLS and raiding fur farms and laboratories will not themselves ignite revolutionary change, and are more rear-guard, defensive actions. The project to emancipate animals, in other words, is integrally related to the struggle to emancipate humans and the battle for a viable natural world. To the extent that the animal liberation movement grasps the big picture that links animal and human oppression struggles as one, and seeks to uncover the roots of hierarchy including that of humans over nature, they can be viewed as a profound new liberation movement that has a crucial place in the planetary struggles against injustice, oppression, exploitation, war, violence, capitalist neo-liberalism, and the destruction of the natural world and biodiversity.

Yet, given the profound relation between the human domination of animals and the crisis—social, ethical, and environmental—in the human world and its relation to the natural world, the animal liberation movement is in a unique position to articulate the importance of new relations between human and human, human and animal, and human and nature.

New social movements and Greens have failed to realize their radical potential. They have abandoned their original demands for radical social change and become integrated into capitalist structures that have eliminated "existing socialist countries" as well as social democracies within the present neoliberal globalization which has become dominant. A new revolutionary force must therefore emerge, one that will build on the achievements of classical democratic, libertarian socialist, and anarchist traditions; incorporate radical green, feminist, and indigenous struggles; synthesize animal, Earth, and human liberation standpoints; and build a global social-ecological revolution capable of abolishing transnational capitalism so that just and ecological societies can be constructed in its place.

Notes

For Feinstein's pathetic capitulation to the Green Scare and her sordid alliance with neo-McCarthyite Senator James "Global Warming Is a Myth" Inhofe (R-Okla.), see her press release. . . .

The text of the "Animal Enterprise Protection Act of 1992" is available online.

In states such as Oregon and California, related legislation has already passed which declares it a felony terrorist offense to enter any animal facility with a camera or video recorder "with the intent to defame the facility or facility's owner." See Steven Best, "It's War: The Escalating Battle Between Activists and the Corporate-State Complex," in *Terrorists or Freedom Fighters? Reflections on the Liberation of Animals* (Lantern Books, 2004), pp. 300–339 (eds. Steven Best and Anthony J. Nocella II).

For a more detailed analysis of the SHAC struggle in the context of political economy, see Steven Best and Richard Kahn, "Trial By Fire: The SHAC 7, Globalization, and the Future of Democracy," *Animal Liberation Philosophy and Policy Journal,* Volume II, Issue 2, 2004 . . .

On the SHAC 7 trial, see Steven Best and Richard Kahn, "Trial By Fire: The SHAC7, Globalization, and the Future of Democracy."

For the text of S3880, the final bill that passed in both houses, see . . .

Will Potter, "Analysis of Animal Enterprise Terrorism Act."

"Why Oppose AETA."

. . . Kucinich also challenged the AETA as being redundant and created a "specific classification" to repress legitimate dissent.

The ACLU letter to Congress is available at . . .

For a list of animal advocacy groups opposed to the AETA, see . . .

For Potter's testimony before the House Committee on the Judiciary Subcommittee on Crime, Terrorism, and Homeland Security see . . .

Steven Best is an associate professor of philosophy at the University of Texas, El Paso. His most recent book (coauthored with Anthony J. Nocella) is *Igniting a Revolution: Voices in Defense of the Earth* (AK Press, 2006). According to his website (www.drstevebest.org/), "He has come under fire for his uncompromising advocacy of 'total liberation' (humans, animals, and the earth) and has been banned from the UK for the power of his thoughts."

EXPLORING THE ISSUE

Is "Animal Rights" Just Another Excuse for Terrorism?

Critical Thinking and Reflection

1. What is the difference between the "animal rights" and the "animal welfare" movements?
2. Why must drugs be tested for safety and efficacy?
3. Should extreme forms of protest be restrained for the good of society?
4. Do all animals (including cockroaches, for instance) have rights? If not, where do we draw the line?

Is There Common Ground?

Both the animal welfare and animal rights movements are rooted in awareness of past abuses of animals. Unfortunately, animal abuse is not just in the past. It shows up far too often in the daily news.

1. Check your local paper (or favorite news site) for stories on animal abuse. They may involve puppy mills, farms, dog tracks, dog or cock fighting, and more. Discuss what is being done about these cases, and by whom (animal welfare or animal rights groups).
2. Do some animals seem more deserving of "rights" than others? Does intelligence matter? Or, how closely are they related to us? (There have been proposals to grant great apes legal rights very similar to human rights; in Spain, in 2008, such rights were actually granted; see www.time.com/time/world/article/0,8599,1824206,00.html.)
3. How is animal welfare protected in your state? (See www.animallaw.com/.)

Create Central

www.mhhe.com/createcentral

Additional Resources

P. Michael Conn and James V. Parker, *The Animal Research War* (Palgrave Macmillan, 2008).

John Hadley, "Animal Rights Extremism and the Terrorism Question," *Journal of Social Philosophy* (Fall 2009).

Manfred Liebsch, et al., "Alternatives to Animal Testing: Current Status and Future Perspectives," *Archives of Toxicology* (August 2011).

Tom Regan, *Empty Cages: Facing the Challenge of Animal Rights* (Rowman and Littlefield, 2005).

Internet References . . .

Center for Alternatives to Animal Testing

The Johns Hopkins Center for Alternatives to Animal Testing (CAAT) promotes humane science by supporting the creation, development, validation, and use of alternatives to animals in research, product safety testing, and education.

http://caat.jhsph.edu/

Americans for Medical Progress

Americans for Medical Progress (AMP) nurtures public understanding of and support for the humane, necessary and valuable use of animals in medicine.

www.amprogress.org/animal-research

Selected, Edited, and with Issue Framing Material by:
Thomas A. Easton, *Thomas College*

ISSUE

Should We Reject the "Transhumanist" Goal of the Genetically, Electronically, and Mechanically Enhanced Human Being?

YES: M. J. McNamee and S. D. Edwards, from "Transhumanism, Medical Technology, and Slippery Slopes," *Journal of Medical Ethics* (September 2006)

NO: Maxwell J. Mehlman, from "Biomedical Enhancements: Entering a New Era," *Issues in Science and Technology* (Spring 2009)

Learning Outcomes

After studying this issue, students will be able to:

- Explain what transhumanism is.
- Explain why ethicists worry about "slippery slopes."
- Discuss why some people find the idea of enhancing the human body and mind objectionable.
- Discuss whether government should subsidize technologies that hold the potential to exacerbate differences among people.

ISSUE SUMMARY

YES: M. J. McNamee and S. D. Edwards argue that the difficulty of showing that the human body *should* (rather than *can*) be enhanced in ways espoused by the transhumanists amounts to an objection to transhumanism.

NO: Maxwell J. Mehlman argues that the era of routine biomedical enhancements is coming. Since the technology cannot be banned, it must be regulated and even subsidized to ensure that it does not create an unfair society.

In the early 1970s, scientists first discovered that it was technically possible to move genes—biological material that determines a living organism's physical makeup—from one organism to another and thus (in principle) to give bacteria, plants, and animals new features and to correct genetic defects of the sort that cause many diseases, such as cystic fibrosis. Most researchers in molecular genetics were excited by the potentialities that suddenly seemed within their grasp. However, a few researchers—as well as many people outside the field—were disturbed by the idea. Among other things, they feared that we were on the verge of an era when people would be so modified that they were no longer human. Some critics were also suspicious of the researchers' motives. Andrew Kimbrell, *The Human Body Shop: The Engineering and Marketing of Life* (HarperSanFrancisco, 1993), thought the development of genetic engineering was so marked by scandal, ambition, and moral blindness that society should be deeply suspicious of its purported benefits.

Since then the idea that human beings will one day be enhanced has grown. The idea now encompasses genetic changes to cure or prevent disease and modify height, muscle strength, and cognitive capabilities, the use of chemicals to improve performance in sports, and even the incorporation in the human body of electronic and robotic elements to add senses and enhance memory, thinking abilities, strength, and a great deal more. In fact, the idea has become a movement known as transhumanism that "promotes an interdisciplinary approach to understanding and evaluating the opportunities for enhancing the human condition and the human organism opened up by the advancement of technology" (see the Humanity+ site at http://humanityplus.org/). The goal is to eliminate aging, disease, and suffering. The transhumanist vision extends to "post-humanism," when what human beings become will make present-day humans look like chimpanzees by comparison. It even includes the possibility of uploading human minds into computers! See George Dvorsky, "Better Living Through

Transhumanism," *Journal of Evolution & Technology* (September 2008).

Some people find this vision frightening. Francis Fukuyama, "Transhumanism," *Foreign Policy* (September/October 2004), has called transhumanism "the world's most dangerous idea." Critics find changing human form and capability objectionable because they believe the result is in some sense unnatural. They believe that making some people more capable will exacerbate social distinctions and put those who can afford the changes in the position of old-fashioned aristocracies. Life will be even more unfair than it is today. Tom Koch, "Enhancing Who? Enhancing What? Ethics, Bioethics, and Transhumanism," *Journal of Medicine & Philosophy* (December 2010), finds transhumanism "a new riff on the old eugenics tune," and the result must be destructive.

Michael Bess, "Icarus 2.0: A Historian's Perspective on Human Biological Enhancement," *Technology and Culture* (January 2008), finds transhumanism in essence dehumanizing: "The technologies of enhancement threaten human dignity precisely because they tempt us to think of a person as an entity that can be 'improved.' To take this step is to break down human personhood into a series of quantifiable traits—resistance to disease, intelligence, and so forth—that are subject to augmentation or alteration. The danger in doing this lies in reducing individuals to the status of products, artifacts to be modified and reshaped according to our own preferences, like any other commodity. In this act, inevitably, we risk losing touch with the quality of intrinsic value that all humans share equally, no matter what their traits may be. In this sense, the well-intentioned effort to enhance a person can result in treating them as a mere *thing*."

Josh Fischman, "A Better Life with Bionics," *National Geographic* (January 2010), describes current work in developing prostheses controlled by nerve signals from nerves that have been surgically rerouted to communicate more effectively with the artificial limb's circuitry, a clear example of "improvement" of the human being. He also discusses electronic cochlear implants and artificial retinas. An accompanying editorial comment says that "Bionics is technology at its most ingenious and humane." Among the most recent developments in this line is an electronic implant that can give the paralyzed robotic arms; see Ian Sample, "Brain Implant Allows Paralysed Woman to Control a Robot with Her Thoughts," *The Guardian* (May 16, 2012) (www.guardian.co.uk/science/2012/may/16/brain-implant-paralysed-woman-robot-thoughts).

Among those who favor transhumanism, few come through more strongly than James Hughes, executive director of the Institute for Ethics and Emerging Technologies (http://ieet.org/). He has argued vigorously that enhancement technologies such as genetic engineering offer "such good that the risks are dwarfed" and finds "faith in the potential unlimited improvability of human nature and expansion of human powers far more satisfying than a resignation to our current limits." See his "Embracing Change with All Four Arms: A Post-Humanist Defense of Genetic Engineering," *Eubios Journal of Asian and International Bioethics* (June 1996). Nicholas Agar, "Whereto Transhumanism? The Literature Reaches Critical Mass," *Hastings Center Report* (May–June 2007), finds that "transhumanism is a movement brimming with fresh ideas. Transhumanists succeed in making the intuitive appeal of posthumanity obvious even if they don't yet have the arguments to compel everybody else to accept their vision." Julian Savalescu and Nick Bostrom (a prominent founder of the transhumanism movement) provide a very positive overview in *Human Enhancement* (Oxford University Press, 2009). Susan Schneider, "Future Minds: Transhumanism, Cognitive Enhancement and the Nature of Persons," in Vardit Ravitsky, Autumn Fiester, and Arthur L. Caplan, eds., *The Penn Center Guide to Bioethics* (Springer, 2009), considers the question of whether people who have undergone extreme modifications are still the people they were before. Is personhood affected? Is the soul? "There are," she writes, "some serious issues which require working out." James Wilson, "Transhumanism and Moral Equality," *Bioethics* (October, 2007), finds that objections to transhumanism on the grounds that enhanced humans will be considered morally superior to unenhanced humans are groundless, for "once we understand the basis for human equality, it is clear that anyone who now has sufficient capacities to count as a person from the moral point of view will continue to count as one even if others are fundamentally enhanced; and it is [a mistake] to think that a creature which had even far greater capacities than an unenhanced human being should count as more than an equal from the moral point of view." David Gelles, "Immortality 2.0," *The Futurist* (January–February 2009), concludes that "skepticism of transhumanism is, arguably, natural. At the deepest level, living forever interferes with everything we understand about the world. . . . But such concerns may not matter any more." The change is already under way, and we may be underestimating how far it will go. See also Jonathan Weiner, *Long for This World: The Strange Science of Immortality* (Ecco, 2010). However, A. Rajczi, "One Danger of Biomedical Enhancements," *Bioethics* (July 2008), cautions that "By spending too much time, energy, and resources on enhancements, we could set back our pursuit of our deepest goals such as living happily and leading ethical lives." Philippe Verdoux, "Transhumanism, Progress and the Future," *Journal of Evolution & Technology* (July 2009), finds pursuing the transhumanist dream the safest route into the future. Philip Hefner, "The Animal that Aspires to be an Angel: The Challenge of Transhumanism," *Dialog: A Journal of Theology* (Summer 2009), finds that transhumanism "represents a fundamental challenge to our understanding of human nature, and in particular [with] what God has created us to become." Joanna Zylinska, "Playing God, Playing Adam: The Politics and Ethics of Enhancement," *Journal of Bioethical Inquiry* (June 2010), takes a different view of humanity's deepest goals and nature, for humanity coevolves with technology.

Maxwell J. Mehlman examines the future implications in *Transhumanist Dreams and Dystopian Nightmares: The Promise and Peril of Genetic Engineering* (Johns Hopkins University Press, 2012).

One way in which the change is already upon us appears in the realm of sports. Steven Kotler, "Juicing 3.0," *Popular Science* (August 2008), notes that the use by athletes of many enhancement techniques—reaction time stimulants, hormones that affect muscle, gene replacement, and even mechanical replacements for missing limbs—are going to become commonplace in the next few years. It may be necessary to accept enhancements as a legitimate part of athletics and other realms of endeavor. See Ivo Van Hilvoorde and Laurens Landeweerd, "Enhancing Disabilities: Transhumanism under the Veil of Inclusion?" *Disability & Rehabilitation* (December 2010), and Brendan Burkett, Mike McNamee, and Wolfgand Potthast, "Shifting Boundaries in Sports Technology and Disability: Equal Rights or Unfair Advantage in the Case of Oscar Pistorius?" *Disability & Society* (August 2011).

In the YES selection, M. J. McNamee and S. D. Edwards discuss the idea that even to start on the transhumanist agenda is to set humanity on a "slippery slope" leading to disaster. They argue that of the several types of slippery slope, the one most threatening to transhumanism is the "arbitrary" slippery slope, meaning that the progression from the first change to the last is not based on any sense of the moral good, but only on subjective preference. They argue that this poses a challenge to transhumanists, to show that the changes they embrace *should* be embraced rather than just *can* be embraced. In the NO selection, Professor of Bioethics Maxwell J. Mehlman argues that the era of routine biomedical enhancements is coming. Since the technology cannot be banned, it must be regulated and even subsidized to ensure that it does not create an unfair society.

YES

M. J. McNamee and S. D. Edwards

Transhumanism, Medical Technology, and Slippery Slopes

No less a figure than Francis Fukuyama recently labelled transhumanism as "the world's most dangerous idea." Such an eye-catching condemnation almost certainly denotes an issue worthy of serious consideration, especially given the centrality of biomedical technology to its aims. In this article, we consider transhumanism as an ideology that seeks to evangelise its human-enhancing aims. Given that transhumanism covers a broad range of ideas, we distinguish moderate conceptions from strong ones and find the strong conceptions more problematic than the moderate ones. We also offer a critique of Boström's position published in this journal. We discuss various forms of slippery slope arguments that may be used for and against transhumanism and highlight one particular criticism, moral arbitrariness, which undermines both forms of transhumanism.

What Is Transhumanism?

At the beginning of the 21st century, we find ourselves in strange times; facts and fantasy find their way together in ethics, medicine and philosophy journals and websites. Key sites of contestation include the very idea of human nature, the place of embodiment within medical ethics and, more specifically, the systematic reflections on the place of medical and other technologies in conceptions of the good life. A reflection of this situation is captured by Dyens who writes,

> What we are witnessing today is the very convergence of environments, systems, bodies, and ontology toward and into the intelligent matter. We can no longer speak of the human condition or even of the posthuman condition. We must now refer to the intelligent condition.

We wish to evaluate the contents of such dialogue and to discuss, if not the death of human nature, then at least its dislocation and derogation in the thinkers who label themselves transhumanists.

One difficulty for critics of transhumanism is that a wide range of views fall under its label. Not merely are there idiosyncrasies of individual academics, but there does not seem to exist an absolutely agreed on definition of transhumanism. One can find not only substantial differences between key authors and the disparate disciplinary nuances of their exhortations, but also subtle variations of its chief representatives in the offerings of people. It is to be expected that any ideology transforms over time and not least of all in response to internal and external criticism. Yet, the transhumanism critic faces a further problem of identifying a robust target that stays still sufficiently long to locate it properly in these web-driven days without constructing a "straw man" to knock over with the slightest philosophical breeze. For the purposes of targeting a sufficiently substantial target, we identify the writings of one of its clearest and intellectually robust proponents, the Oxford philosopher and cofounder of the World Transhumanist Association, Nick Boström, who has written recently in these pages of transhumanism's desire to make good the "half-baked" project that is human nature.

Before specifically evaluating Boström's position, it is best first to offer a global definition for transhumanism and then to locate it among the range of views that fall under the heading. One of the most celebrated advocates of transhumanism is Max More, whose website reads "no more gods, nor more faith, no more timid holding back. The future belongs to posthumanity." We will have a clearer idea then of the kinds of position transhumanism stands in direct opposition to. Specifically, More asserts,

> "Transhumanism" is a blanket term given to the school of thought that refuses to accept traditional human limitations such as death, disease and other biological frailties. Transhumans are typically interested in a variety of futurist topics, including space migration, mind uploading and cryonic suspension. Transhumans are also extremely interested in more immediate subjects such as bio- and nano-technology, computers and neurology. Transhumans deplore the standard paradigms that attempt to render our world comfortable at the sake of human fulfilment.

Strong transhumanism advocates see themselves engaged in a project, the purpose of which is to overcome the limits of human nature. Whether this is the foundational claim, or merely the central claim, is not clear. These limitations—one may describe them simply as features of human nature, as the idea of labelling them as limitations is itself to take up a negative stance towards them—concern appearance, human sensory capacities, intelligence, lifespan and vulnerability to harm. According to the extreme transhumanism programme, technology can be used to vastly enhance a person's intelligence; to tailor their appearance to what they desire; to lengthen their lifespan, perhaps to immortality; and to reduce vastly their vulnerability to harm. This can be done by exploitation of various kinds of technology, including genetic engineering, cybernetics, computation and nanotechnology. Whether technology will continue to progress sufficiently, and sufficiently predictably, is of course quite another matter.

Advocates of transhumanism argue that recruitment or deployment of these various types of technology can produce people who are intelligent and immortal, but who are not members of the species *Homo sapiens*. Their species type will be ambiguous—for example, if they are cyborgs (part human, part machine)—or, if they are wholly machines, they will lack any common genetic features with human beings. A legion of labels covers this possibility; we find in Dyen's recently translated book a variety of cultural bodies, perhaps the most extreme being cyberpunks:

> . . . a profound misalignment between existence and its manifestation. This misalignment produces bodies so transformed, so dissociated, and so asynchronized, that their only outcome is gross mutation. Cyberpunk bodies are horrible, strange and mysterious (think of *Alien, Robocop, Terminator*, etc.), for they have no real attachment to any biological structure.

Perhaps a reasonable claim is encapsulated in the idea that such entities will be posthuman. The extent to which posthuman might be synonymous with transhumanism is not clear. Extreme transhumanists strongly support such developments.

At the other end of transhumanism is a much less radical project, which is simply the project to use technology to enhance human characteristics—for example, beauty, lifespan and resistance to disease. In this less extreme project, there is no necessary aspiration to shed human nature or human genetic constitution, just to augment it with technology where possible and where desired by the person.

Who Is for Transhumanism?

At present it seems to be a movement based mostly in North America, although there are some adherents from the UK. Among its most intellectually sophisticated proponents is Nick Boström. Perhaps the most outspoken supporters of transhumanism are people who see it simply as an issue of free choice. It may simply be the case that moderate transhumanists are libertarians at the core. In that case, transhumanism merely supplies an overt technological dimension to libertarianism. If certain technological developments are possible, which they as competent choosers desire, then they should not be prevented from acquiring the technologically driven enhancements they desire. One obvious line of criticism here may be in relation to the inequality that necessarily arises with respect to scarce goods and services distributed by market mechanisms. We will elaborate this point in the Transhumanism and slippery slopes section.

So, one group of people for the transhumanism project sees it simply as a way of improving their own life by their own standards of what counts as an improvement. For example, they may choose to purchase an intervention, which will make them more intelligent or even extend their life by 200 years. (Of course it is not self-evident that everyone would regard this as an improvement.) A less vociferous group sees the transhumanism project as not so much bound to the expansion of autonomy (notwithstanding our criticism that will necessarily be effected only in the sphere of economic consumer choice) as one that has the potential to improve the quality of life for humans in general. For this group, the relationship between transhumanism and the general good is what makes transhumanism worthy of support. For the other group, the worth of transhumanism is in its connection with their own conception of what is good for them, with the extension of their personal life choices.

What Can Be Said in Its Favour?

Of the many points for transhumanism, we note three. Firstly, transhumanism seems to facilitate two aims that have commanded much support. The use of technology to improve humans is something we pretty much take for granted. Much good has been achieved with low-level technology in the promotion of public health. The construction of sewage systems, clean water supplies, etc, is all work to facilitate this aim and is surely good work, work which aims at, and in this case achieves, a good. Moreover, a large portion of the modern biomedical enterprise is another example of a project that aims at generating this good too.

Secondly, proponents of transhumanism say it presents an opportunity to plan the future development of human beings, the species *Homo sapiens*. Instead of this being left to the evolutionary process and its exploitation of random mutations, transhumanism presents a hitherto unavailable option: tailoring the development of human beings to an ideal blueprint. Precisely whose ideal gets blueprinted is a point that we deal with later.

Thirdly, in the spirit of work in ethics that makes use of a technical idea of personhood, the view that moral status is independent of membership of a particular species (or indeed any biological species), transhumanism presents a way in which moral status can be shown to be bound to intellectual capacity rather than to human embodiment as such or human vulnerability in the capacity of embodiment.

What Can Be Said Against It?

Critics point to consequences of transhumanism, which they find unpalatable. One possible consequence feared by some commentators is that, in effect, transhumanism will lead to the existence of two distinct types of being, the human and the posthuman. The human may be incapable of breeding with the posthuman and will be seen as having a much lower moral standing. Given that, as Buchanan *et al.* note, much moral progress, in the West at least, is founded on the category of the human in terms of rights claims, if we no longer have a common humanity, what rights, if any, ought to be enjoyed by transhumans? This can be viewed either as a criticism (we poor humans are no longer at the top of the evolutionary tree) or simply as a critical concern that invites further argumentation. We shall return to this idea in the final section, by way of identifying a deeper problem with the open-endedness of transhumanism that builds on this recognition.

In the same vein, critics may argue that transhumanism will increase inequalities between the rich and the poor. The rich can afford to make use of transhumanism, but the poor will not be able to. Indeed, we may come to think of such people as deficient, failing to achieve a new heightened level of normal functioning. In the opposing direction, critical observers may say that transhumanism is, in reality, an irrelevance, as very few will be able to use the technological developments even if they ever manifest themselves. A further possibility is that transhumanism could lead to the extinction of humans and posthumans, for things are just as likely to turn out for the worse as for the better (e.g., those for precautionary principle).

One of the deeper philosophical objections comes from a very traditional source. Like all such utopian visions, transhumanism rests on some conception of good. So just as humanism is founded on the idea that humans are the measure of all things and that their fulfilment is to be found in the powers of reason extolled and extended in culture and education, so too transhumanism has a vision of the good, albeit one loosely shared. For one group of transhumanists, the good is the expansion of personal choice. Given that autonomy is so widely valued, why not remove the barriers to enhanced autonomy by various technological interventions? Theological critics especially, but not exclusively, object to what they see as the imperialising of autonomy. Elshtain lists the three c's: choice, consent and control. These, she asserts, are the dominant motifs of modern American culture. And there is, of course, an army of communitarians ready to provide support in general moral and political matters to this line of criticism. One extension of this line of transhumanism thinking is to align the valorisation of autonomy with economic rationality, for we may as well be motivated by economic concerns as by moral ones where the market is concerned. As noted earlier, only a small minority may be able to access this technology (despite Boström's naive disclaimer for democratic transhumanism), so the technology necessary for transhumanist transformations is unlikely to be prioritised in the context of artificially scarce public health resources. One other population attracted to transhumanism will be the elite sports world, fuelled by the media commercialisation complex—where mere mortals will get no more than a glimpse of the transhuman in competitive physical contexts. There may be something of a double-binding character to this consumerism. The poor, at once removed from the possibility of such augmentation, pay (per view) for the pleasure of their envy.

If we argue against the idea that the good cannot be equated with what people choose simpliciter, it does not follow that we need to reject the requisite medical technology outright. Against the more moderate transhumanists, who see transhumanism as an opportunity to enhance the general quality of life for humans, it is nevertheless true that their position presupposes some conception of the good. What kind of traits is best engineered into humans: disease resistance or parabolic hearing? And unsurprisingly, transhumanists disagree about precisely what "objective goods" to select for installation into humans or posthumans.

Some radical critics of transhumanism see it as a threat to morality itself. This is because they see morality as necessarily connected to the kind of vulnerability that accompanies human nature. Think of the idea of human rights and the power this has had in voicing concern about the plight of especially vulnerable human beings. As noted earlier a transhumanist may be thought to be beyond humanity and as neither enjoying its rights nor its obligations. Why would a transhuman be moved by appeals to human solidarity? Once the prospect of posthumanism emerges, the whole of morality is thus threatened because the existence of human nature itself is under threat.

One further objection voiced by Habermas is that interfering with the process of human conception, and by implication human constitution, deprives humans of the "naturalness which so far has been a part of the taken-for-granted background of our self-understanding as a species" and "Getting used to having human life biotechnologically at the disposal of our contingent preferences cannot help but change our normative self-understanding."

On this account, our self-understanding would include, for example, our essential vulnerability to disease, ageing and death. Suppose the strong transhumanism project is realised. We are no longer thus vulnerable: immortality is a real prospect. Nevertheless, conceptual caution must be exercised here—even transhumanists will be susceptible in the manner that Hobbes noted. Even the strongest are vulnerable in their sleep. But the kind of vulnerability transhumanism seeks to overcome is of the internal kind (not Hobbes's external threats). We are reminded of Woody Allen's famous remark that he wanted to become immortal, not by doing great deeds but simply by not dying. This will result in a radical change in our self-understanding, which has inescapably normative elements to it that need to be challenged. Most radically, this change in self-understanding may take the form of a change in what we view as a good life. Hitherto a human life, this would have been assumed to be finite. Transhumanists suggest that even now this may change with appropriate technology and the "right" motivation.

Do the changes in self-understanding presented by transhumanists (and genetic manipulation) necessarily have to represent a change for the worse? As discussed earlier, it may be that the technology that generates the possibility of transhumanism can be used for the good of humans—for example, to promote immunity to disease or to increase quality of life. Is there really an intrinsic connection between acquisition of the capacity to bring about transhumanism and moral decline? Perhaps Habermas's point is that moral decline is simply more likely to occur once radical enhancement technologies are adopted as a practice that is not intrinsically evil or morally objectionable. But how can this be known in advance? This raises the spectre of slippery slope arguments.

But before we discuss such slopes, let us note that the kind of approach (whether characterised as closed-minded or sceptical) Boström seems to dislike is one he calls speculative. He dismisses as speculative the idea that offspring may think themselves lesser beings, commodifications of their parents' egoistic desires (or some such). None the less, having pointed out the lack of epistemological standing of such speculation, he invites us to his own apparently more congenial position:

> We might speculate, instead, that germ-line enhancements will lead to more love and parental dedication. Some mothers and fathers might find it easier to love a child who, thanks to enhancements, is bright, beautiful, healthy, and happy. The practice of germ-line enhancement might lead to better treatment of people with disabilities, because a general demystification of the genetic contributions to human traits could make it clearer that people with disabilities are not to blame for their disabilities and a decreased incidence of some disabilities could lead to more assistance being available for the remaining affected people to enable them to live full, unrestricted lives through various technological and social supports. Speculating about possible psychological or cultural effects of germ-line engineering can therefore cut both ways. Good consequences no less than bad ones are possible. In the absence of sound arguments for the view that the negative consequences would predominate, such speculations provide no reason against moving forward with the technology. Ruminations over hypothetical side effects may serve to make us aware of things that could go wrong so that we can be on the lookout for untoward developments. By being aware of the perils in advance, we will be in a better position to take preventive countermeasures.

Following Boström's speculation then, what grounds for hope exist? Beyond speculation, what kinds of arguments does Boström offer? Well, most people may think that the burden of proof should fall to the transhumanists. Not so, according to Boström. Assuming the likely enormous benefits, he turns the tables on this intuition—not by argument but by skilful rhetorical speculation. We quote for accuracy of representation (emphasis added):

> Only after a fair comparison of the risks with the likely positive consequences can any conclusion based on a cost-benefit analysis be reached. In the case of germ-line enhancements, the potential gains are enormous. Only rarely, however, are the potential gains discussed, perhaps because they are too obvious to be of much theoretical interest. By contrast, uncovering subtle and non-trivial ways in which manipulating our genome could undermine deep values is philosophically a lot more challenging. But if we think about it, we recognize that the promise of genetic enhancements is anything but insignificant. Being free from severe genetic diseases would be good, as would having a mind that can learn more quickly, or having a more robust immune system. Healthier, wittier, happier people may be able to reach new levels culturally. To achieve a significant enhancement of human capacities would be to embark on the transhuman journey of exploration of some of the modes of being that are not accessible to us as we are currently constituted, possibly to discover and to instantiate important new values. On an even more basic level, genetic engineering holds great potential for alleviating unnecessary human suffering. Every day that the introduction of effective human genetic enhancement is delayed is a day of lost individual and cultural potential, and a day of torment for many unfortunate sufferers of diseases that could have been prevented. Seen in this light, *proponents of a ban or a moratorium on human genetic modification must take on a heavy burden of proof* in order to have the balance of reason tilt in their favor.

Now one way in which such a balance of reason may be had is in the idea of a slippery slope argument. We now turn to that.

Transhumanism and Slippery Slopes

A proper assessment of transhumanism requires consideration of the objection that acceptance of the main claims of transhumanism will place us on a slippery slope. Yet, paradoxically, both proponents and detractors of transhumanism may exploit slippery slope arguments in support of their position. It is necessary therefore to set out the various arguments that fall under this title so that we can better characterise arguments for and against transhumanism. We shall therefore examine three such attempts but argue that the arbitrary slippery slope may undermine all versions of transhumanists, although not every enhancement proposed by them.

Schauer offers the following essentialist analysis of slippery slope arguments. A "pure" slippery slope is one where a "particular act, seemingly innocuous when taken in isolation, may yet lead to a future host of similar but increasingly pernicious events." Abortion and euthanasia are classic candidates for slippery slope arguments in public discussion and policy making. Against this, however, there is no reason to suppose that the future events (acts or policies) down the slope need to display similarities—indeed we may propose that they will lead to a whole range of different, although equally unwished for, consequences. The vast array of enhancements proposed by transhumanists would not be captured under this conception of a slippery slope because of their heterogeneity. Moreover, as Sternglantz notes, Schauer undermines his case when arguing that greater linguistic precision undermines the slippery slope and that indirect consequences often bolster slippery slope arguments. It is as if the slippery slopes would cease in a world with greater linguistic precision or when applied only to direct consequences. These views do not find support in the later literature. Schauer does, however, identify three non-slippery slope arguments where the advocate's aim is (a) to show that the bottom of a proposed slope has been arrived at; (b) to show that a principle is excessively broad; (c) to highlight how granting authority to X will make it more likely that an undesirable outcome will be achieved. Clearly (a) cannot properly be called a slippery slope argument in itself, while (b) and (c) often have some role in slippery slope arguments.

The excessive breadth principle can be subsumed under Bernard Williams's distinction between slippery slope arguments with (a) horrible results and (b) arbitrary results. According to Williams, the nature of the bottom of the slope allows us to determine which category a particular argument falls under. Clearly, the most common form is the slippery slope to a horrible result argument. Walton goes further in distinguishing three types: (a) thin end of the wedge or precedent arguments; (b) Sorites arguments; and (c) domino-effect arguments. Importantly, these arguments may be used both by antagonists and also by advocates of transhumanism. We shall consider the advocates of transhumanism first.

In the thin end of the wedge slippery slopes, allowing P will set a precedent that will allow further precedents (Pn) taken to an unspecified problematic terminus. Is it necessary that the end point has to be bad? Of course this is the typical linguistic meaning of the phrase "slippery slopes." Nevertheless, we may turn the tables here and argue that [the] slopes may be viewed positively too. Perhaps a new phrase will be required to capture ineluctable slides (ascents?) to such end points. This would be somewhat analogous to the ideas of vicious and virtuous cycles. So transhumanists could argue that, once the artificial generation of life through technologies of in vitro fertilisation was thought permissible, the slope was foreseeable, and transhumanists are doing no more than extending that life-creating and fashioning impulse.

In Sorites arguments, the inability to draw clear distinctions has the effect that allowing P will not allow us to consistently deny Pn. This slope follows the form of the Sorites paradox, where taking a grain of sand from a heap does not prevent our recognising or describing the heap as such, even though it is not identical with its former state. At the heart of the problem with such arguments is the idea of conceptual vagueness. Yet the logical distinctions used by philosophers are often inapplicable in the real world. Transhumanists may well seize on this vagueness and apply a Sorites argument as follows: as therapeutic interventions are currently morally permissible, and there is no clear distinction between treatment and enhancement, enhancement interventions are morally permissible too. They may ask whether we can really distinguish categorically between the added functionality of certain prosthetic devices and sonar senses.

In domino-effect arguments, the domino conception of the slippery slope, we have what others often refer to as a causal slippery slope. Once P is allowed, a causal chain will be effected allowing Pn and so on to follow, which will precipitate increasingly bad consequences.

In what ways can slippery slope arguments be used against transhumanism? What is wrong with transhumanism? Or, better, is there a point at which we can say transhumanism is objectionable? One particular strategy adopted by proponents of transhumanism falls clearly under the aspect of the thin end of the wedge conception of the slippery slope. Although some aspects of their ideology seem aimed at unqualified goods, there seems to be no limit to the aspirations of transhumanism as they cite the powers of other animals and substances as potential modifications for the transhumanist. Although we can admire the sonic capacities of the bat, the elastic strength of lizards' tongues and the endurability of Kevlar in contrast with traditional construction materials used in the body, their transplantation into humans is, to coin Kass's celebrated label, "repugnant."

Although not all transhumanists would support such extreme enhancements (if that is indeed what they are), less radical advocates use justifications that are based on therapeutic lines up front with the more Promethean aims less explicitly advertised. We can find many examples of this manoeuvre. Take, for example, the Cognitive Enhancement Research Institute in California. Prominently displayed on its website front page . . . we read, "Do you know somebody with Alzheimer's disease? Click to see the latest research breakthrough." The mode is simple: treatment by front entrance, enhancement by the back door. Borgmann, in his discussion of the uses of technology in modern society, observed precisely this argumentative strategy more than 20 years ago:

> The main goal of these programs seems to be the domination of nature. But we must be more precise. The desire to dominate does not just spring from a lust of power, from sheer human imperialism. It is from the start connected with the aim of liberating humanity from disease, hunger, and toil and enriching life with learning, art and athletics.

Who would want to deny the powers of viral diseases that can be genetically treated? Would we want to draw the line at the transplantation of non-human capacities (sonar path finding)? Or at in vivo fibre optic communications backbone or anti-degeneration powers? (These would have to be non-human by hypothesis). Or should we consider the scope of technological enhancements that one chief transhumanist, Natasha Vita More, propounds:

> A transhuman is an evolutionary stage from being exclusively biological to becoming post-biological. Post-biological means a continuous shedding of our biology and merging with machines. (. . .) The body, as we transform ourselves over time, will take on different types of appearances and designs and materials. (. . .)
>
> For hiking a mountain, I'd like extended leg strength, stamina, a skin-sheath to protect me from damaging environmental aspects, self-moisturizing, cool-down capability, extended hearing and augmented vision (Network of sonar sensors depicts data through solid mass and map images onto visual field. Overlay window shifts spectrum frequencies. Visual scratch pad relays mental ideas to visual recognition bots. Global Satellite interface at micro-zoom range).
>
> For a party, I'd like an eclectic look—a glistening bronze skin with emerald green highlights, enhanced height to tower above other people, a sophisticated internal sound system so that I could alter the music to suit my own taste, memory enhance device, emotional-select for feel-good people so I wouldn't get dragged into anyone's inappropriate conversations. And parabolic hearing so that I could listen in on conversations across the room if the one I was currently in started winding down.

Notwithstanding the difficulty of bringing together transhumanism under one movement, the sheer variety of proposals merely contained within Vita More's catalogue means that we cannot determinately point to a precise station at which we can say, "Here, this is the end we said things would naturally progress to." But does this pose a problem? Well, it certainly makes it difficult to specify exactly a "horrible result" that is supposed to be at the bottom of the slope. Equally, it is extremely difficult to say that if we allow precedent X, it will allow practices Y or Z to follow as it is not clear how these practices Y or Z are (if at all) connected with the precedent X. So it is not clear that a form of precedent-setting slippery slope can be strictly used in every case against transhumanism, although it may be applicable in some.

Nevertheless, we contend, in contrast with Boström that the burden of proof would fall to the transhumanist. Consider in this light, a Sorites-type slope. The transhumanist would have to show how the relationship between the therapeutic practices and the enhancements are indeed transitive. We know night from day without being able to specify exactly when this occurs. So simply because we cannot determine a precise distinction between, say, genetic treatments G1, G2 and G3, and transhumanism enhancements T1, T2 and so on, it does not follow that there are no important moral distinctions between G1 and T20. According to Williams, this kind of indeterminacy arises because of the conceptual vagueness of certain terms. Yet, the indeterminacy of so open a predicate "heap" is not equally true of "therapy" or "enhancement." The latitude they permit is nowhere near so wide.

Instead of objecting to Pn on the grounds that Pn is morally objectionable (i.e., to depict a horrible result), we may instead, after Williams, object that the slide from P to Pn is simply morally arbitrary, when it ought not to be. Here, we may say, without specifying a horrible result, that it would be difficult to know what, in principle, can ever be objected to. And this is, quite literally, what is troublesome. It seems to us that this criticism applies to all categories of transhumanism, although not necessarily to all enhancements proposed by them. Clearly, the somewhat loose identity of the movement—and the variations between strong and moderate versions—makes it difficult to sustain this argument unequivocally. Still the transhumanist may be justified in asking, "What is wrong with arbitrariness?" Let us consider one brief example. In aspects of our lives, as a widely shared intuition, we may think that in the absence of good reasons, we ought not to discriminate among people arbitrarily. Healthcare may be considered to be precisely one such case. Given the ever-increasing demand for public healthcare services and products, it may be argued that access to them typically ought to be governed by publicly disputable criteria such as clinical need or potential benefit, as opposed to individual choices of an arbitrary or subjective nature. And nothing in transhumanism seems to allow for such objective dispute, let alone prioritisation. Of course, transhumanists such as More find no such disquietude. His phrase "No more timidity" is a typical token of transhumanist slogans. We applaud advances in therapeutic medical technologies such as those from new genetically based organ regeneration to more familiar prosthetic devices. Here the ends of the interventions are clearly medically defined and the means regulated closely. This is what prevents transhumanists from adopting a Sorites-type slippery slope. But in the absence of a telos, of clearly and substantively specified ends (beyond the mere banner of enhancement), we suggest that the public, medical professionals and bioethicists alike ought to resist the potentially open-ended transformations of human nature. For if all transformations are in principle enhancements, then surely none are. The very application of the word may become redundant. Thus it seems that one strong argument against transhumanism generally—the arbitrary slippery slope—presents a challenge to transhumanism, to show that all of what are described as transhumanist enhancements are imbued with positive normative force and are not merely technological extensions of libertarianism, whose conception of the good is merely an extension of individual choice and consumption.

Limits of Transhumanist Arguments for Medical Technology and Practice

Already, we have seen the misuse of a host of therapeutically designed drugs used by non-therapeutic populations for enhancements. Consider the non-therapeutic use of human growth hormone in non-clinical populations. Such is the present perception of height as a positional good in society that Cuttler *et al.* report that the proportion of doctors who recommended human growth hormone treatment of short non-growth hormone deficient children ranged from 1% to 74%. This is despite its contrary indication in professional literature, such as that of the Pediatric Endocrine Society, and considerable doubt about its efficacy. Moreover, evidence supports the view that recreational body builders will use the technology, given the evidence of their use or misuse of steroids and other biotechnological products. Finally, in the sphere of elite sport, which so valorises embodied capacities that may be found elsewhere in greater degree, precision and sophistication in the animal kingdom or in the computer laboratory, biomedical enhancers may latch onto the genetically determined capacities and adopt or adapt them for their own commercially driven ends.

The arguments and examples presented here do no more than to warn us of the enhancement ideologies, such as transhumanism, which seek to predicate their futuristic agendas on the bedrock of medical technological progress aimed at therapeutic ends and are secondarily extended to loosely defined enhancement ends. In discussion and in bioethical literatures, the future of genetic engineering is often challenged by slippery slope arguments that lead policy and practice to a horrible result. Instead of pointing to the undesirability of the ends to which transhumanism leads, we have pointed out the failure to specify their telos beyond the slogans of "overcoming timidity" or Boström's exhortation that the passive acceptance of ageing is an example of "reckless and dangerous barriers to urgently needed action in the biomedical sphere."

We propose that greater care be taken to distinguish the slippery slope arguments that are used in the emotionally loaded exhortations of transhumanism to come to a more judicious perspective on the technologically driven agenda for biomedical enhancement. Perhaps we would do better to consider those other all-too-human frailties such as violent aggression, wanton self-harming and so on, before we turn too readily to the richer imaginations of biomedical technologists.

M. J. McNamee is a reader in philosophy at the Centre for Philosophy, Humanities and Law in Healthcare, School of Health Science, University of Wales, Swansea, UK.

S. D. Edwards is a researcher at the Centre for Philosophy, Humanities and Law in Healthcare, School of Health Science, University of Wales, Swansea, UK.

Maxwell J. Mehlman

NO

Biomedical Enhancements: Entering a New Era

Recently, the Food and Drug Administration (FDA) approved a drug to lengthen and darken eyelashes. Botox and other wrinkle-reducing injections have joined facelifts, tummy tucks, and vaginal reconstruction to combat the effects of aging. To gain a competitive edge, athletes use everything from steroids and blood transfusions to recombinant-DNA–manufactured hormones, Lasik surgery, and artificial atmospheres. Students supplement caffeine-containing energy drinks with Ritalin and the new alertness drug modafinil. The military spends millions of dollars every year on biological research to increase the warfighting abilities of our soldiers. Parents perform genetic tests on their children to determine whether they have a genetic predisposition to excel at explosive or endurance sports. All of these are examples of biomedical enhancements: interventions that use medical and biological technology to improve performance, appearance, or capability in addition to what is necessary to achieve, sustain, or restore health.

The use of biomedical enhancements, of course, is not new. Amphetamines were doled out to troops during World War II. Athletes at the turn of the 20th century ingested narcotics. The cognitive benefits of caffeine have been known for at least a millennium. Ancient Greek athletes swallowed herbal infusions before competitions. The Egyptians brewed a drink containing a relative of Viagra at least 1,000 years before Christ. But modern drug development and improvements in surgical technique are yielding biomedical enhancements that achieve safer, larger, and more targeted enhancement effects than their predecessors, and more extraordinary technologies are expected to emerge from ongoing discoveries in human genetics. (In addition, there are biomechanical enhancements that involve the use of computer implants and nanotechnology, which are beyond the scope of this article.)

What is also new is that biomedical enhancements have become controversial. Some commentators want to outlaw them altogether. Others are concerned about their use by athletes and children. Still others fret that only the well-off will be able to afford them, thereby exacerbating social inequality.

Banning enhancements, however, is misguided. Still, it is important to try to ensure that they are as safe and effective as possible, that vulnerable populations such as children are not forced into using them, and that they are not available only to the well-off. This will require effective government and private action.

A Misguided View

Despite the long history of enhancement use, there recently has emerged a view that it is wrong. The first manifestation of this hostility resulted from the use of performance enhancements in sports in the 1950s, especially steroids and amphetamines. European nations began adopting anti-doping laws in the mid-1960s, and the Olympic Games began testing athletes in 1968. In 1980, Congress amended the Federal Food, Drug, and Cosmetic Act (FFDCA) to make it a felony to distribute anabolic steroids for nonmedical purposes. Two years later, Congress made steroids a Schedule III controlled substance and substituted human growth hormone in the steroid provision of the FFDCA. Between 2003 and 2005, Congress held hearings lambasting professional sports for not imposing adequate testing regimens. Drug testing has also been instituted in high-school and collegiate sports.

The antipathy toward biomedical enhancements extends well beyond sports, however. Officially, at least, the National Institutes of Health (NIH) will not fund research to develop genetic technologies for human enhancement purposes, although it has funded studies in animals that the researchers tout as a step toward developing human enhancements. It is a federal crime to use steroids to increase strength even if the user is not an athlete. Human growth hormone is in a unique regulatory category in that it is a felony to prescribe it for any purpose other than a specific use approved by the FDA. (For example, the FDA has not approved it for anti-aging purposes.) There is an ongoing controversy about whether musicians, especially string players, should be allowed to use beta blockers to steady their hands. And who hasn't heard of objections to the use of mood-altering drugs to make "normal" people happier? There's even a campaign against caffeine.

If the critics had their way, the government would ban the use of biomedical enhancements. It might seem that this would merely entail extending the War on Drugs to a larger number of drugs. But remember that enhancements include not just drugs, but cosmetic surgery and information technologies, such as genetic testing to identify nondisease traits. So a War on Enhancements would have to extend to a broader range of technologies, and because many are delivered within the patient-physician relationship, the government would have to intrude into that relationship in significant new ways. Moreover, the FDA is likely to have approved many enhancement drugs for legitimate medical purposes, with enhancement use taking place on an "off-label" basis. So there would have to be some way for the enhancement police to identify people for whom the drugs had been legally prescribed to treat illness, but who were misusing them for enhancement purposes.

This leads to a far more profound difficulty. The War on Drugs targets only manufacture, distribution, and possession. There is virtually no effort to punish people merely for using an illegal substance. But a successful ban on biomedical enhancement would have to prevent people from obtaining benefits from enhancements that persisted after they no longer possessed the enhancements themselves, such as the muscles built with the aid of steroids or the cognitive improvement that lasts for several weeks after normal people stop taking a certain medicine that treats memory loss in Alzheimer's patients. In short, a ban on enhancements would have to aim at use as well as possession and sale.

To imagine what this would be like, think about the campaign against doping in elite sports, where athletes must notify anti-doping officials of their whereabouts at all times and are subject to unannounced, intrusive, and often indecent drug tests at any hour of the day or night. Even in the improbable event that regular citizens were willing to endure such an unprecedented loss of privacy, the economic cost of maintaining such a regime, given how widespread the use of highly effective biomedical enhancements might be, would be prohibitive.

A ban on biomedical enhancements would be not only unworkable but unjustifiable. Consider the objections to enhancement in sports. Why are enhancements against the rules? Is it because they are unsafe? Not all of them are: Anti-doping rules in sports go after many substances that pose no significant health risks, such as caffeine and Sudafed. (A Romanian gymnast forfeited her Olympic gold medal after she accidentally took a couple of Sudafed to treat a cold.) Even in the case of vilified products such as steroids, safety concerns stem largely from the fact that athletes are forced to use the drugs covertly, without medical supervision. Do enhancements give athletes an "unfair" advantage? They do so only if the enhancements are hard to obtain, so that only a few competitors obtain the edge. But the opposite seems to be true: Enhancements are everywhere. Besides, athletes are also tested for substances that have no known performance-enhancing effects, such as marijuana. Are the rewards from enhancements "unearned"? Not necessarily. Athletes still need to train hard. Indeed, the benefit from steroids comes chiefly from allowing athletes to train harder without injuring themselves. In any event, success in sports comes from factors that athletes have done nothing to deserve, such as natural talent and the good luck to have been born to encouraging parents or to avoid getting hurt. Would the use of enhancements confound recordkeeping? This doesn't seem to have stopped the adoption of new equipment that improves performance, such as carbon-fiber vaulting poles, metal skis, and oversized tennis racquets. If one athlete used enhancements, would every athlete have to, so that the benefit would be nullified? No, there would still be the benefit of improved performance across the board—bigger lifts, faster times, higher jumps. In any case, the same thing happens whenever an advance takes place that improves performance.

The final objection to athletic enhancement, in the words of the international Olympic movement, is that it is against the "spirit of sport." It is hard to know what this means. It certainly can't mean that enhancements destroy an earlier idyll in which sports were enhancement-free; as we saw before, this never was the case. Nor can it stand for the proposition that a physical competition played with the aid of enhancements necessarily is not a "sport." There are many sporting events in which the organizers do not bother to test participants, from certain types of "strong-man" and powerlifting meets to your neighborhood pickup basketball game. There are several interesting historical explanations for why athletic enhancement has gained such a bad rap, but ultimately, the objection about "the spirit of sport" boils down to the fact that some people simply don't like the idea of athletes using enhancements. Well, not exactly. You see, many biomedical enhancements are perfectly permissible, including dietary supplements, sports psychology, carbohydrate loading, electrolyte-containing beverages, and sleeping at altitude (or in artificial environments that simulate it). Despite the labor of innumerable philosophers of sport, no one has ever come up with a rational explanation for why these things are legal and others aren't. In the end, they are just arbitrary distinctions.

But that's perfectly okay. Lots of rules in sports are arbitrary, like how many players are on a team or how far the boundary lines stretch. If you don't like being all alone in the outfield, don't play baseball. If you are bothered by midnight drug tests, don't become an Olympian.

The problem comes when the opponents of enhancement use in sports try to impose their arbitrary dislikes on the wider world. We already have observed how intrusive and expensive this would be. Beyond that, there are strong constitutional objections to using the power of the law to enforce arbitrary rules. But most important, a ban on the use of enhancements outside of sports would sacrifice an enormous amount of societal benefit. Wouldn't we want automobile drivers to use alertness drugs if doing so could prevent accidents? Shouldn't surgeons be allowed to use beta blockers to steady their hands? Why not let medical researchers take cognitive enhancers if it would lead to faster cures, or let workers take them to be more productive? Why stop soldiers from achieving greater combat effectiveness, rescue workers from lifting heavier objects, and men and women from leading better sex lives? Competent adults who want to use enhancements should be permitted to. In some instances, such as in combat or when performing dangerous jobs, they should even be required to.

Protecting the Vulnerable

Rejecting the idea of banning enhancements doesn't mean that their use should be unregulated. The government has several crucial roles to play in helping to ensure that the benefits from enhancement use outweigh the costs.

In the first place, the government needs to protect people who are incapable of making rational decisions about whether to use enhancements. In the language of biomedical ethics, these are populations that are "vulnerable," and a number of them are well recognized. One such group, of course, is people with severe mental disabilities. The law requires surrogates to make decisions for these individuals based on what is in their best interests.

Another vulnerable population is children. There can be little disagreement that kids should not be allowed to decide on their own to consume powerful, potentially dangerous enhancement substances. Not only do they lack decisionmaking capacity, but they may be much more susceptible than adults to harm. This is clearly the case with steroids, which can interfere with bone growth in children and adolescents.

The more difficult question is whether parents should be free to give enhancements to their children. Parents face powerful social pressures to help their children excel. Some parents may be willing to improve their children's academic or athletic performance even at a substantial risk of injury to the child. There are many stories of parents who allow their adolescent daughters to have cosmetic surgery, including breast augmentation. In general, the law gives parents considerable discretion in determining how to raise their children. The basic legal constraint on parental discretion is the prohibition in state law against abuse or neglect, and this generally is interpreted to defer to parental decisionmaking so long as the child does not suffer serious net harm. There are no reported instances in which parents have been sanctioned for giving their children biomedical enhancements, and the authorities might conclude that the benefits conferred by the use of an enhancement outweighed even a fairly significant risk of injury.

Beyond the actions of parents, there remains the question of whether some biomedical enhancements are so benign that children should be allowed to purchase them themselves. At present, for instance, there is no law in the United States against children purchasing coffee, caffeinated soft drinks, and even high-caffeine–containing energy drinks. (Laws prohibiting children from buying energy drinks have been enacted in some other countries.)

At the same time, it may be a mistake to lump youngsters together with older adolescents into one category of children. Older adolescents, although still under the legal age of majority, have greater cognitive and judgmental capacities than younger children. The law recognizes this by allowing certain adolescents, deemed "mature" or "emancipated" minors, to make legally binding decisions, such as decisions to receive medical treatment. Older adolescents similarly may deserve some degree of latitude in making decisions about using biomedical enhancements.

Children may be vulnerable to pressure to use enhancements not only from their parents, but from their educators. Under programs such as No Child Left Behind, public school teachers and administrators are rewarded and punished based on student performance on standardized tests. Private schools compete with one another in terms of where their graduates are accepted for further education. There is also intense competition in school athletics, especially at the collegiate level. Students in these environments may be bull-dozed into using enhancements to increase their academic and athletic abilities. Numerous anecdotes, for example, tell of parents who are informed by teachers that their children need medication to "help them focus"; the medication class in question typically is the cognition-enhancing amphetamines, and many of these children do not have diagnoses that would warrant the use of these drugs.

Beyond students, athletes in general are vulnerable to pressure from coaches, sponsors, family, and teammates to use hazardous enhancements. For example, at the 2005 congressional hearings on steroid use in baseball, a father testified that his son committed suicide after using steroids, when in fact he killed himself after his family caught him using steroids, which the boy had turned to in an effort to meet his family's athletic aspirations.

Another group that could be vulnerable to coercion is workers. Employers might condition employment or promotion on the use of enhancements that increased productivity. For example, an employer might require its nighttime work force to take the alertness drug modafinil, which is now approved for use by sleep-deprived swing-shift workers. Current labor law does not clearly forbid this so long as the drug is relatively safe. From an era in which employees are tested to make sure they aren't taking drugs, we might see a new approach in which employers test them to make sure they are.

Members of the military may also be forced to use enhancements. The military now conducts the largest known biomedical enhancement research project. Under battlefield conditions, superiors may order the use of enhancements, leaving soldiers no lawful option to refuse. A notorious example is the use of amphetamines by combat pilots. Technically, the pilots are required to give their consent to the use of the pep pills, but if they refuse, they are barred from flying the missions.

The ability of government regulation to protect vulnerable groups varies depending on the group. It is important that educators not be allowed to give students dangerous enhancements without parental permission and that parents not be pressured into making unreasonable decisions by fearful, overzealous, or inadequate educators. The law can mandate the former, but not easily prevent the latter. Coaches and trainers who cause injury to athletes by giving them dangerous enhancements or by unduly encouraging their use should be subject to criminal and civil liability. The same goes for employers. But the realities of military life make it extremely difficult to protect soldiers from the orders of their superiors.

Moreover, individuals may feel pressure to use enhancements not only from outside sources, but from within. Students may be driven to do well in order to satisfy parents, gain admittance to more prestigious schools, or establish better careers. Athletes take all sorts of risks to increase their chances of winning. Workers may be desperate to save their jobs or bring in a bigger paycheck, especially in economically uncertain times. Soldiers better able to complete their missions are likely to live longer.

Surprisingly, while acknowledging the need to protect people from outside pressures, bioethicists generally maintain that we do not need to protect them from harmful decisions motivated by internal pressures. This position stems, it seems, from the recognition that, with the exception of decisions that are purely random, everything we decide to do is dictated at least in part by internal pressures, and in many cases, these pressures can be so strong that the decisions may no longer appear to be voluntary. Take, for example, seriously ill cancer patients contemplating whether or not to undergo harsh chemotherapy regimens. Bioethicists worry that, if we focused on the pressures and lack of options created by the patients' dire condition, we might not let the patients receive the treatment, or, in the guise of protecting the patients from harm, might create procedural hurdles that would rob them of their decisionmaking autonomy. Similarly, these bioethicists might object to restricting the ability of workers, say, to use biomedical enhancements merely because their choices are highly constrained by their fear of losing their jobs. But even if we accept this argument, that doesn't mean that we must be indifferent to the dangers posed by overwhelming internal pressure. As we will see, the government still must take steps to minimize the harm that could result.

Individuals may be vulnerable to harm not only from using enhancements, but from participating in experiments to see if an enhancement is safe and effective. Research subjects are protected by a fairly elaborate set of rules, collectively known as the "Common Rule," that are designed to ensure that the risks of the research are outweighed by the potential benefits and that the subjects have given their informed consent to their participation. But there are many weaknesses in this regulatory scheme. For one thing, these rules apply only to experiments conducted by government-funded institutions or that are submitted to the FDA in support of licensing applications, and therefore they do not cover a great deal of research performed by private industry. Moreover, the rules were written with medically oriented research in mind, and it is not clear how they should be interpreted and applied to enhancement research. For example, the rules permit children to be enrolled as experimental subjects in trials that present "more than minimal risk" if, among other things, the research offers the possibility of "direct benefit" to the subject, but the rules do not say whether an enhancement benefit can count as a direct benefit. Specific research protections extend to other vulnerable populations besides children, such as prisoners and pregnant women, but do not explicitly cover students, workers, or athletes. In reports of a project several colleagues and I recently completed for the NIH, we suggest a number of changes to current regulations that would provide better protection for these populations.

Ensuring Safety and Effectiveness

Beginning with the enactment of the Pure Food and Drug Act in 1906, we have turned to the government to protect us from unsafe, ineffective, and fraudulent biomedical products and services. Regardless of how much freedom individuals should have to decide whether or not to use biomedical enhancements, they cannot make good decisions without accurate information about how well enhancements work. In regard to enhancements in the form of drugs and medical devices, the FDA has the legal responsibility to make sure that this information exists.

The FDA's ability to discharge this responsibility, however, is limited. In the first place, the FDA has tended to rely on information from highly stylized clinical trials that do not reflect the conditions under which enhancements would be used by the general public. Moreover, the deficiencies of clinical trials are becoming more apparent as we learn about pharmacogenetics—the degree to which individual responses to medical interventions vary depending on the individual's genes. The FDA is beginning to revise its rules to require manufacturers to take pharmacogenetics into consideration in studying safety and efficacy, but it will be many years, if ever, before robust pharmacogenetic information is publicly available. The solution is to rely more on data from actual use. Recently the agency has become more adamant about monitoring real-world experience after products reach the market, but this information comes from self-reports by physicians and manufacturers who have little incentive to cooperate. The agency needs to be able to conduct its own surveillance of actual use, with the costs borne by the manufacturers.

Many biomedical enhancements fall outside the scope of FDA authority. They include dietary supplements, many of which are used for enhancement purposes rather than to promote health. You only have to turn on late-night TV to be bombarded with claims for substances to make you stronger or more virile. Occasionally the Federal Trade Commission cracks down on hucksters, but it needs far greater resources to do an effective job. The FDA needs to exert greater authority to regulate dietary supplements, including those used for enhancement.

The FDA also lacks jurisdiction over the "practice of medicine." Consequently, it has no oversight over cosmetic surgery, except when the surgeon employs a new medical device. This limitation also complicates the agency's efforts to exert authority over reproductive and genetic practices. This would include the genetic modification of embryos to improve their traits, which promises to be one of the most effective enhancement techniques. Because organized medicine fiercely protects this limit on the FDA, consumers will have to continue to rely on physicians and other health care professionals to provide them with the information they need to make decisions about these types of enhancements. Medical experts need to stay on top of advances in enhancement technology.

Even with regard to drugs and devices that are clearly within the FDA's jurisdiction, its regulatory oversight only goes so far. Once the agency approves a product for a particular use, physicians are free to use it for any other purpose, subject only to liability for malpractice and, in the case of controlled substances, a requirement that the use must comprise legitimate medical practice. Only a handful of products, such as Botox, have received FDA approval for enhancement use; as noted earlier, enhancements predominantly are unapproved, off-label uses of products approved for health-related purposes. Modafinil, for example, one of the most popular drugs for enhancing cognitive performance, is approved only for the treatment of narcolepsy and sleepiness associated with obstructive sleep apnea/hypopnea syndrome and shift-work sleep disorder. Erythropoietin, which athletes use to improve performance, is approved to treat anemias. The FDA needs to be able to require manufacturers of products such as these to pay for the agency to collect and disseminate data on off-label experience. The agency also has to continue to limit the ability of manufacturers to promote drugs for off-label uses, in order to give them an incentive to obtain FDA approval for enhancement labeling.

An enhancement technology that will increase in use is testing to identify genes that are associated with non-disease characteristics. People can use this information to make lifestyle choices, such as playing sports at which they have the genes to excel, or in reproduction, such as deciding which of a number of embryos fertilized in vitro will be implanted in the uterus. An area of special concern is genetic tests that consumers can use at home without the involvement of physicians or genetic counselors to help them interpret the results. Regulatory authority over genetic testing is widely believed to be inadequate, in part because it is split among the FDA and several other federal agencies, and there are growing calls for revamping this regulatory scheme that need to be heeded.

Any attempt to regulate biomedical enhancement will be undercut by people who obtain enhancements abroad. The best hope for protecting these "enhancement tourists" against unsafe or ineffective products and services lies in international cooperation, but this is costly and subject to varying degrees of compliance.

To make intelligent decisions about enhancement use, consumers need information not only about safety and effectiveness, but about whether they are worth the money. Should they pay for Botox injections, for example, or try to get rid of facial wrinkles with cheaper creams and lotions? When the FDA approved Botox for cosmetic use, it ignored this question of cost-effectiveness because it has no statutory authority to consider it. In the case of medical care, consumers may get some help in making efficient spending decisions from their health insurers, who have an incentive to avoid paying for unnecessarily costly products or services. But insurance does not cover enhancements. The new administration is proposing to create a federal commission to conduct health care cost-effectiveness analyses, among other things, and it is important that such a body pay attention to enhancements as well as other biomedical interventions.

Subsidizing Enhancement

In these times of economic distress, when we already question whether the nation can afford to increase spending on health care, infrastructure, and other basic necessities, it may seem foolish to consider whether the government has an obligation to make biomedical enhancements available to all. Yet if enhancements enable people to enjoy a significantly better life, this may not be so outlandish, and if universal access avoids a degree of inequality so great that it undermines our democratic way of life, it may be inescapable.

There is no need for everyone to have access to all available enhancements. Some may add little to an individual's abilities. Others may be so hazardous that they offer little net benefit to the user. But imagine that a pill is discovered that substantially improves a person's cognitive facility, not just their memory but abilities such as executive function—the highest form of problem-solving capacity—or creativity. Now imagine if this pill were available only to those who already were well-off and could afford to purchase it with personal funds. If such a pill were sufficiently effective, so that those who took it had a lock on the best schools, careers, and mates, wealth-based access could drive an insurmountable wedge between the haves and have-nots, a gap so wide and deep that we could no longer pretend that there is equality of opportunity in our society. At that point, it is doubtful that a liberal democratic state could survive.

So it may be necessary for the government to regard such a success-determining enhancement as a basic necessity, and, after driving the cost down to the lowest amount possible, subsidize access for those unable to purchase it themselves. Even if this merely maintained preexisting differences in cognitive ability, it would be justified in order to prevent further erosion of equality of opportunity.

The need for effective regulation of biomedical enhancement is only going to increase as we enter an era of increasingly sophisticated technologies. Existing schemes, such as the rules governing human subjects research, must be reviewed to determine whether additions or changes are needed to accommodate this class of interventions. Government agencies and private organizations need to be aware of both the promise and the peril of enhancements and devote an appropriate amount of resources in order to regulate, rather than stop, their use.

MAXWELL J. MEHLMAN is the Arthur E. Petersilge Professor of Law, director of the Law-Medicine Center, and professor of bioethics at Case Western Reserve University. His latest books are *The Price of Perfection: The Individual and Society in the Era of Biomedical Enhancement* (Johns Hopkins University Press, 2009) and *Transhumanist Dreams and Dystopian Nightmares: The Promise and Peril of Genetic Engineering* (Johns Hopkins University Press, 2012).

EXPLORING THE ISSUE

Should We Reject the "Transhumanist" Goal of the Genetically, Electronically, and Mechanically Enhanced Human Being?

Critical Thinking and Reflection

1. What is transhumanism?
2. What is a "slippery slope" argument?
3. What bodily or mental enhancements would you find desirable? Why?
4. Should government subsidize biomedical enhancements for those who cannot afford them? Why or why not?

Is There Common Ground?

"Common ground" is difficult to find here, for many of those who object to enhancing the human mind and body seem to draw rather arbitrary lines to distinguish between enhancements they find acceptable and those they do not.

1. Is the line between internal and external enhancements, or between new and old? Consider eyeglasses versus lens implants (done when cataracts must be removed), hearing aids versus cochlear implants, crutches and canes versus artificial hips and knees.
2. Do computers give us fundamentally new abilities for communication and memory expansion? Do we accept these abilities? Will it make a difference when we can implant our computers inside our heads?
3. What other technological enhancements of the human body and mind do most of us accept readily?
4. Does the list of acceptable enhancements expand as time goes on and technology progresses?

Create Central

www.mhhe.com/createcentral

Additional Resources

Josh Fischman, "A Better Life with Bionics," *National Geographic* (January 2010).

Andrew Kimbrell, *The Human Body Shop: The Engineering and Marketing of Life* (HarperSanFrancisco, 1993).

Julian Savalescu and Nick Bostrom, *Human Enhancement* (Oxford University Press, 2009).

Internet Reference . . .

Humanity+

Humanity+ is the leading transhumanist association, dedicating to promoting understanding, interest, and participation in the field of human enhancement.

http://humanityplus.org/